THE BETTMAN ARCHIVE

BOOKS BY JOSEPH GIES:

Bridges and Men

Adventure Undergound: The Story of the World's Great Tunnels

A Matter of Morals

They Never Had It So Good

BRIDGES

and

MEN

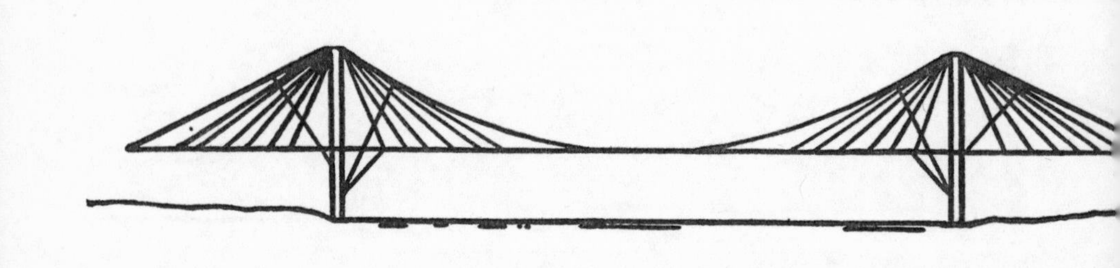

BRIDGES and MEN

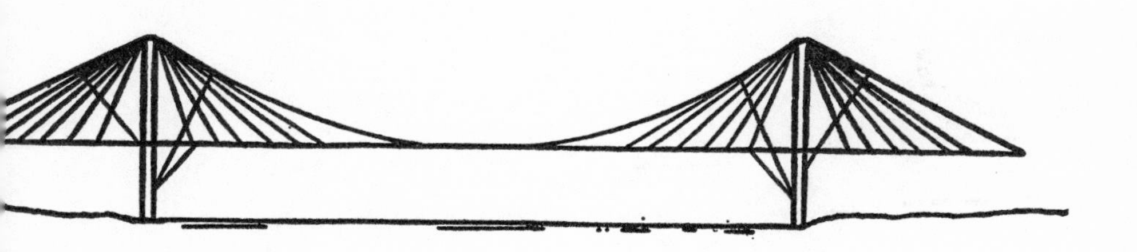

JOSEPH GIES

with drawings by Jane Orth Ware

Doubleday & Company, Inc., Garden City, N.Y.

The lines from Hart Crane's "The Bridge" in *The Collected Poems of Hart Crane* are reprinted by permission of Liveright, Publishers, N.Y. Copyright © R-1961 by Liveright Publishing Corp.

The lines from "In Time of War" from *The Collected Poetry of W. H. Auden*, copyright, 1945, by W. H. Auden, are reprinted by permission of Random House, Inc.

Library of Congress Catalog Card Number 63–18202

Contents

Illustrations

Foreword

WHEN a layman sets out to write a book on a technical subject, he needs help. If his book is in the realm of civil engineering he is fortunate, because engineers, as Ogden Nash once observed in reference to the locomotive variety, are exceptionally friendly, helpful, and courteous. The most distinguished of living bridge engineers, Othmar H. Ammann, stopped working on the world's biggest bridge (the Verrazano-Narrows, Chapter 24) long enough to tell me about the world's worst bridge construction disaster (Quebec, 1907, Chapter 20), which he helped investigate. Dr. Jacob Feld, an eminent New York consulting engineer, advised me about another disaster (Chapter 14, "The Mystery of the Firth of Tay"). Dr. Feld read the pertinent documents in that celebrated mid-Victorian tragedy and helped explain why the bridge over the Tay fell down one December night in 1879.

Professor J. M. Garrelts, head of the Department of Civil Engineering at Columbia University, read several chapters and suggested emendations. Professor Lawrence C. Maugh, acting head of the Department of Civil Engineering at the University of Michigan, my own alma mater, did the same, and in addition took some of his valuable time to make me understand (or at least think I understood) such recondite terms as static determination and the Von Karman effect.

I ventured to ask a question or two of James Kip Finch, Dean Emeritus and Renwick Professor of Civil Engineering at Columbia and author of many writings on engineering history, including the excellent one-volume *The Story of Engineering*. Professor Finch not only answered my questions but read my first drafts of Chapters 8 ("The 'Flying Arch': Jean-Rodolphe Perronet") and 11 ("The Yankee Bridge") and made suggestions that led to complete revision of both chapters. In addition he lent excellent copies of eighteenth-century prints of the Pont de Neuilly and other bridges, and clarified some stubbornly obscure points on ancient and modern engineering.

Several other engineers, at the headquarters of the American Society of Civil Engineers in New York and elsewhere, set me straight on various important aspects of bridge history, especially of the modern era. The A.S.C.E. also opened its picture files to my profit.

Mike Chenoweth, manager of the Bureau of Information of the A.S.C.E., not only performed the valuable service of putting me in touch with most of the above authorities, but also gave me much other assistance as well. I enjoyed the privileges of the incomparable Engineering Societies Library of the United Engineering Center thanks to Mike and to Dr. Ralph Phelps, director of the library.

I should mention also the Engineering Library of the University of Michigan and the University of Michigan News and Information Service.

The vast resources of the New York Public Library were indispensable for several chapters, and the courteous, intelligent help of the personnel, especially in the Technical and Oriental divisions, was much appreciated.

The U. S. Army, through Lieutenant Colonel Howard Gardner Stevenson of the Army Information Service in New York, lent the pictures of the capture of the Remagen Bridge, and also answered questions about bridge demolition. French, Italian, and British cultural information services helped with pictures and with corrections of text material; I should especially mention Dr. Lucia Pallavicini of the Italian Cultural Division. The justly famous pictures of Galloping Gertie in action were sent to me by Professor F. B. Farquharson, the foremost living expert on the memorable event.

Frank Davidson, President of Technical Studies, Inc., the American company that is determined to build either a tunnel under or a bridge over the English Channel, told or gave me everything I know about the picturesque Channel bridge project, including the artist's representation of the Schneider-Hersent cantilever of 1889.

In obtaining many other pictures I had the expert help of Mrs. Marianne Tyrrasch, picture researcher of *This Week Magazine*. This brings me to another category of assistance. Mention that you are writing a book on bridges and you will be amazed at the number of people who will tell you something you never knew about bridges, real or fictional. Ed McCarthy, managing editor of *This Week,* supplied most of the material on the bridge in art in Chapter 26. Eric Lasher and Stewart Beach, also of *This Week,* gave me respectively tips on that lively bridge form, the logger's flume, and the far-echoing episode of American history that took place at North Bridge, Concord, Massachusetts, one April morning in 1775 (see Chapter 25). So many other people made suggestions, answered questions, volunteered information, or supplied material that to list them all would be impossible. I should like to single out one—Mrs. Stella de Banzie, formerly of Doubleday and Company, who introduced me to that immortal Scots bard, William McGonagall of Dundee, author of the verses at the beginning of Chapter 14.

Today practically every writer's acknowledgments conclude with a mention of his wife, who helped with editing, typing, and researching, and whose intelligent interest made his book possible. I follow this tradition, and add that the contribution Frances Carney Gies made to certain chapters (for example, "The Endless Bridge"), went far beyond these familiar categories.

JOSEPH GIES

Wilton, Connecticut, 1963

1.

How Bridges Were Invented

THE history of anything—bathing suits, furniture, baseball, cooking—is a part of the history of everything, but some of the threads are more fundamental to the whole tapestry than others. Few of man's inventions are more basic than the bridge. The oldest engineering work devised by man, it is the only one universally employed by him in his precivilized state. In the Dartmoor district of England you may still see streams or dry stream beds into which huge monolithic slabs of granite were dragged to serve as the vertical piers and horizontal beams of millennia-old crossings. In other places, timber piles have survived the ages to reveal the engineering capacities of our remote ancestors.

What is incredible is that our distant forebears in many parts of the globe, struggling to overcome the transportation problems of their primitive trail-worlds, invented not only the simple beam bridge but also the far more sophisticated, even ultramodern forms of suspension and cantilever. In the interior of South America men first learned to swing across a chasm on a vine, like monkeys. Then the vine's end was fastened to the farther side to be available for the return journey. Next it was made secure and crossed repeatedly by hand-over-hand acrobatics. Several vines fastened together were stronger: two or three such cables fixed parallel to each other made the crossing less hazardous. Eventually the idea developed of laying a floor of transverse branches, which later became more solid. Prescott gives this description of spans found by the Spaniards in the Inca Empire:

> Over some of the boldest streams it was necessary to construct suspension bridges, as they are termed [Prescott is writing in 1847], made of the

tough fibres of the maguey, or of the osier of the country, which has an extraordinary degree of tenacity and strength. These osiers were woven into cables of the thickness of a man's body. The huge ropes, then stretched across the water, were conducted through rings or holes cut in immense buttresses of stone raised on the opposite banks of the river, and there secured to heavy pieces of timber. Several of these enormous cables, bound together, formed a bridge, which, covered with planks, well secured and defended by a railing of the same osier materials on the sides, afforded a safe passage for the traveller. The length of this aerial bridge, sometimes exceeding two hundred feet, caused it, confined as it was only at the extremities, to dip with an alarming inclination towards the centre, while the motion given to it by the passenger occasioned an oscillation still more frightful, as his eye wandered over the dark abyss of waters that foamed and tumbled many a fathom beneath.

Yet these light and fragile fabrics were crossed without fear by the Peruvians, and are still retained by the Spaniards. . . .

Despite the precariousness, these Peruvian suspension spans were used not only for pedestrian traffic but also for burden-bearing llamas.

In northeast India, suspension bridges consisting of single bamboo cables were stretched across streams. The bamboo was taut, like a tightrope. The traveler wishing to cross performed what amounted to a circus feat. Armed with a loop of bamboo, he climbed the tree to which the cable was fastened, fitted his loop on the tightrope, and dropped his weight onto it, causing the cable to sag. With increasing velocity, he shot out over the torrent, as the cable sagged deeper and deeper; his momentum even carried him partway up the other side. Then, grasping the cable with his hands and holding the loop with his legs, he pulled himself the rest of the distance into the tree that served as the tower on the far bank.

Such "transporter" bridges were still common in Tibet and northeast India in the nineteenth century. Usually by this time the passenger simply rode in the loop, which was hauled across by a light cable. On the opposite side of the world, in the Shetland Islands north of Scotland, one of the outlying crags was connected to a bigger island by the same kind of bridge as late as a hundred years ago. In South America a basket was hung on the main cable, and the passenger, seated in the basket, pulled himself across by hauling on a movable cable.

But in Assam and Burma, as in Peru, real suspension bridges, with floors and handrails, evolved from these beginnings. Some were hundreds of feet long, stiffened at intervals to keep the floor from closing in on the traveler. On the west coast of Africa, too, suspension bridges were made of tough roots plaited together and hung from trees on either side of a stream.

Nobody knows when the first cantilever bridge was built, but it was in the very distant past, in China. A cantilever is a balanced structure extending laterally in two directions, from a base or pier—like a V on a pedestal, or a cocktail glass—which can be raised on each side of a river either to meet in the middle or to support a suspended span (*Figure 1*).

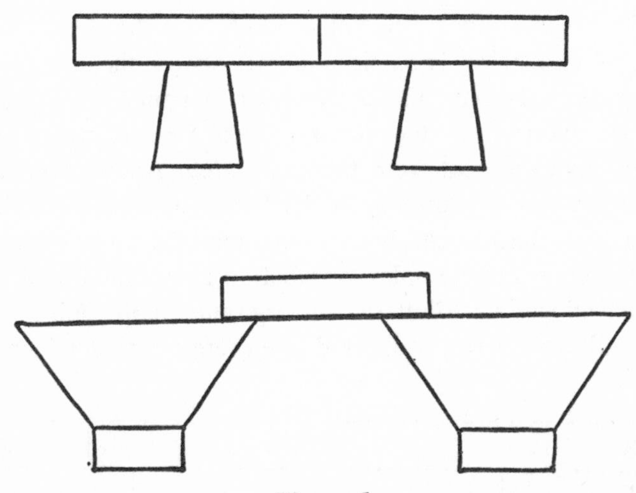

Figure 1

In China cantilevers were built by extending heavy timbers outward from a solid stone abutment. The stones were fitted together without mortar. The timbers were roughly hewn treetrunks, projected in pairs, placed with an upward slant, usually in three or four pairs, with the inner ends held by the weight of the stone abutment, the outer ends bound together (*Figure 2*).

For early man, with his limited access to materials and his limited means of refining them, these bridge forms, ingenious as they were, had only very restricted value. They served for narrow crossings under favorable circumstances. Civilization demanded something better. Above all, the invention of the wheel, with its dramatic train of carts, wagons, roads, highways, merchants, wealth, towns, and cities, brought the problem of river crossings to the fore.

The invention that solved the bridge problem of ancient civili-

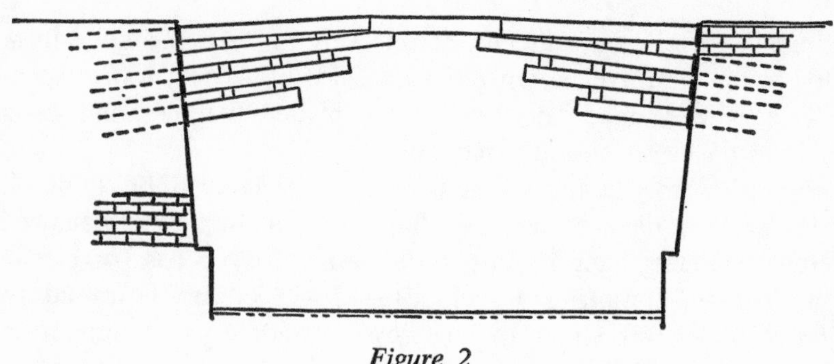

Figure 2

zation ranks second only to the wheel itself. It is the arch. How this marvel came into being is as deep a mystery as the origin of the wheel. Engineers discount the older guess that man built arches in imitation of nature, for the natural arch formed by erosion is structurally quite different from the stone arch. Another guess, that bridging of streams by dumping rocks led to a sudden insight also is farfetched. Archaeologists have found that the arch appeared in tombs and underground temples long before it was used as a bridge. Recent excavations have disclosed underground vaults going back to the fourth millennium B.C. at Ur and elsewhere in ancient Sumer, the

Figure 3

earliest Tigris-Euphrates civilization. Egyptians, too, knew vaulting by the year 3000 B.C.

The Sumerians and Babylonians apparently had the "false arch" at a very early date, and perhaps derived the true arch from it. The difference between the two is interesting. The false arch, built of overlapping bricks laid horizontally and held together by mortar, will stand, but it will not carry a load. A true arch, on the other hand, will sustain an enormous weight, even without any mortar (*Figure 3*).

Who built the first arch bridge? Diodorus of Sicily describes a bridge across the Euphrates built by "Queen Semiramis of Babylon" about 2000 B.C. But even if we overlook the legendary character of this queen, Diodorus' description indicates that the bridge consisted not of arch spans but of simple beams on piers twelve feet apart. This construction was quite possible over the Euphrates, which was reduced to a trickle in the dry season. Herodotus ascribes a bridge over the Euphrates to another queen, Nitocris, and gives it stone piers with wooden flooring. A modern writer places the bridge in Nebuchadnezzar's reign (sixth century B.C.). If so, then it was not the first stone arch, even assuming it was an arch. The oldest surviving stone arch is at Smyrna, in Turkey, over the Meles River. It dates at least from the ninth century B.C., and is said to have been crossed by St. Paul. Several stone-arch bridges in Israel antedate the Christian era (even though the Old Testament does not contain a single bridge reference).

Stone arches are not necessarily semicircular, though this is the form we usually think of (and by far the commonest in bridging).

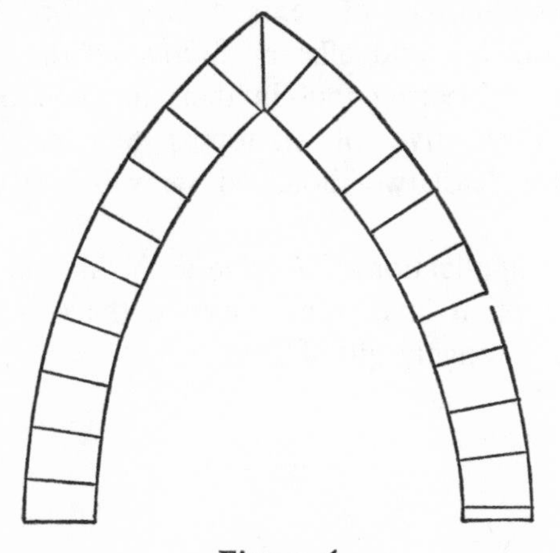

Figure 4

Early stone arches of the eastern Mediterranean were pointed (*Figure 4*). Pointed brick arches in drainage tunnels have been found in the supposed palace of Nimrod on the Tigris, dating from 1300 B.C. A mud-brick pointed arch at Nippur goes back to the fourth millennium B.C. Semi-circular "voussoir" arches—that is, true arches made with wedge-shaped stones—have been found at the ruins of Khorsabad near Ninevah, dating from about the reign of Sargon II of Assyria (722–705 B.C.).

The semicircular arch has an obvious advantage over the pointed arch when it comes to bridging—fewer piers are needed in the river. The pointed arch has an advantage too, but bridge builders did not discover it for a long time (*Figure 5*).

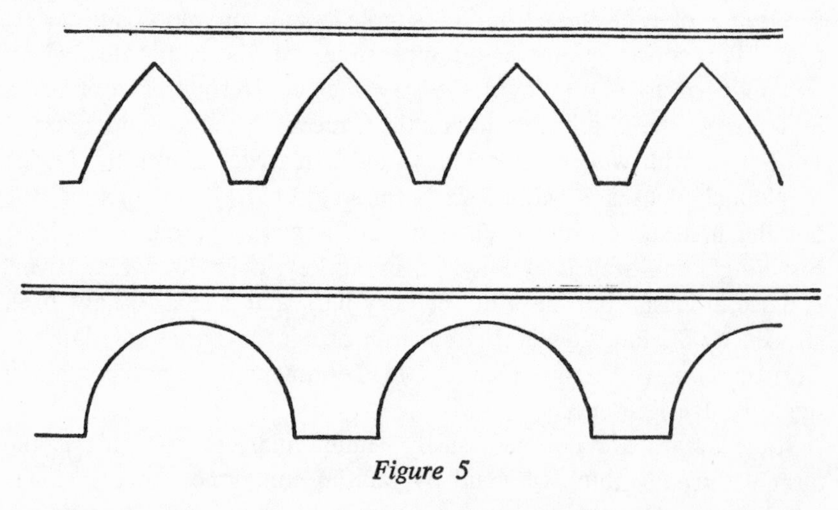

Figure 5

Hundreds and hundreds of years passed before kings and pharaohs and their officials and officers discovered the great application of the priceless engineering tool in their hands. Restricted to what amounted to a decorative role in tombs, temples, and palaces, the arch existed for at least two thousand years before it was ever used as a bridge.

For its serious application, the stone arch, like many other Greek, Persian, and Egyptian inventions, awaited the coming of the pragmatic, inartistic, strangely gifted Romans.

2.

The Mighty Roman Arch

THE Tarquins, Etruscan kings of Rome in its remote pre-Republican stage, brought Etruscan experts to their Tiber principality in the seventh century B.C. to solve a civil-engineering problem that has persisted into modern times: sewage disposal. Their vaulted tunnel, the Cloaca Maxima, exists today, the oldest of all Roman stone-arch structures. Not long after, the first known Roman stone-arch bridge, the Pons Solarus, was built to cross the Teverone, a small tributary of the Tiber. The Pons Solarus has vanished completely, and we know little about its design. All the early Roman bridges are shrouded in the mists of prehistory. What we know for sure is that Roman engineers learned to sink foundations of remarkable endurance to carry semicircular stone arches of considerable size, and that in the end they left behind them bridges at whose majestic dimensions we gaze in undiminished awe today.

To appreciate the Roman achievements one should first take some note of the basic problems involved in bridging a wide, deep river. To a layman examining a bridge engineer's problems for the first time, perhaps the biggest single surprise is the disproportionate amount of effort that must be made under the water. Looking at the Brooklyn Bridge, for example, one scarcely suspects the years of night-and-day struggle by gangs of workmen and engineers below the surface of the East River before the suspension cables could even be begun. For the Romans it was no different. To bridge a river with five stone arches required four piers in the stream, two of them near the middle. The bottom of a river is mud. How do you build a pier on a mud river bottom? To support a heavy stone arch, it should be observed, a pier of considerable dimensions is demanded. Actually, for reasons we shall see in a moment, the Roman engineers made their piers thicker and broader than necessary. But on what could such a huge mass of masonry rest? How could the stones be fastened together under the water? And how could the pier, once built, be protected against scour—the wearing action of moving sand? Scour occurs at the bottom of any river against any obstacle, natural or man-made. But its effect is heightened by the speed of the current, and the bigger the obstacle created in the river by the piers, the more rapid the current.

The Roman engineers of the second and first centuries B.C. solved all these problems. The only arch they knew, the semicircular, rests half its weight on each of its two supporting piers. When two piers are built, they will support one arch, even in the absence of the rest of the bridge, provided that each of them is at least one third as thick as the length of the arch span. The Romans built the abutments first, then added one pier and one arch at a time, working in the summer and fall and letting the incomplete structure stand through winter and spring. Each pier was massive enough to support the equivalent of a whole arch (*Figure 6*).

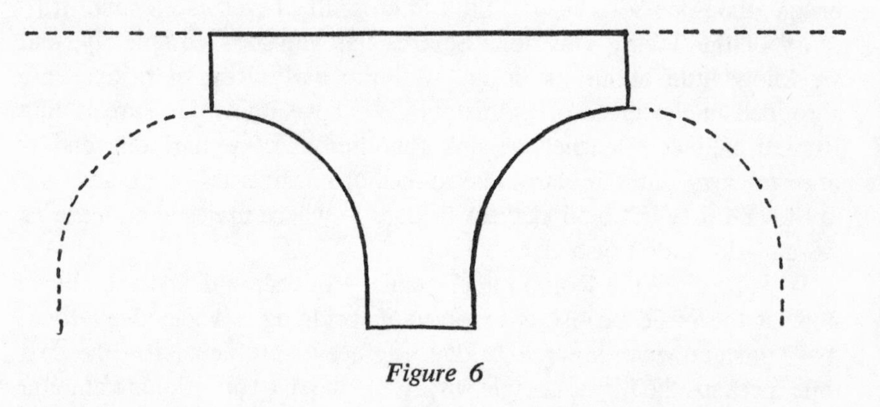

Figure 6

The longer the arch span, the thicker the pier. The Romans usually made their arches from fifty to ninety feet in span, and their piers from eighteen to thirty-six feet thick. All the arches of a bridge were not necessarily the same length; more frequently the center span or two center spans were longer than the outside spans. The Tiber being from 400 to 500 feet wide in Rome, it could be bridged with from five to seven such arches.

But how to construct a foundation for a pier some 25 or 30 feet square (the Roman roadway was generally about that wide)? The answer was piling—timber poles driven deep into the riverbed. But if the river was deeper than a man's height, how drive such piles? To support a stone pier, the piles had to go well in. A stone-arch bridge was an expensive improvement on a timber bridge and, to be worth it, had to last. Yet the most impressive masonry above the water was only as strong as the timber piling underneath it.

The Roman solution was the cofferdam. A wide circle of piles was driven around the pier site. Then a second circle was driven just inside the first. Between the two concentric circles clay—impervious to water—was dumped. Then a bucket gang was set to work emptying the enclosed space. Naturally the water flowed back through the river bottom almost as fast as it could be drained. While hundreds of men—probably slaves—manned the buckets, hundreds of others dug away at the river mud. If they could hit bedrock within a few feet, the bridge would have an excellent foundation. This would have been a rare occurrence; far more often the excavators dug as far as they could, perhaps till they were neck-deep in water, while their comrades desperately plied the buckets, and then the piles were driven for the foundation. These were of alder, olive, or oak, charred before driving.

For the pile-driving a machine was used. The Romans developed several such machines. The earliest, and probably the one most commonly used for bridges, was a weight lifted by a capstan wheel. A gang pushed the capstan bar and raised a heavy stone, which then was tripped and dropped on the pile head. Slowly, blow by blow, to a rhythmic shout, not to mention the curses of the foreman, the pile was driven.

Crushings and drownings must have been frequent. But the timber piles were driven, close together, with stone and mortar filling the interstices, and when they were as deep as they would go, they were sawed off evenly and the rock foundations were begun on their tops. A volcanic clay called pozzolana, found in great quantities at Puteoli (Pozzuoli), near Naples, made a wonderful mortar, unaffected by water.

To diminish the effect of the current on the piers, especially in flood times, the Romans extended their pier fronts forward into the current in a prow shape (*Figure 7*).

These cutwaters, sometimes called starlings, were extended downstream too when Roman engineers discovered that the waters swirling out from the narrow arch openings had a dangerous effect on the downstream side of the foundations.

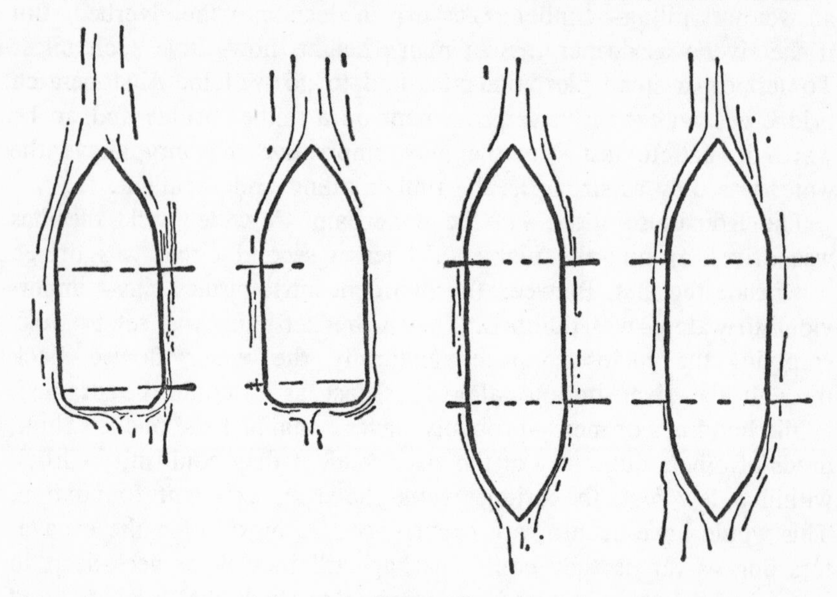

Figure 7

Thus the piers were built. The arches were sprung from about mean water level. As work was recommenced after the spring floods, a pier might stand completed halfway out in the river, sixty feet from its neighbor, which was already joined by a complete arch to the next pier or the shore abutment (*Figure 8*). To link the two piers

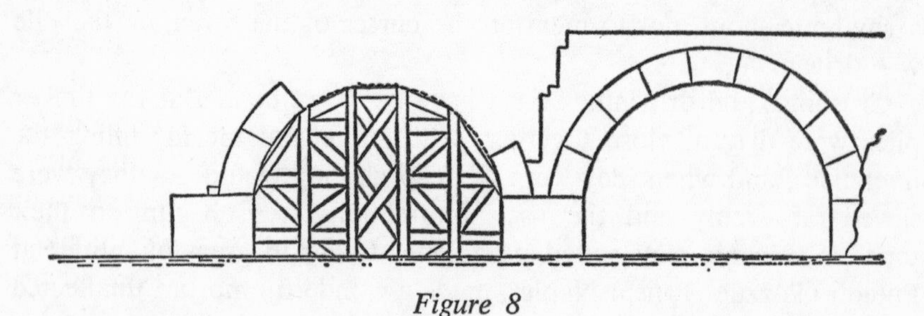

Figure 8

a timber "falsework" or "centering" was built. This falsework was braced partly against the nearside pier, partly against the far pier, partly on intermediate pilings driven into the river bottom. On this timber web the voussoirs—the wedge-shaped stones of the arch ring—were placed in their ascending curve one by one. These were of travertine—a deposit of calcium carbonate—while the invisible core was of a volcanic tufa.

Remarkably, especially in view of the Roman possession of a good mortar, the voussoirs were held together by their shape alone. Sometimes iron was employed to clamp stones in place during construction, but to give the bridges permanence, to make them last as long as Rome itself, the Roman engineer relied simply on the precision of his stone-dressing. Despite the crudeness of his iron tools, he managed to chip stone with an accuracy that made the finished arch stand solidly without mortar.

Laterally, the stones were laid in overlapping rows for maximum stability (*Figure 9*). The vault was solid, not ribbed. Passing under

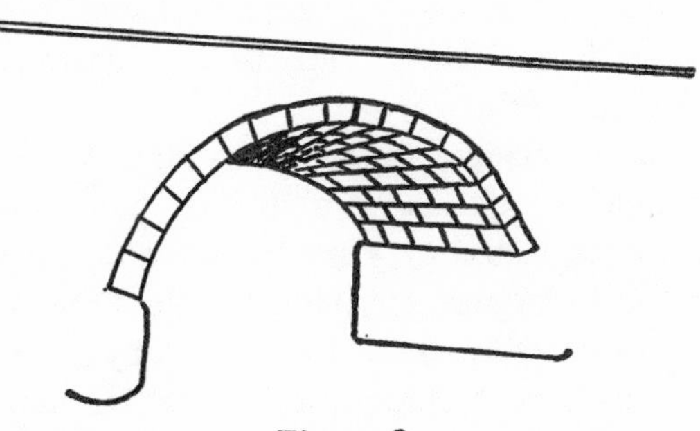

Figure 9

one of these Roman bridges today, through the narrow opening vaulted by the massive arch, one has a sense of the tremendous power and weight of the Roman Empire. This translation of engineering into political terms is somewhat misleading. The Roman bridgebuilders certainly reflected the economic and technical resources of their country in the care with which they worked, and in the determination and confidence with which they attacked truly prodigious problems. But the massive quality of their bridges is owing also to their theoretical limitations. They built exclusively semicircular arches because they did not realize that an elliptical arch could be supported much more easily—a revolutionary engineering advance that came, as we shall see, long after Rome's decline and fall. Also, the Roman engineers, despite their skill in using cofferdams, did not succeed completely in mastering the bottom of the river. They had to build their piers where they could rely on the riverbed, usually where the water was not too deep. This meant unequal spaces between piers, which in turn meant unequal arch spans, an arrangement secure only with the use of semicircular arches and very thick piers.

The first bridges to span the Tiber were of course wooden, like the very ancient Pons Sublicius that Horatius defended. These frequently were carried away by floods, and as the city grew powerful and prosperous they were replaced one by one by stone and masonry. Most of the city's eight stone arches fell into disrepair during the general decay of the Middle Ages; today five are standing in a partly original, partly restored form. One amazingly survives intact, the Pons Fabricius, now known as the Ponte Quattro Capi, built in the consulship of Cicero (62 B.C.), at the height of the Roman Republic. Its inscription records that the contractor would have his deposit returned over a period of forty years—apparently a guarantee of the permanence of the bridge. Thus these Roman bridges were constructed, at least in part, by private enterprise.

The Fabricius, named for a Roman commissioner of roads, was built at a point where the Tiber is divided by a tiny island called in ancient times the Island of Aesculapius, now the Isola Tiberina. The isle was joined to the left bank by the Fabricius, and to the right by the Pons Cestius, built 60–36 B.C. by Lucius Cestius, the city's governor. A novel technique was used for founding the piers of the Cestius, and perhaps for some other Roman bridges. A shoal of rock and masonry was sunk across the river from the island to the right bank at low-water time; as this heavy mass settled, it provided a solid foundation for piers. The Tiberina, which has a natural boat shape, was ornamented with prow and bulwarks of stone and a little temple to Aesculapius, the god of healing. On the Fabrician bridge itself a famous statue was erected, a four-headed figure from which the popular Italian name for the bridge—Ponte Quattro Capi—is derived. This figure has been erroneously identified as the god Janus and even, for some reason or other, as Jason; actually it is a representation of Hermes, herald of the gods, and guardian of streets and boundaries; his four-headed statues, called *hermae* (plural of Hermes), marked the ancient city's boundary.

Varying fragments of four other ancient Tiber bridges still stand. The Ponte Sisto, built in the fifteenth century, contains Roman foundations, and the Ponte Rotto (Broken Bridge), one of Rome's most arresting sights, is all that remains of the Pons Aemilianus—a single arch of uncertain age, standing alone in the river, immediately north of the modern Ponte Palatino.

Two truer survivors played memorable roles in history. The Pons Milvius (today the Ponte Milvio or the Ponte Molle; every Roman bridge has at least two and often three names), built by the censor Marcus Aemilius Scaurus in 109 B.C., is known to every third-year Latin student through Cicero's orations. Here, in 63 B.C., Cicero, then consul, captured the emissaries of the Allobroges when they were en route to a secret rendezvous with Catiline. Almost four centuries later the bridge was the scene of one of the most celebrated battles of ancient history, that in which Constantine the Great defeated his rival Maxentius and secured his claim to the crown of both the Eastern and Western Roman Empire. The day before the battle, marching down the Flaminian Way, according to the famous legend, Constantine saw in the sky a flaming cross with the words, "*In hōc signō vincēs,*" "In this sign you will conquer." Promptly embracing the Christian religion, he caused its symbols to be affixed to the standards of the legions, and the following day won the battle. The body of the slain Maxentius, theretofore Emperor of the West, was flung from the Pons Milvius into the Tiber.

The Milvius fell into the disrepair that overtook so many Roman structures in the Middle Ages, but in the fifteenth century it was securely rebuilt, two of its original arches being retained. In 1944–45, the ancient edifice carried the heavy traffic of modern war as German, Italian, and American armies, including tanks, crossed it in succession. Its only drawback was its narrow (24-foot) width. Otherwise it served as well as on Constantine's day of victory.

Finest of all is the splendid Pons Aelius, built at the height of Rome's glory by the Emperor Hadrian (Aelius Hadrianus) to connect the Campus Martius with the handsome castle he designed as his mausoleum. The foundations of this bridge were extraordinarily broad and were laid with exceptional care, with large blocks of dressed stone anchored together in all directions by stone keys and iron clamps. The 24-foot piers support main spans of about 60 feet; there were originally seven arches, including small side arches discovered only in reconstruction at the end of the nineteenth century.

Completed A.D. 134, the bridge stood intact through the Middle Ages, though changing its name. In the pontificate of Gregory the Great (590–604), a plague raged in the city; the Pope crossed the bridge on his way to the Vatican to pray for the end of the pestilence. In the sky above Hadrian's Tomb he saw an angel in the act of sheathing a flaming sword—a sign that God's wrath was appeased and that the plague would soon end. When it did presently end, the tomb of the pagan emperor was promptly converted into a Christian monument by altering its name to the Castel Sant'Angelo, and that of the bridge to the Ponte Sant'Angelo. The tomb itself had undergone a previous alteration; the soldierly Emperor Aurelian, discerning on the horizon of the third century the future menace of the barbarians, built a new wall around Rome and converted his predecessor's tomb into a bridgehead fortress surrounded by a turreted wall. The castle had a memorable history through the Middle Ages, but by the fifteenth century it was in such disrepair as to require complete rebuilding, a process carried out under Pope Nicholas V. A gate in Aurelian's wall gave access in Renaissance days to the Vatican via the Passaggetto, which was used by Popes Alexander VI in 1494 and Clement VII in 1527 as an escape route from the Vatican to the fortress when foreign armies entered Rome. Clement VII was besieged in the castle by the ruffianly German army of the Emperor Charles V, whose famous French commander, the Constable de Bourbon, was slain by an arrow shot from the castle by Benvenuto Cellini.

The same Renaissance Pope, Clement VII, placed the statues of St. Peter and St. Paul at the end of the bridge. The iron balustrade and the ten statues of angels above the piers, designed by Giovanni Bernini, were installed by Clement IX.

But the most remarkable testimony to the genius of Roman bridge engineers lies far from the city of Rome. Of the hundreds of stone-arch bridges and aqueducts with which these formidable builders strewed Europe, Africa, and western Asia, five in particular, built in widely separated corners of the vast Empire, testify to the remarkable qualities of Western man's mightiest social-political edifice. The Pons Augustus at Rimini, Trajan's Bridge over the Danube, the Puente Alcántara and the Segovian Aqueduct in Spain, and the Pont du Gard in southern France could have been built only in the first or second centuries, the era of the Twelve Caesars and the Five Good Emperors. After Marcus Aurelius, Roman engineering declined, and after the fall of Rome, Europe was as incapable of building great bridges as of writing masterpieces of poetry. The great—and despite everything, the civilized—power that was Rome is perhaps better expressed, in fact, in these four bridges than in all the ruins of the Forum.

The Pons Augustus. Built, as its name indicates, in the shining Roman summer of the Augustan Age (31 B.C.–A.D. 14), this bridge over the Ariminus (now the Marecchia) at Rimini, at the end of the Flaminian Way, is universally considered the finest river bridge of the ancient world. The famous Renaissance architect Palladio first pronounced this opinion, and he copied the span many times in his own sixteenth-century constructions. Because Palladio's own bridges were in turn widely copied, the Pons Augustus, at a second remove, can be seen today in many European cities.

The original was of modest size, with five spans varying from 23 to 28 feet. Each spandrel (pier-side wall) carries a classic niche. The balustrade is solid, as in all Roman bridges, and the cornice running along the roadway's edge projects strongly, carried by dentils—toothlike stone supports.

The Pont du Gard. In the Augustan Age too was built this most soaring of all Roman aqueducts, designed to carry water over the Gard River to the city of Nîmes in southern Gaul. Augustus' administrative aide, general, and son-in-law, Marcus Vipsanius Agrippa, is credited with the conception. The breathtaking beauty of the bridge, owing to the combination of its lofty height and its superb location, almost overshadows its remarkable technical character. To reach the height of 155 feet above the river (as high as the Straits of Mackinac Bridge in Michigan), the engineers built three separate tiers of arches. The first is of six arches, from 51 to 80 feet, the largest spanning the river. The arches of the second tier are of the same dimensions, but eleven in number, to reach across the widening valley. The third tier consists of thirty-five smaller (15-foot) arches. Only in the topmost tier, which extends 885 feet from bank to bank, is mortar used. In the two great lower tiers, not an iron clamp, not a pound of mortar holds the enormous blocks together. For twenty centuries they have stood linked in simple, majestic harmony, every stone so carefully cut that it is supported by, and in turn supports, its neighbors.

In the picture (illustration 7), note the projecting stones at various points on the face of the arches and spandrels. These supported the scaffolding on which the workmen stood while building the second and third tiers of arches.

Agrippa's Pont du Gard was not only an achievement but also an education for Roman engineers. At the end of the first century, Trajan ordered an aqueduct built to bring water to Segovia from the Guadarrama Mountains, sixty miles away. To carry the water into the city a 2700-foot aqueduct 119 feet high was required. We do not know the name of the engineer, but Segovia represents the type of advance in design over the Pont du Gard that comes from confidence gained by success. The two tiers of arches are equal in span, but the lower tier is mounted on tall piers only eight feet in breadth. Compared with its massive French predecessor, the Segovia is more slender, more economical, more sophisticated.

Even more striking is another Spanish construction of Trajan's reign, the *Puente de Alcántara* over the Tagus. The name is curiously redundant, as "Alcántara" is the Arabic "El Kántara"—"the bridge." Several bridges in Spain and North Africa are known by this same name, including the famous arch at Toledo painted by El Greco. The great Roman span crosses the Tagus close to the Portuguese border, and the town also is called Alcántara. This towering work was built by the Emperor Trajan to provide a secure roadway over the steep, narrow Tagus River, which turns into a roaring torrent in floodtimes. Floodwaters are said actually to have touched the soffits (undersides) of the arches, 140 feet above low-water level. The bridge is made of granite blocks laid, like the stones of the Pont du Gard, without mortar. The six arches have spans of from 92 to 98 feet, probably the longest ever undertaken in stone by a Roman engineer. One of the unusual things about the Alcántara is that we know the name of the engineer—Caius Julius Lacer, whose tomb is nearby, and whose inscription has survived, like his work, two thousand years: *Pontem perpetui mansuram in saecula mundi* (I leave a bridge forever in the centuries of the world).

Fifteen hundred miles from the Spanish corner of the Roman Empire, at Turnu Severin, Romania, east of the Iron Gate rapids of the Danube, traces still exist of what is perhaps the most interesting architectural revelation of the texture of Roman greatness. In the beginning of the second century of our era, the ninth century of Rome's, the same Emperor Trajan conquered the trans-Danubian region that today is Romania and added it to the Roman Empire under the name of Dacia. To guarantee the supply line of the legions garrisoned in that wild, forested country, Trajan ordered a bridge more than half a mile long built across the Danube. The engineer was probably Trajan's tamed lieutenant, Apollodorus of Damascus. Two records, somewhat at variance on details, describe the bridge—the inscription on Trajan's Column in the Forum and the history of Dion Cassius, written a hundred years later. The bridge stood on twenty piers of stone, each 150 feet high, 60 feet wide, and 50 feet thick, placed 170 feet apart (center to center)—the whole span stretching over 3000 feet. The piers in deep water probably were founded by dumping rocks clamped together. The Roman legionary was a man of exceptional physical fitness and capacity, accustomed to building his own fortified camp in the midst of enemy territory at a moment's notice. Slaves were used to help haul stones, cut, clamp, float out, and then sink them in position. How many stones? On a basis of rocks cut to two-foot cubes, no fewer than one million, one hundred and twenty-five thousand! These twenty piers, in a broad, deep river on a remote and roadless frontier, supplied remarkable testimony of the supple strength of Rome. The lower Danube was not bridged again till the nineteenth century. As a comparison, note that the Mississippi was bridged for the first time at St. Louis in the 1870s, the East River at New York in the 1880s, the Hudson at New York in the 1930s.

The twenty great stone piers were joined by timber arches, both a quicker and easier method than the use of stone. For well over a thousand years, the 170-foot spans remained the longest constructed in the world.

But possibly even more extraordinary than the construction of Trajan's bridge was its sequel. More than a century and a half later, another emperor, Aurelian, confronted with a more dangerous array of barbarian enemies, decided to abandon Dacia. The legions were pulled back to hold the line of the Danube. The Roman colonists who had been planted in Dacia were left to become the ancestors of the modern Romanians. And Trajan's mighty bridge was destroyed—an operation of military engineering that has been executed a hundred thousand times on every conceivable scale, but never in a more dramatic historical circumstance. The vast military empire, pressed on all sides, carried out a systematic withdrawal to a new and stronger line of defense, destroying as it retreated the first bridge ever thrown across the Danube. Sixteen centuries passed before the second was built. Twelve centuries passed before a bridge of greater span was built anywhere.

Before looking ahead to the fragmentation of the ancient world and the disappearance of Roman engineering skill, hear a famous Roman engineer and architect speak his apostrophe. Marcus Vitruvius Pollio, a contemporary of Caesar and Augustus, author of *De*

Architectura, thus summarized the qualities demanded of a Roman architect (that is, a civil engineer):

An architect should be ingenious, and apt in the acquisition of knowledge; . . . he should be a good writer, a skillful draughtsman, versed in geometry and optics, expert at figures, acquainted with history, informed on the principles of natural and moral philosophy, somewhat of a musician, not ignorant of the sciences both of law and physics, nor of the motions, laws, and relations to each other of the heavenly bodies. . . . Moral philosophy will teach the architect to be above meanness in his dealings and to avoid arrogance; it will make him just, compliant, and faithful to his employer; and, what is of the highest importance, it will prevent avarice gaining an ascendancy over him; for he should not be occupied with the thoughts of filling his coffers, nor with the desire of grasping everything in the shape of gain, but by the gravity of his manners and a good character should be careful to preserve his dignity.

Such was a Roman engineer, perhaps the noblest Roman of them all. His fellow citizens over whom the barbarian shadow was falling might well have added, "We shall not live to see his like again."

3.

The Engineer Vanishes from Europe but Appears in Asia

AFTER the fourth century, no Roman bridges were built. Bridge engineering, together with road engineering and practically every other kind of engineering, vanished from Europe for seven hundred years.

The fragmentation of the Roman Empire after the barbarian invasions was accelerated by the sudden eruption of Islam in the seventh century. The loss of European trade routes in the Mediterranean followed, and the decomposition of the European economy into the small, self-contained units of feudalism. Some of the early barbarian successor states of the Empire tried to maintain roads and bridges, but as the basic political units grew smaller, the great highways were allowed to fall into disrepair. The little feudal agricultural states of the eighth and ninth centuries could not find the resources for important engineering works, and had very little motivation for them anyway. From the point of view of defense, streams and rivers were better left unbridged. Only at crossings important to the few, declining cities were bridges built, and these were cheap timber spans constantly swept away by flood or destroyed by fire.

At the beginning of the ninth century, Charlemagne, the barbarian prince who restored the name and a semblance of the political reality of empire to western Europe, made vigorous efforts to organize a regular road-and-bridge service. At least one of Charlemagne's laws, the *corvée*, a tax paid in labor on roads and bridges, had real effect and provided a solid basis for highway maintenance in later centuries. But civilization, timidly reviving, received a new blow from the

Norsemen who struck at all the European coasts and penetrated far inland in the ninth and tenth centuries. In 886 they besieged Paris, at that time a single island in the Seine, with two wooden bridges. Around the towers that protected the heads of these bridges the battle raged, the defenders pouring down burning oil, wax, and pitch on the heads of their assailants, who finally retired, wounded and snarling, to winter in Burgundy.

Eventually, as the fierce intruders from the North either settled down or were resisted better, trade reappeared. Peddlers carried packs of merchandise on their backs and, if they prospered, on mules. In the tenth and eleventh centuries, wagons could hardly travel in Europe. The fords could not be used even by pack mules for many months of the year. The ferrymen extorted outrageous tolls or slew and robbed their customers.

"In all Europe," Chateaubriand asserted with only slight exaggeration, "there were no roads, no inns, no protection of any kind. Its woods were full of robbers and assassins, and its laws were without force, or rather there were no laws. Religion, like a great column, arose in the midst of ruins and alone offered shelter."

Before we discover how religion offered shelter, and in fact went much further toward solving Europe's transportation problems, we will turn to another part of the medieval world. At the very time that bridge engineers so conspicuously vanished from the European scene, they became extraordinarily active in Asia, where several civilizations were entering a period of lustrous contrast to the Dark Ages.

In the third century, Rome suffered one of her few major military reverses when the Emperor Valerian was defeated and taken prisoner with his army by the Sassanid Persians under Shapor I. Shapor took advantage of his captives' engineering skill to employ them on a bridge-building project. "Valerian's Bridge" over the Karun River in Khuzistan spanned 1700 feet on forty arches mounted on exceptionally heavy piers, for the bridge was designed to act partly as a dam. The substantial structure lasted until 1888.

The Sassanids built many more bridges during the next two centuries, and ruins of some of them still survive. Persian bridges of the Middle Ages were built of brick, with pointed arches, long before brick was used in Europe. The old bridge at Dizful, first built in the fourth century, was rebuilt in part by the Moslem rulers of the ninth century, and was further restored during succeeding periods, though most of the original piers have lasted.

By this time the Roman arch had gone far beyond Persia. The Chinese silk merchants of the Han dynasty (206 B.C.–A.D. 221) had direct contact with the Parthians and other people on the fringe of the Roman Empire. The stone arch made its earliest appearance in the Far East in the center of the Han power, around Chengtu. The "Ten Thousand Li" bridge outside the South Gate of Chengtu consisted of sixty-eight semicircular arches across the wide, shallow Wei River.

Chinese roadways commonly followed the arch line in a "camel's back," rising high enough over a stream for junks to pass beneath, but making it difficult for donkeys to climb over. Considerable development took place in the stone arch in China, but we know little about its chronology. Bridge-building in China was an imperial government activity even in predynastic times (third millennium B.C.), and the Yangtse Delta, where every square mile contained twenty-five miles of running water, demanded bridges. Long before the arch arrived from the West, stone was used in the Delta to give more permanence to the endlessly reconstructed wooden spans. Even if the superstructure had to be rebuilt every year, stone piers made the work relatively easy.

The Chinese cantilever was such a combination of stone piers and timber spans. Originally the piers were made by filling wooden caissons with stone rubble to hold the projecting timbers in place. As time went on, the piers were made of masonry, with slots to receive the timbers. The cantilever was apparently exported from China to India: elaborate cantilever structures made their appearance in Kashmir, where the cantilever chords were made of cedar and the roadway carried houses.

This was a fair exchange, for several important bridge developments began in India and moved to China. The old deck type of suspension bridge, in which the roadway was laid directly on top of the tautly drawn cables, was improved by a decisive change introduced in the northern India-Himalaya region. Two main cables of plaited rope were allowed to sag in a gentle curve. Short lateral strands were hung in U-form between them, and on these the roadway was laid. It was a significant move toward the modern suspended roadway. This new type of suspension apparently reached China in late Roman times.

The main problem with these light suspension spans for foot and pack-animal traffic was the rotting of the plaited bamboo cables. Once more the solution came from India. The Indus Valley in northwest

India was an advanced region and was geographically close to vigorous, progressive Sassanid Persia. Iron was known and worked with great skill in Sassanid Persia, and this knowledge probably reached northwest India fairly soon. A very interesting pair of Chinese chronicles give ground for speculation. The first is the record of a journey to India by the Buddhist monk Fa Hsien in A.D. 399 in search of sacred writings. Fa Hsien, who eventually reached Ceylon and returned to China by sea after several years' absence, wrote:

> Keeping to the range, the party journeyed on in a southwesterly direction for fifteen days, over a difficult, dangerous, and precipitous road, the side of the mountain being like a stone wall sixteen thousand feet in height.
>
> On nearing the edge, the eye becomes confused, and wishing to advance, the foot finds no resting place. Below is a river, named the Indus. The men of former times had cut away the rock to make a way down. There are seven hundred rock steps, and when these and the ladders have been negotiated the river is crossed by a suspension bridge of ropes. The two banks of the river are somewhat less than eighty paces apart.

Fa Hsien thought the bridge "very old." Almost two and a half centuries later, another Buddhist scholar, Hsuan-Tsang, made a similar pilgrimage to India (A.D. 630). Hsuan-Tsang reported crossing "bridges of iron," clearly meaning bridges suspended from iron chains. The bridge over the Indus that made such an impression on the earlier traveler evidently had been given a permanent character by this innovation, far ahead of any comparable European use of iron. Similar iron-link suspension chains made their appearance in China soon after, and it is very possible that Hsuan-Tsang's account was responsible for them. In the eighth century, a Chinese suspension span over the Kin-sha River hung from iron chains, and similar bridges were built in Yunnan and in the mountains of Tibet.

The old bamboo-strip suspension cables were improved considerably in durability by a refinement in their construction. The toughest, inner part of the bamboo was made the core of a cable around which the strips of the outer part were plaited in such a way that when tension was applied to the cable the plaited outer section gripped the hard inner core. There was nothing wrong with these bamboo cables from the point of view of strength. A Danish engineer, H. Fugl-Meyer, who tested some, reported that a two-inch bamboo rope could carry a four-ton weight without breaking. From eight to twelve such cables supported the roadways of long suspension spans.

In the tenth century, Chinese bridge engineering took a dramatic turn. The Sung Dynasty (960–1280) gave fresh vigor to an Imperial tradition of bridge- and road-building. In Fukien, in southeast China, appeared a bridge form never seen before and never repeated anywhere in the world. Fugl-Meyer has given it the name "stone truss," apparently a bad translation of stone trestle. Actually it was a cantilever built up of stones of a size that even the Romans would have considered stupendous. "Each of the three stones composing the truss [trestle] weighed two hundred tons." The unknown means by which these monster rocks were manhandled into position amounts to as baffling a feat as the construction of the Great Wall itself. On these incredibly massive piers huge monolithic slabs were laid to carry the roadway.

Under the Sungs, the stone arch also achieved new stature. Marco Polo, who toured China toward the end of the thirteenth century, was impressed with Chinese bridges as, indeed, he was with nearly everything Chinese. The Pulisang Bridge, with its twenty-four arches, particularly struck the Venetian, who asserts that ten horsemen abreast could cross it. He ascribed twelve hundred bridges to Hangchow, the southern capital, a city that today has little water and few bridges, but in the thirteenth century was an Oriental Venice. To Soochow, Marco Polo gives six thousand bridges, "all of stone, and so lofty that a galley, or even two galleys at once, could pass underneath," but this we must put down to the famous traveler's notorious memory: historians credit Soochow with perhaps two hundred bridges. Even allowing for exaggerations, Marco Polo's account makes it very evident that Chinese engineering had surpassed European in the centuries after Rome's fall. Well-built cofferdams were indispensable to bridging in the muddy deltas, where rivulets turned to roaring torrents in the spring. Chinese engineers in the Yangtse region devised an ingenious arch that could deform without rupturing as foundations settled. Their stone-dressing was on a par with the Roman; the Chinese used no mortar and, indeed, possessed nothing comparable to the Roman pozzolana. During construction they usually clamped large arches with iron keys. By the thirteenth century, the Chinese possessed not only the semicircular arch, but also the pointed, apparently an import from western Asia, and the segmental (less than half a circle). They carried many of their arches high over floodwaters ("so lofty that a galley, or even two galleys at once, could pass underneath").

The Chinese arch was much more economically built than the Roman. Instead of the ponderous, wasteful solid stone, the Chinese engineers built a thin shell of stone and filled it with loose sand and gravel. This practice of using earth fill had a curious effect—plants grew inside the bridges, and foliage sprouted out on the spandrels of the arches. Often a stone bridge face was completely shrouded in leafy covering.

More deliberately conceived decorations were also a prominent feature of Chinese bridge design. Stone lions were particularly favored, as in the "Marco Polo Bridge" over the Yungtin southwest of Peking, though dragons and other beasts often stood as guardians. In Pnom-Penh, Cambodia, an old stone bridge is guarded by seven-headed cobras. Citizens of Peking in the early twentieth century still felt strongly enough about this time-honored tradition to add a stone dragon to a French-built reinforced-concrete arch. Attention was given to other aspects of the bridge's appearance. Arches were often faced with marble (as the eleven semicircular arches of the "Marco Polo"), and balustrades were introduced long before their appearance in Europe. In the Imperial Court outside Peking, at a somewhat later date, breath-taking beauty was achieved in serpentine arches of marble, the most famous of which are in the seventeen-arch Summer Palace Bridge.

Thus bridge engineering in Asia made great strides during a period when the European engineer had disappeared in the stagnation and ignorance of the Dark Ages.

But by the time of Marco Polo's journey, the European engineer had achieved a dramatic reincarnation, though clad in an unlikely costume. One of the stimuli to Chinese bridge-building during the period we have reviewed was a Buddhist exhortation, "If you have money, spend it in digging wells in a dry land, in building bridges where streams run deep." This rule may have derived from Zoroastrianism, from which Mahayana (Chinese) Buddhism acquired a list of good deeds. This form of Buddhism did not penetrate India, where, save in the Indus Valley and the Himalayas, bridge-building was not extensive. (A tradition survives of a bridge from the Indian tip to Ceylon, but even in its legendary form this appears to have been a causeway or dike rather than a bridge.) But in China, bridges multiplied as wealthy old sinners spent fortunes on public bridges to insure their own safe crossing into heaven.

In Europe too, at this same time, religion was pronouncing bridges to be "pious works," and thereby stimulating a great engineering resurgence.

4.

The Bridge Brothers Build the Pont d'Avignon

"Men of all countries, of all ranks, of all states, foreigners or citizens, pilgrims or merchants, whether on foot or on horseback, whether poor or rich, whether with carriages or with horses loaded or unloaded, or with other animals, or in whatever manner they travel, can by virtue of our concession, without being held to any toll, pass freely over this bridge."

—Inscription on eleventh-century bridge at Tours, built by Count Eudes "in order to be useful to posterity and consequently agreeable to God."

A CONNECTION between bridges and religion was nothing new. Since ancient times, bridges had had spiritual significance. Greek "priests of the bridge" were posted as guardians at certain sacred crossings. Roman priests played active roles in construction of the early Tiber bridges, which often involved propitiatory ceremonials and human sacrifice. Later the propitiation was merely simulated: men made of straw were thrown from the bridges.

The priestly connection with bridges accounts for the title of the chief Roman priest—Pontifex [*pontis* and *factus*] Maximus, Greatest Bridge-builder. In the fourth century, the Christian bishops of Rome took over the title from their pagan predecessors, and it is borne by the Pope to this day. The pontiff is literally the bridge-builder, a metaphorical felicity that has been remarked often.

In the Middle Ages, this centuries-old tradition of clerical interest was fortified by the new position of the Christian Church. Not only was the Church the chief guardian of civilized values, as Chateaubriand pointed out, but also it was virtually the sole repository of scientific knowledge in the West. Further, it was the only far-ranging social authority amid the swarm of truculent little feudal states. And, finally, the Church possessed a means of rewarding labor, by classing bridges and roads with churches themselves as "pious works" that would bring salvation to their builders.

The scientific knowledge that the literate churchmen of medieval Christianity preserved from the Romans and Greeks was fortified from the eleventh century on by the development of Gothic architecture. The great cathedrals of Laon, Chartres, Amiens, Poitiers, and Notre Dame de Paris, all built or begun in the twelfth century, were schools of civil engineering, from which graduated a corps of master builders, stonecutters, and masons. The vaulting technique appeared in the West for the first time since Roman days, the earlier Christian church-builders having been constrained to use simple timber roofs to economize on bearing walls. Hans Straub, in his *History of Civil Engineering,* mentions four structural developments of the Gothic cathedrals that had wide application elsewhere, including use of bridges:

1. the distinction between bearing pillars and non-bearing walls;
2. the pointed arch, which is statically efficient—that is, can carry a heavy loading;
3. vault-supporting ribs (the old Roman vaults always had been solid, a much more expensive method of construction);
4. buttresses and flying buttresses.

Thus the Christian Church of the eleventh century united remarkable new engineering techniques with a powerful ideology and broad social-political authority to launch a revival in bridge-building in the West. This revival continued uninterrupted for eight hundred years, with new forces, new ideologies, and new techniques joining in the long advance one by one. The bridge engineer of the East had had his day, and when he at last reappeared in modern Japan, China, and India, he was armed with the technical knowledge and skill of the West.

This knowledge and this skill were accumulated slowly. As commerce and industry rose, flourished, or flagged in one place or another in western Europe, the bridge engineer moved from country to country, from region to region. The first place in which he wrote a significant chapter in history was the sunny Rhône Valley of southeastern France. By 1200, bridge-building was a reviving accompaniment to growing trade routes in France, Germany, Italy, and England. Most of the new bridges were of timber, sometimes of timber beams mounted on stone piers. But the stone arch made its reappearance in a modest way in Provence, first in a little span over the Tarn at Ste.-Enimie. We know little about who built these early medieval arches, but we do know that the Church, especially through its "regular" (monastic) clergy, already was taking an active role. Before the end of the eleventh century, a monastic order was founded in Florence devoted specifically to building hospices and serving as bridge and ferry wardens to guarantee safety for travelers at crossings that had grown notorious. The order soon crossed into France, where it was called the *Hospitaliers de St. Jacques de Haut Pas* and was responsible for arch bridges, with hospices for travelers, at Mirabeau, Malbort, and Cavaillon. In the twelfth century, Benedictines, Trappists, Carthusians, Cistercians, and other orders joined in the good work of protecting travelers at the dangerous river crossings. New brotherhoods were organized in France, England, and other countries, divided into "master builders," "assistant masters," and "certified workers," which undertook not only to guard ferry crossings but to supplant them with bridges. In doing so they wrote one of bridge-building's most beautiful chapters. Among the many bridges they built, one stands out as an artistic chef-d'oeuvre as well as an engineering triumph: the storied Pont d'Avignon.

The lower Rhône Valley was a prosperous region in which literature and music as well as commerce flourished. Its principal town, Avignon, has been described as "the freest, happiest city of the time." On September 14, 1178, a literal shadow suddenly fell on the sunny town: a total eclipse. This natural phenomenon, associated with the crucifixion of Christ, frequently was a serious cause of alarm in the Middle Ages. According to Robert d'Auxerre, the pious chronicler who wrote about it thirty-three years later, a frightened throng gathered in the marketplace.

Under the apocalyptic sky, the bishop began a sermon. In the middle of it, a ragged shepherd youth ran up, shouting that God had commanded him to build a bridge. The interruption of the bishop's sermon was almost as shocking an event as the eclipse, and to claim to have received commands directly from God without the help of the Church was blasphemy, as Joan of Arc learned later. The shepherd boy was banished from the city. But he presently returned and had the hardihood to repeat his words. This time he was put to a test: he was required to carry an enormous stone, far too heavy for an ordinary man, to the river. Picking up the stone, he bore it to the shore, placed it at the water's edge, and declared his project begun by God's command. At once the crowd rallied to his side, and amid scenes of enthusiasm, a collection was taken up, amounting to 5000 sous, evidently an impressive sum.

Viollet-le-Duc, the nineteenth-century restorer and expert on medieval architecture, says that Petit-Bénoît, the shepherd lad of the legend, was the same Bénoît who already had built a bridge over the Durance at Maupas in 1164—that is, fourteen years earlier. This bridge was built to supersede a ferry, the reputation of whose landing, a favorite ambush for robbers, gave the place its name (Maupas—evil passage). After the bridge and its accompanying hospice were built, the place was renamed Bonpas. Bénoît and the brother monks who had done the job took the name *Frères du Bonpas*. In the next few years, this energetic brotherhood built two bridges over the Rhône, one at Lyon and one at Pont St.-Esprit, a few miles above Avignon. They now changed their name to *Frères du Pont*—Brothers of the Bridge.

However Bénoît was inspired to build his bridge at Avignon, it was boldly planned, brilliantly designed, admirably executed. Today only a beautiful fragment survives of the Pont d'Avignon, and its original form has been a matter for conjecture. Viollet-le-Duc believed that the four arches were left from a total of twenty-one; some more recent writers think there were only twenty. At Avignon the Rhône divides into two channels, with the Isle of Barthelasse between them (*Figure 10*). The west branch, called the Grand-Rhône, is larger; the east branch, the Petit-Rhône, is where the four surviving arches stand. The total length of the bridge was not quite 3000 feet, by far the longest bridge built since Roman times, and not soon to be exceeded. If we except aqueducts, the Pont d'Avignon was the longest stone-masonry bridge ever built. No permanent Roman bridge equaled it. The four arches standing today range from 101 to 110 feet, and it is likely that some of the vanished arches must have been longer. Emiland Gauthey, in his seventeenth-century classic *Histoire de la Construction des Ponts*, gives the spans as from 65 to 115.

One of the most striking features of the bridge's design is the sharp angle (thirty degrees) that Bénoît caused it to make in the Grand-

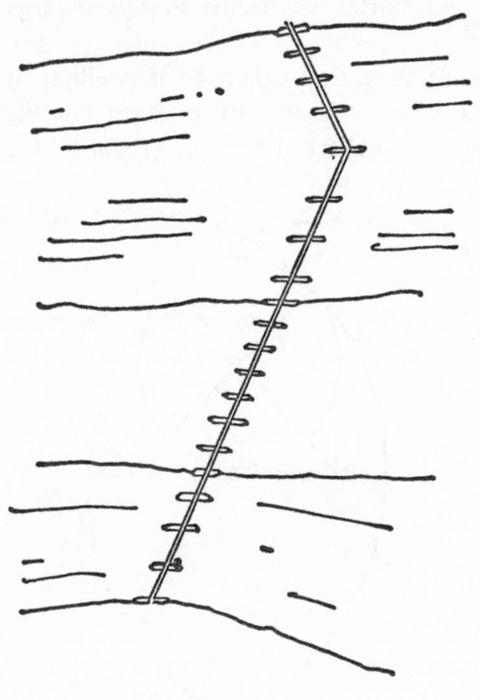

Figure 10

Rhône, in opposition to the current. According to Viollet-le-Duc, Bénoît employed this innovation, which he had previously tried at the Pont St.-Esprit, to resist floods. The Rhône is a notorious river, with tortuous channels and an enormous drainage area, resulting in spring floods as high as twenty-five feet. The arches stood only about thirty-five feet above mean low water. To meet emergency waters, floodways—small arched openings—were built into the abutments above the pier levels, and the usual Roman sub-arches were incorporated in the spandrels.

The voussoirs of Avignon are laid dry, in the Roman fashion, though the blocks are much smaller than those used in the Pont du Gard, which stood as a model only twenty miles away. The Avignon voussoirs are $3 \times 1\frac{1}{2} \times \frac{1}{2}$ feet—of a size that two men could carry without difficulty. The pier stones are bigger—$4 \times 1 \times 2$ feet. (The chronicler does not record the size of the famous stone that Bénoît carried to the river's edge.) The stonecutting is expert despite the volunteer labor force, working principally for spiritual rewards. Later medieval bridges did not enjoy so high a standard of workmanship, and mortar was nearly always employed to hold their arches together.

Bénoît's arch form is itself original—it is elliptical, with the long axis vertical, an effect achieved by constructing the arch of three separate circles, the smallest at the top (*Figure 11*).

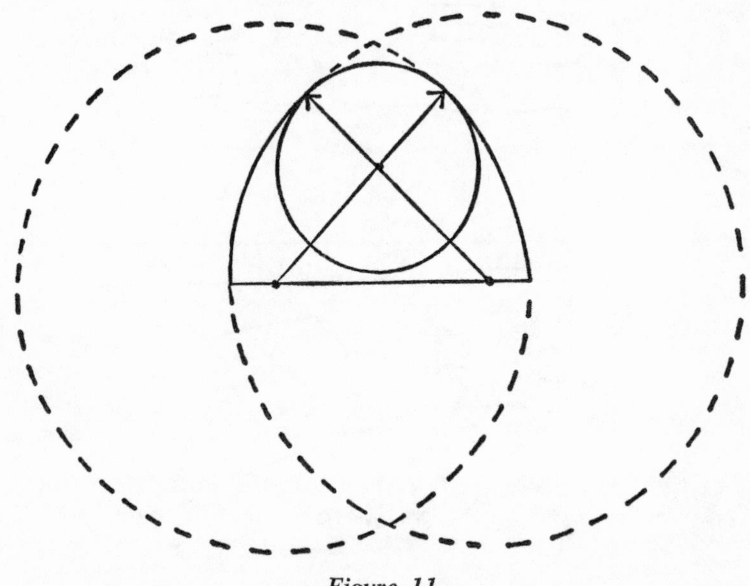

Figure 11

Bénoît's arch required a pier of only one fourth the arch span instead of from one third to one half as did the Roman semicircular arch. The taller arches carried the roadway higher above the water. Thus the Pont d'Avignon represented a real engineering advance in the direction of a freer waterway and a bridge more secure against flood.

Bénoît's cutwaters projected in both directions. His previous experience with the swift Rhône current (six feet per second) had taught him the necessity for protection against scour on the downstream side as well as on the upstream. The foundations were carried to bedrock, twenty feet below the riverbed, by the old Roman method during the summer season.

The roadway of the Pont d'Avignon was of a shape that would have mystified the Romans. Of irregular width, it was exceptionally narrow—sixteen feet at its widest. At a point on the Avignon side, it squeezed down to only six and a half feet. Whatever for, a perplexed Roman engineer might have asked? For two very medieval reasons. First, at this point Bénoît built a chapel, which took up most of the roadway. Second, a six-foot-wide space can be defended easily, and the angle in the bridge section over the Grand-Rhône may also have been inspired partly by military considerations.

The chapel had more than a religious function: it was also a toll station. The Bridge Brothers bought the right to charge tolls from one Alasaccia, who owned the ferry concession.

The charges were not excessive:

Horse and rider	2 deniers
Donkey, cow or sheep	½ denier
Wagon	4 deniers
Pig	1 obole

An obole was a coin of somewhat varying value, but less than a denier, a medieval French penny, the twelfth part of a sou. No charge was made for pedestrians.

Bénoît died in 1184, three years before completion of his masterpiece, and was buried in the chapel—which still stands on the part of the span that survives. Eventually he was canonized by the Church as St. Bénézet.

The Bridge Brothers built a number of other bridges and acquired various ferry and mooring rights along the Rhône. A papal bull from Clement III confirmed these in 1191.

The Pont d'Avignon stood intact, one of the wonders of Europe, through the Rhône floods of the thirteenth century. At the beginning of the fourteenth century the French king, Philip IV, placed the Pope in "Babylonian captivity," in Avignon, a fief of the Holy Roman Empire just across the Rhône from French territory. To command the bridge, Philip built a formidable tower at Villeneuve, on the right bank. The Pope presently built a fortified chalet on his own side. A later Pope had a section of the bridge destroyed; another restored it, but in a weakened condition. During the Hundred Years' War, the famed Breton hero, Bertrand du Guesclin, once defended the tower. In 1395 a Spanish force besieging the Pope's palace cut the bridge; in 1418 the town, once more at peace, repaired it.

Through the sixteenth century, as Protestant battled Catholic in a bitter war that flamed and smoldered and flamed again, the bridge survived. But in 1602 a terrific flood collapsed an arch, one of those rebuilt after destruction. The roaring torrent carried three neighboring arches with it. Repairing this catastrophic gap was something to give pause, and in 1633 two more arches were carried away. In 1670 an exceptionally severe winter produced unheard-of ice floes; they crashed into the piers and collapsed several more arches. At last only four were left.

It is a curious fact that the Pont d'Avignon has lost none of its fame because of its ruined condition. If anything, it is better known today all over the world than when it stood intact athwart the island of Barthelasse. The French children's song and dance, *"Sur le pont d'Avignon,"* actually dates only from the seventeenth or eighteenth century, when the bridge was already a ruin.

Many of the bridges built by the Frères du Pont and the other orders were taken over and fortified by rapacious feudal lords. Yet even they were forced to keep the bridges in repair in order to collect tolls. Some of these medieval bridges still stand in southern France, in fortunate areas bypassed by the wars of old and modern times:

The Pont de Valentré at Cahors (early fourteenth century) has "the aspect of a well-disciplined warrior," in Charles Whitney's apt phrase. To cross it, a traveler must pass through three tall towers with crenellated pier tops, from which fire could be directed against boats in the river as well as approaching troops. Its six pointed arches are of fifty-four-foot span. On the upstream side, the cutwaters extend up to the level of the narrow roadway, to form refuge bays, enabling traffic to pass.

The Pont de la Guillotière, Lyon. The earlier wooden structure at this point broke down under the baggage trains of Philip Augustus and Richard the Lion-Hearted en route to the Third Crusade. The construction of the stone bridge, begun with the stimulus of massive indulgences in 1245, dragged along for nearly four centuries, not being completed until 1570. Of its twenty stone arches, nine are over the Rhône.

The Pont St.-Esprit. Begun in 1265, completed in 1307, damaged in the Second World War, but repaired and still in use today, its twenty-three arches across the Rhône twenty miles above Avignon may constitute the longest surviving stone bridge in the world. It crosses the river in an oblique direction, probably for convenience in pier-founding. The money for the bridge was raised largely by offerings collected at a Chapel of the Holy Ghost, accounting for the name of the bridge and the town that soon grew up.

The Pont d'Espalion over the Lot at Espalion. It was at one time believed that this bridge dated from Charlemagne's reign, but apparently the bridge built by Charlemagne was a wooden structure that was replaced by the present red sandstone, ogival-arched bridge in the eleventh or twelfth century. The high-pointed ogival arch was brought back from the East by returning Crusaders.

The Pont d'Orthez over the Gave de Pau, completed by the middle of the thirteenth century, is one of the most picturesque as well as most historic of medieval bridges, with its three pointed arches and two high piers springing from rocky banks. The high octagonal tower on the center pier was originally matched by another at the opposite end of the large span (which is not the middle span). After the capture and sack of Orthez in 1560, the Huguenot soldiers are said to have thrown the Catholic priests taken prisoner through the windows of the bridge parapet, giving these openings their name, Priests' Windows. In 1814, Marshal Soult, retreating before Wellington's Anglo-Spanish-Portuguese army, posted a company of forty-five riflemen in the 600-year-old tower; they held up the enemy's advance guard for the entire day on February 27.

The Pont de Montauban. This seven-arched bridge has been called the "finest French medieval bridge still intact." Six hundred and fifty feet long, its roadway runs sixty-five feet above the Tarn. We know the names of its builders, who finished it in 1335; Étienne de Ferrières and Mathieu de Verdun. Defensive towers originally stood at either end.

Medieval bridge-building was not, of course, limited to France. Stone arches were constructed in many other European countries, especially Italy and, after the Norman Conquest, England. One bridge of Norman England actually antedates the Pont d'Avignon in its commencement, though it was not completed till several years after the Avignon. This remarkable bridge has so many claims to fame—in fact it may well be the most famous bridge ever built—that its story demands a separate chapter.

5.

Weird and Wonderful, Appalling and Amazing Old London Bridge

London Bridge is broken down,
Dance o'er my Lady Lee:
London Bridge is broken down,
With a gay lady . . .

Build it up with stone so strong
Dance o'er my Lady Lee,
Huzza, 'twill last for ages long,
With a gay lady.

THE nursery rhyme and dance-in-the-round of the eighteenth century (or possibly earlier), more frequently sung in modern times as "London Bridge is falling down," aptly commemorate the most famous bridge that the English-speaking world ever has known. Its tendency to fall down but somehow stand up was only one of the arresting characteristics of this long-standing, ever-tottering wonder of the world. For most of its six hundred years of life it was, preposterously, the only crossing of the river that divided the world's busiest metropolis. If there is one bridge more than any other that the historian, the antiquarian, and the bridge lover (though hardly the art lover) must lament, it is Old London Bridge. For that matter, many Americans who have sung the nursery rhyme are unaware that the incredible old structure has been gone since early in the nineteenth century.

What a bridge! A contemporary of St. Bénézet's beautiful and rational Pont d'Avignon, London Bridge was as homely as Avignon was graceful, as illogical as Avignon was intelligent. The least one can say of it is that there has never been a bridge like it.

The Romans probably built the first bridge over the Thames at London, though the evidence is slight and rather odd. When foundations were being laid for John Rennie's New London Bridge in the 1820s, an astonishing number of Roman coins were found in the riverbed, leading to speculation that the Romans had a good-luck tradition in connection with their bridge. But many of the coins obviously had been new when thrown in. Was a boat swamped while carrying the legions' pay? This implies a ferry rather than a bridge crossing. The number and dispersion of the coins apparently suggest some more recondite accident. And how explain a bronze head of the Emperor Hadrian? As for whether the Romans built a bridge or relied on a ferry, it seems that there is, or was, at least some evidence of iron-shod timber piling. Quite aside from this, it is hard to believe that the skilled and businesslike conquerors who built a permanent road network and a 73-mile fortified wall did not bridge the Thames.

We do know that there was no bridge when the Romans arrived, and if there was one when they left, it must have been timber and could not have lasted long without replacement. Roman London itself (*Londinium*) vanished without trace, as far as historical records go, in A.D. 457. For the next several centuries, there as everywhere in western Europe, construction was meager, records even more meager. Suddenly in the tenth century there is a reference to a London Bridge. Like so much connected with this long-lived historical structure, the reference is peculiar. A widow was tied to a pier at low water and left to drown for having stuck pins in a model of a man she disliked—whether her husband or someone else is not quite clear.

This bridge apparently was swept away soon, its place being taken by a privately operated ferry that produced an excellent revenue for its owner, one John Audrey, or Overy. John was reputed to be as miserly as he was wealthy, and his parsimony caused his untimely demise. Shamming death in the hope of inducing his servants to fast for twenty-four hours, he was mightily disappointed when they greeted the news of the master's departure with feasting and carousing at the expense of the estate. He made the mistake of jumping up from his death bed to rate them, and somebody, taking him for a ghost, brained him with an oar. Old John's daughter Mary had a fiancé. When, according to the story, this young man galloped off to carry the melancholy news, his horse stumbled and he was thrown and killed. Poor Mary Audrey, or Overy, inheriting her father's wealth and ferryboats, and losing her lover at the same moment, founded a church, St. Mary Overy, which supported a chapter of monks.

These monks, like their Continental brothers, became bridge builders. In 993 they constructed a timber bridge, mentioned in the laws of Ethelred the Unready. During the next year, 994, the Danish invasion struck; Sweyn Fork-Beard, son of Harold Bluetooth, sailing up the river to sack London, ran afoul of the bridge with his ships. In the ensuing fight, the Londoners successfully repelled the invader. Sweyn's comrade in arms, Olaf, who became a sort of Scandinavian Roland, returned later and, sailing his ships close under the bridge, made lines fast to the pilings. Then he turned and rowed away, pulling the bridge down. Olaf's subsequent victory is celebrated in the Norwegian Olaf Sagas:

> London Bridge is broken down,
> Gold is won and bright renown.
> Shields resounding,
> War horns sounding,
> Heldure shouting in the din;
> Arrows singing,
> Mailcoats ringing,
> Odin makes our Olaf win.

How many times the Scandinavian corsairs repeated their forays is not known, nor how many timber bridges were carried away by the fires of war or peaceful accidents. We do know that Sweyn's son Knute, invading England in 1016, ran up against a wooden Thames bridge and that he circumvented it by digging a canal through the marshes south of London, drawing his ships west and blockading the town.

When the Normans arrived in 1066, a timber bridge existed, but it was swept away in 1091. William the Conqueror's successor, William Rufus, levied a heavy tax for a new bridge, which was erected in 1097. Forty years later, this bridge or, more likely, another was destroyed by fire. From this fire arose the idea of building a permanent stone bridge.

St. Mary Overy Church stood in a district known as Colechurch. A twelfth-century chaplain, Peter of Colechurch, finally built the London Bridge of stone, song, and history. Of the contributions that came from many sources, probably the largest, of a thousand marks, was from the Papal legate.

The Thames is a little over nine hundred feet wide at this point in the heart of ancient and modern London. In it the tide flows swiftly west from the ocean, flooding the inland countryside; twelve hours later it flows swiftly back. Its level varies with the seasons, and in medieval times, before embankments, weirs, dikes, and the like, it varied dramatically. In 1114, its level dropped so low that men, women, and children waded across. This well-known peculiarity of the Thames perhaps lent color to the explanation of the construction of London Bridge given by Stow, an early historian of the city:

> The course of the river for the time was turned another way about by a trench cast for that purpose beginning as is supposed, east about Rotherhithe, and ending in the west about Patricksey, now Battersea.

Stow's explanation does not stand critical analysis, however. Not only would it have been an extremely difficult and massive engineering work for the twelfth century to divert a river the size of the Thames, but also had such a project been carried out, leaving the old riverbed dry, the bridge could have been built in far less than thirty-three years, and would scarcely have been disfigured by the peculiar design that actually was followed. Rather, the semicircular arches were built one by one, season after season,

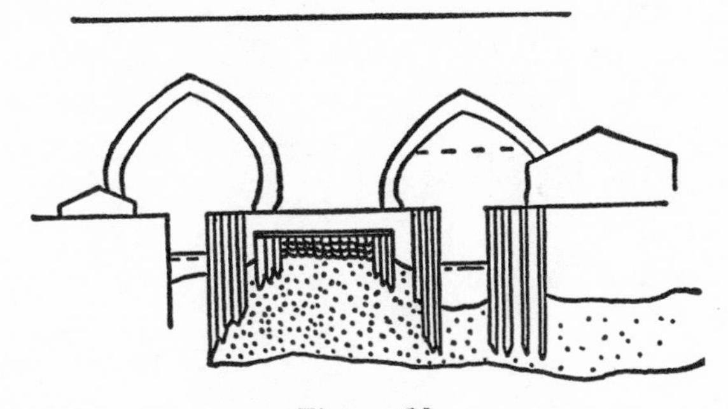

Figure 12

in Roman fashion, except that frequently a season passed without the building of an arch. Cofferdams were staked out in the river, one after another. In the shallow water and mud inside them, piles—later found to have been "sapling oak and some elm"—were driven to found boat-shaped piers of eccentrically varying sizes, mostly from 36 to 54 feet long. The interior was filled with rocks, planks were bolted over the top, and the masonry of the pier foundations was laid on (*Figure 12*).

Gordon Home, chief modern historian of London Bridge, pictures the pier-building as it would have looked to a contemporary spectator:

> As pier after pier was added to the structure, the difficulties produced by the great rush of water through the narrowing space left to it must have made the pile-driving and other work increasingly difficult and hazardous. It is in fact quite possible that some two hundred and fifty lives were lost during the work. Year after year it continued, an arch being completed on the average every eighteen months.

The pile drivers were huge weights lifted by winding on a capstan. Perhaps horses or donkeys were used to turn the capstan, perhaps men. As the work proceeded out into the stream, the whole contraption was mounted on a barge.

> Loungers . . . would have watched the long winding up followed by the sudden drop of the heavy weights which inch by inch brought the

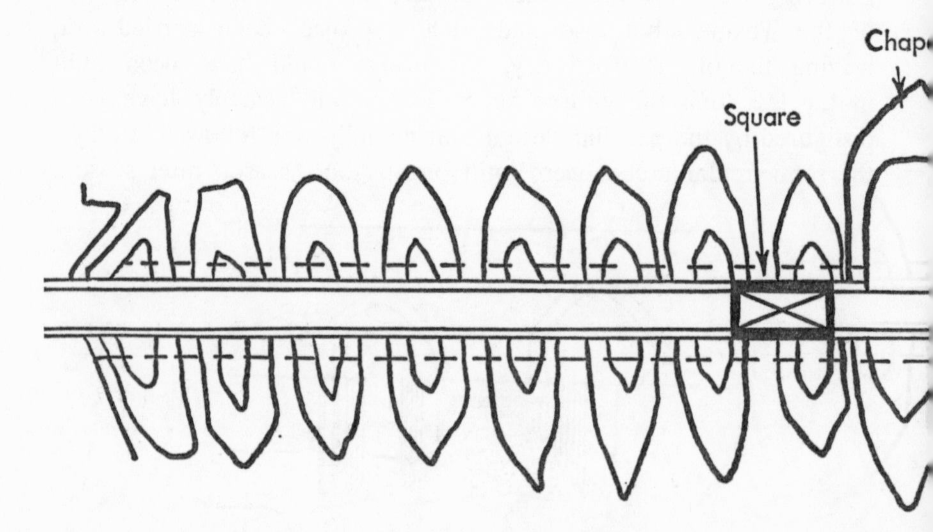

pile down to the level of low water. They would have watched the hoisting of the blocks of stone from the barges, the difficulty of getting the lowest course of masonry placed on the foundations just exposed at low tide, and the pouring in of hot pitch, and later on would have seen the carpenters fixing their wooden centering upon which were placed the carefully shaped voussoirs of the arch stones.

Altogether there were no fewer than nineteen arches in the river (*Figure 13*). Probably Peter of Colechurch never tried to calculate in advance the exact position of his piers, or perhaps even their number, but simply built year after year, as weather, economy, and politics permitted. The ninth pier from the London side he made a sort of king pier, 95 feet long (twice or more the length of any of the others) and 36 feet wide. On this massive tower of masonry he designed a two-story chapel dedicated to St. Thomas à Becket, the London-born Archbishop of Canterbury whom the agents of King Henry II murdered just six years before the bridge was commenced in 1176. The chapel was very popular, attracting contributions that, as an English Protestant writer of the nineteenth century observed, "might better have been expended on the bridge." The bridge was neglected by the combative Richard the Lion-Hearted, and it was completed only in 1209 after his militarily unsuccessful brother John, of Magna Charta fame, inherited the throne. Peter of Colechurch did not live to see its completion; like Bénézet, he was buried in his own chapel. The work was finished,

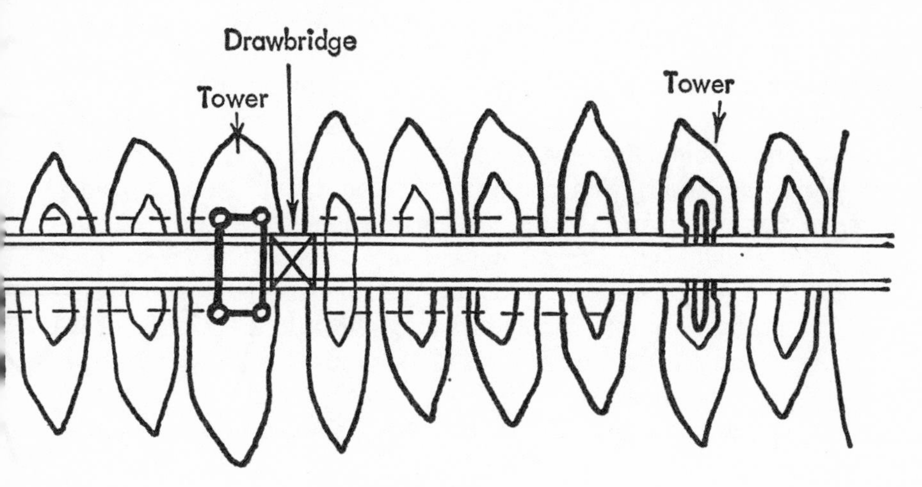

Figure 13

according to the unreliable Stow, by three London merchants; according to another account, by a French bridge expert named Isembert, from Saintes. Very likely both versions are true, and the three London merchants joined their financial and civic powers to the know-how of the French engineer.

The end result was something for which neither a Gothic architect nor a Roman engineer would have claimed credit. The bridge was a miracle of asymmetry. No two piers were alike. At the same time, all were extraordinarily thick. Nineteen arches were crowded into the space of 936 feet. Their piers occupied a total width of 420 feet, leaving only 516 feet for the waterway, or rather for the nineteen separate and unequal rivulets. The widest arch was 34 feet, 5 inches; the narrowest, 15 feet. (We are indebted for these exact measurements to French-Swiss engineer Charles Labelye, who built the second Thames Bridge, Westminster, in the eighteenth century.) The starlings, or cutwaters, which naturally projected both upstream and downstream because the river flowed both ways, were wider than the piers and reduced the waterway still more. An eighteenth-century writer calculated the total waterway when the tide was out and the river level fell below the starlings at 194 feet. The fourteenth arch from the north (London) side was a drawbridge, not primarily for permitting ships to pass, a function for which it was too small, but for military purposes. Either at the outset or a little later, two defensive towers were added, one fronting the drawbridge, and one, especially powerful, at the Southwark end of the bridge. These served their purpose on more than one occasion.

When the tide was running full, in either direction, barely five feet of headroom for shipping remained. From the point of view of navigation, nothing remotely like London Bridge ever obstructed a river, and when we find shipping interests at a later date violently combating the erection of bridges fifty and more feet above the water, with intervals of hundreds of feet between piers, we can only conclude that Thames boatmen had surprisingly little political influence. Besides presenting vessels with a choice of nineteen narrow passageways, the bridge so constricted the river that the nineteen rivulets came torrenting through the arches like so many cataracts. Steering a boat through one of these roaring passages was known as "shooting the bridge." Small vessels were capsized by the score over the bridge's 600-year life; large vessels, of course, could not pass at all. It took a daring boatman to come careening in on the torrent, pointing his prow hopefully at an opening, ready to jump for it if the piled-up waters hurled him against a pier. One such incident is recorded because it involved a nobleman: the Duke of Norfolk crashed into the piling in 1428 and barely escaped with his life by leaping onto the starling, whence he was hauled up to the roadway by a rope.

Prudent passengers sailing down the Thames habitually changed boats, beaching the upriver craft when they came within sound of the roar of the cataracts, proceeding on foot, and embarking in a second boat downriver from the bridge.

The bridge was barely completed when the first, and apparently severest, of its many mishaps occurred. On July 10, 1212, one of London's numerous fires broke out. The account given by Stow is somewhat elliptical, but evidently a great number of Londoners rushed onto the bridge in order to enjoy the conflagration, which, somehow spreading simultaneously to both ends of the bridge, trapped them in the middle. Of the multitude who flung themselves into the river to escape the flames, no fewer than three thousand perished, Stow assures us, which may be taken as the usual extremely pessimistic figure favored by the old chroniclers.

Were there houses on London Bridge at the time of the fire? We do not know. As the bridge had been standing complete for three years, it is quite possible, but there is no clear evidence. To restore the bridge after the fire, a special halfpenny tax was levied on foreign merchants, which suggests that neither bridge rents nor "pontage"—bridge tolls—had been thought of then.

In 1263 the rebuilt bridge was the scene of vivid political disturbances. Henry II, founder of the Plantagenet dynasty, had married the famous French heiress Eleanor of Aquitaine, thereby doubling his kingdom. But the new queen was far from popular with Londoners, who supported the barons' demands for implementation of Magna Charta. When Eleanor prepared to shoot the bridge in her royal barge, the citizens expressed their antidynastic feelings by crowding onto the roadway to throw things, including rocks, at her. Shortly after, when the popular feeling heightened to armed insurrection, Simon de Montfort, a French adventurer with a claim to an English title of nobility, led the rebel forces to the Southwark gate. A sort of incomprehensible medieval scuffle took place in which somebody threw the keys to the bridge gate into the river, nearly trapping Montfort and a few followers. But the London citizenry broke the gate down, thronged across the bridge, and rescued the rebel leader, who survived to found Parliament.

By Simon de Montfort's time there definitely were houses on the bridge, the rents being paid to the Hospital of St. Catherine, a religious institution charged with repairs—already needed—for the structure. But in 1269, Henry gave the bridge rents to Eleanor, who apparently spent the money and failed to perform any maintenance. When Henry died in 1274, the city complained to the new king, Edward I, and the rents and responsibility of the bridge eventually were entrusted to the city. Two bridge wardens were appointed, and took up their station in the Bridge House near the south end. The repair problem evidently was pressing; in 1281 tolls were levied for the first time:

Pedestrian	1 farthing
Horseman	1 penny
Pack horse	½ penny

The tolls came too late to save the bridge from an exceptionally severe winter: at the end of the year five arches collapsed under the pressure of ice.

Reconstruction was undertaken at once, and by 1305 a far more complex schedule of "pontage" was put into effect. Cheese, butter, tallow, lead, wax, almonds, barley, Brazil wood, frankincense, "verdigrease" (verdigris—then used as a medicine), cinnamon, quicksilver, sulfur, figs, raisins, sheepskins, wolves' skins, arrowheads, and dozens of other commodities were taxed. At the same time, boats were charged for passing under the bridge, which certainly seems like adding insult to injury.

By this time the bridge had gained a new and barbarous distinction. Edward was attempting the conquest of Scotland and encountering strong opposition, so the Scottish leader William Wallace became an object of profoundest opprobrium in England. Finally captured, he was tortured and executed and his head, together with that of his comrade Simon Frisell, was put on public display on the northern tower of London Bridge. This charming custom was continued for three hundred years. Usually the victim's body, divided into four quarters, was dispatched to four provincial cities to decorate local bridges. Occasionally during the Middle Ages executions appear to have taken place on London Bridge. Another medieval English bridge, at Haddington, was regularly so used, thieves and other malefactors being left to die a lingering death on an iron hook. The hook was last used in 1745, not for an execution, but to display the severed hand of one of Bonnie Prince Charlie's adherents. The hand, blackened and shriveled, remained there for ten years.

By the end of the fourteenth century, houses and shops—gabled, chimneyed, multistoried—occupied both sides of the roadway and projected out over the river, haphazardly braced from the spandrel walls and the cutwaters. Most met over the roadway, forming an arcade tunnel. Some had basements under the roadway, incredible as that may sound. The space reserved for traffic on the bridge was nearly as limited as that beneath it. Of an original breadth of forty feet, no more than twenty feet were left at the widest points, and in many places this narrowed to twelve or even ten feet. Only three openings along the entire span permitted a brief view of the river to the traveler, who otherwise made his way with horses, mules, cattle, sheep, wagons, carts, and carriages through the dark narrow, filthy, and frequently hazardous passage.

Despite the danger of fire, the bridge was a high-rent area. It was a good shop location. In Tudor days it was especially favored by pin-and-needle-makers, though it had many other kinds of establishments, including one of London's most celebrated taverns, The Bear, founded by a man with the inappropriate name of Thomas Drynkewater.

Priestly processions, triumphal entries of monarchs (such as that of Henry V after Agincourt), royal funerals, and other parades filed through the narrow passageway. One of the most extraordinary events ever to take place on this or any other bridge occurred in 1390. Scottish chronicler Hector Boethius tells how Lord Wells, the ambassador of Richard II to Scotland, challenged a boastful Scottish knight named Sir David Lindsay (afterward Earl of Crawford) to a passage at arms. The Scottish king having agreed, Lord Wells named London Bridge as the place, and Sir David chivalrously proposed St. George's Day (April 23), the English national holiday, for the event. With twenty-nine retainers, and provided with a safe-conduct that still is extant, Sir David traveled to London. Armed with square-cut spears, the two knights clashed on the bridge at a point clear of houses, affording spectators on the shore a good view. At the first onset, neither knight fell; so firm was Sir David in his saddle that the spectators, who naturally favored the home-town champion, cried out that the Scot was tied to his saddle. To disprove this allegation, Sir David leaped nimbly from his horse and vaulted aboard again. A second course followed, equally indecisive. At the third, Lord Wells was unhorsed and injured; in true knightly fashion, his Scottish adversary assisted him from the field and stayed over in London to visit his hospitalized opponent until the Englishman recovered.

Many more lances were splintered in another sport that was carried on under the bridge. This was bridge-tilting, an invention of London youths who shot the bridge, lance (or staff) in hand, and attempted to shiver their weapon against a target fixed to one of the piers. The blow had to be accurately aimed or the staff would not break, whereupon the tilter, standing in his small boat, usually plunged into the stream.

In 1440, Eleanor Cobham, Duchess of Gloucester, was the central figure in another kind of ceremony. The Bishop of Winchester and the Duke of Suffolk, political foes of the Duchess' husband, got the Duchess and a friend of hers named Roger Bolingbroke convicted of witchcraft. Bolingbroke was executed, his head posted on the bridge tower, and his quartered body displayed on bridges at Hereford, Oxford, York, and Cambridge. The Duchess was merely required to do public penance by bearing a two-pound wax taper to St. Paul's barefoot, with an explanatory scroll affixed to her dress.

A decade later one of the most memorable incidents in the bridge's checkered life took place. The English defeat in the Hundred Years' War triggered an insurrection of the peasants of Kent. Their scythe-and-pitchfork army, led by an ex-soldier named Jack Cade, appeared at the Southwark Gate at the beginning of July. London apparently divided sharply along class lines: the rebels were admitted through the Bridge Tower by one part of the population while the more solid citizens took to their heels:

> Jack Cade hath gotten London Bridge, the Citizens
> Fly and forsake their houses,

says Shakespeare (*Henry VI, Part II*). But on July 5, Cade was back in Southwark. A fierce night battle took place on the bridge; the rebels recaptured the drawspan, but were halted in the middle of the bridge. A truce was arranged. Cade was first pardoned and afterward slain. His head was posted on the Bridge Gate (where he recently had placed that of Lord Say, Treasurer and Commander of the Tower) with the heads of twenty-two of his followers.

A little later, in the midst of the War of the Roses, a picturesque desperado called the Bastard of Falconbridge attempted to storm the Bridge, theoretically to free King Henry VI, who had been deposed and imprisoned in the Tower by the York faction. The Bastard was foiled, but burned thirteen of the houses on the roadway.

In 1481 a house of apparently doubtful repute called The Common Stage fell off the bridge into the river, drowning five men. At that time there were well over a hundred lodgings on the bridge. There was even a rent-control problem—at one time tenants were forbidden to sublet at a profit.

In 1497 another peasant rising was crushed by the new Tudor monarch, Henry VII. Originally he planned to post the quarters of the two leaders, Flamoke and Joseph, in their native Cornwall, but, having been advised that this might be taken as an affront by their temperamental Cornish fellow citizens, merely displayed their heads in the usual place on London Bridge.

In 1554 the drawspan was cut down in a skirmish during an insurrection in favor of Mary Queen of Scots. By 1577 the tower north of the drawbridge was so decayed that it had to be dismantled. To compensate for the loss the tower gate, at the end of the bridge, was completely reconstructed in more massive form, four stories high, and crowned by four round turrets. When the new tower was completed the heads were removed from the old one and thoughtfully transferred to the new, which was thenceforth known as "Traitor's Gate."

In the sixteenth century the bridge became a favorite residential street, partly because the river afforded both water supply and sewage disposal, two conveniences lacking in the rest of London. Several very lavish houses made their appearance, and an Elizabethan, Andrew Boorde, expressed the opinion that "such a brydge of pulchritudnes . . . in all the worlde there is none like," one of the few compliments the structure ever received on esthetic grounds.

One of the houses was occupied by William Hewett, a clothmaker who grew wealthy, acquired knighthood, and became Lord Mayor of London. One day the Hewetts' nurse, gazing out of the window, had the misfortune to drop the baby. Little Anne vanished in the torrent below, then bobbed to the surface. An apprentice lad, Edward Osborne, leaped in and heroically rescued her. The grateful father did not forget: years later, though the noble Earl of Shrewsbury courted the heiress, Sir William declared that "Osborne saved her, Osborne should enjoy her." Osborne not only enjoyed the lady, but himself attained the lofty honor of Lord Mayor.

Henry VIII's difficulty with the Church gave Traitor's Gate perhaps its most memorable martyrs and a legend as well. The Pope having sent John Fisher, Bishop of Rochester, a cardinal's hat, Henry commented, "Mother of God, he shall wear it on his shoulders for I will leave him never a head to put it on," and was as good as his word. Cardinal Fisher's head was parboiled before being displayed above the tower gate. But it refused to decay, and after two weeks during which the martyr's face grew ever more shining and attracted ever larger crowds of awed believers, the executioner was ordered to throw it into the river by night. Sir Thomas More's head replaced it, but though the same miracle was repeated, the head that conceived *Utopia* was preserved from the river by the author's daughter, Margaret Roper, who bought it and eventually had it buried with herself.

The religious convulsions of sixteenth-century England had another effect. The celebrated chapel on the great central pier became embarrassing because of its devotion to the memory of St. Thomas à Becket. In 1539–40 the name of the martyr of Canterbury was expunged by a sign painter and replaced by that of Our Lady. A dozen years later the chapel itself was replaced by a grocery.

In 1580 a remarkable mechanical device was added to the bridge's numerous encumbrances. A Dutchman named Peter Moris or Morice obtained permission to install a set of water wheels, turned by the ebb and flow of the river, on the north side. Thames water thus was pumped up at a rate of 216 gallons a minute and distributed by lead pipes to houses in the vicinity. Moris' lease ran for the extraordinary term of five hundred years. His rent for the first year was a trifling ten shillings for occupation of a single arch. The waterworks was so successful that Moris rented a second arch the following year, and eventually left a business that flourished in his family for a hundred years. When it was finally sold in 1701, for £38,000, the water wheels were serving ten thousand customers and occupied four arches—further diminishing the waterway.

Another Dutch contribution was hardly less remarkable. A handsome tall house was built specifically for position on the bridge athwart the pier fronting the drawspan, the position formerly held by the north tower. Shipped to England in sections, this prefabricated mansion, fastened together exclusively by wooden pegs, was for generations one of the most famous and desirable houses in London, universally known as Nonesuch House.

1605: another plot, another head, another miracle. Father Henry Garnet, Principal of the English Jesuits, tried to stop the Gunpowder Plot, but was executed in its aftermath. His head remained as lifelike as Cardinal Fisher's.

In the seventeenth century more wheels were added—wheels to turn miniature corn mills built out on some of the starlings. More and more shops took the place of houses, with competitive advertising. Balsam of chili, for example, was sold by Mr. Tracy at the Three Bibles for one shilling six the bottle, and a broadsheet vigorously attacked a rival, Mr. Stuart, who sold the same item at a shop similarly named. Tobacconists, leather merchants, breeches-makers, stationers, wig-makers, print-sellers, and ribboners shared the bridge with Mr. Tracy.

By this time there was considerable agitation for another crossing. Since Peter of Colechurch's time, London had grown from a town of perhaps twenty-five thousand on the north side of the river to a teeming metropolis of nearly half a million, with a large and rapidly expanding population on the Southwark side. Wheeled traffic had increased enormously, and the congestion on the bridge was universally cursed. Further, Westminster and Lambeth had matured into thriving communities that keenly felt the lack of a crossing farther west. But the influential citizens of the City of London, fearing the diversion of the traffic, wholly funneled into their district, opposed a new bridge with every form of argument to which the government was susceptible. The government of Charles II was well-known to be susceptible to one form of argument above all others. In 1664 the citizens waited upon Charles and respectfully begged him not to ruin them by acquiescing in the erection of a new bridge. The merry monarch agreed to their request, and was promptly thanked in words as grateful as if he had saved the city from a foreign enemy; at the same time the roundish sum of £100,000 was advanced to His Royal Highness by the London Common Council.

Just two years later, in 1666, the Great Fire of London struck, devastating the city north of the bridge, including historic Colechurch. The fire did not spread across the bridge because a previous fire, in 1632, had left a gap in the buildings. Rebuilt five years later the bridge deck remained a favored residential street through the seventeenth century, convenient to the heart of the city and endowed with a splendid view from upper stories and roof platforms. And of course water supply and sewage disposal were still important advantages for bridge-dwellers.

In 1671 a resolution in favor of a new bridge was acrimoniously debated in Parliament, but the Corporation of London narrowly succeeded in getting the motion defeated.

But as the eighteenth century dawned, the creaky old structure was unmistakably entering its decadence. It ceased to be a fashionable place to live. The houses were falling into disrepair and bringing smaller rents to the Bridge House Estates, thus placing more and more of the burden of maintenance on the city itself. Once-magnificent Nonesuch House was falling to pieces and suffered the fate of most elderly city mansions; it was cut up into tenements. In 1725 a fire destroyed the Southwark Gate, ending—one detects an "alas" in the tone of the old historians—the custom of exposing traitors' heads.

In the 1740s it finally became impossible to resist the vehement pressure for a second bridge, and Westminster, a graceful elliptical stone arch, rose to make the old bridge look even worse by comparison. Labelye, the engineer who built Westminster, was commissioned to carry out an extensive reconstruction of Old London. While this was under way, a temporary timber bridge, the first in seven hundred years, was thrown over the Thames—and burned down. The renovation that Labelye carried out was so extensive that when the ancient structure was finally demolished sixty years later, two thirds of the stone belonged to his reconstruction.

Between 1754 and 1759, Labelye removed the houses and other buildings, widened the no-longer-encumbered roadway, and made an effort to expand the waterway by removing the great central pier and the two central arches and replacing them with a single arch. This massive alteration presently proved imprudent, for the added strain on some of the neighboring arches disturbed foundations and threatened the whole precarious structure. John Smeaton, a leading British engineer of the day, was called in; he recommended dumping rock to fill up the cavity left by removal of the central pier and by the scour of the current. But the scouring continued with unabated violence around the piers supporting the new arch. Quantities of stone had to be dumped continuously, leading to the formation of a reef below the bridge, stretching from shore to shore, and nearly uncovered at low tide. The exasperation of Thames boatmen, continuous for six centuries, now possibly reached its height.

Toll schedules of the eighteenth century reveal the increase in the variety of traffic since the bridge's early days, when no charge had been listed for vehicular traffic. In 1756, coaches, chariots, berlins, and calashes all were listed, with three different categories for each

—six-or-more-horse (two shillings), four-horse (one shilling six), less than four-horse (one shilling). The cumbrous medieval practice of charging for merchandise and produce by kind and weight long had been abandoned. "Waggons, wains, carriages, carts" drawn by "four or more horses or other beasts" cost a shilling; the same vehicles with fewer than four animals, sixpence. A horse, mule, or ass was charged the same—one penny—whether laden or unladen, showing the diminished importance of this ancient form of transport. As for pedestrians, they passed over the venerable footway for a ha'penny—except on Sunday, when the charge rose to a penny.

Traffic passing under the bridge continued to be charged toll. Barges, lighters, and other craft of less than five tons' burden paid twopence. Up to ten tons, the boats paid sixpence. Over twenty-five tons, the charge was a shilling. Few vessels much bigger than twenty-five tons ever "shot the bridge." In 1782, tolls were abolished entirely.

Tottering, staggering, not quite falling down, hanging on somehow, like an elderly tippler on his last legs, London Bridge still stood as the nineteenth century dawned. It was the anachronistic marvel of the new age, universally cursed, despised, ridiculed, and loved. At last even Parliament, even the City of London, admitted that it had to go. How it was finally replaced we shall see in a later chapter. We have gone far ahead of our story chronologically in order to keep London Bridge within compact bounds, something history itself was unable to do. On our bridge time-line we are still in the Middle Ages (*Figure 14*).

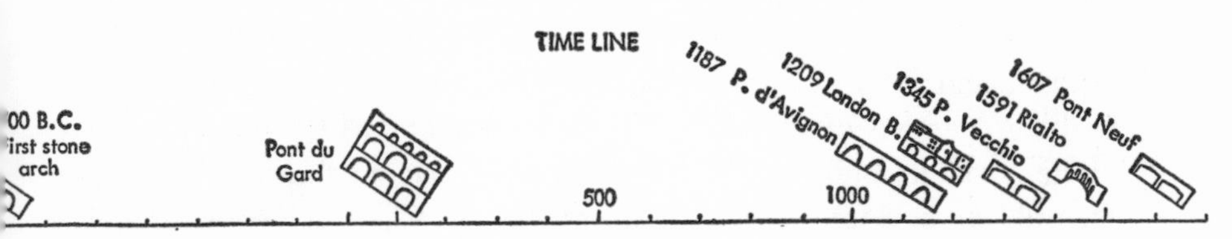

Figure 14

As we have observed, Peter of Colechurch's construction, however fascinating its history, left something to be desired from an engineer's point of view. In the fourteenth and fifteenth centuries several bridges were built that were far ahead of Old London in design, and they scarcely lag behind it in historic interest.

6.

Out of the Middle Ages by the Rialto Bridge

ENGINEERING, like art, develops with commerce and industry, and it is not surprising that the history of the bridge takes us back to Italy in the fourteenth century. Florence was the most advanced manufacturing city in Europe; thither wool grown in agricultural England and turned into rough cloth in Flanders or France was brought for finishing and dyeing. This medieval factory metropolis was very small; hardly more than thirty thousand workers could have been enclosed within its walls. But it was a rich little town, and in 1345 it undertook to build a stone-arch bridge across its river, the 300-foot-wide Arno.

This was a much more sophisticated structure than Old London Bridge, and its very form indicated Florentine leadership. It is the earliest example of a bridge whose arches are wider than a semicircle. How its builder, Taddeo Gaddi, discovered that such a "segmental" arch would stand we do not know. The segmental arch is still part of a circle: it is simply a smaller arc of a larger circle (*Figure 15*).

Such an arch has a profoundly different structural effect from that of the semicircular arch. Where the semicircular arch pressed down in a wholly vertical direction, the segmental arch introduced the element of horizontal thrust. How much of the pressure exerted on a pier by the thrust of an arch of given dimensions was horizontal and how thick did the pier have to be made to withstand it? Fourteenth-century mathematics could not solve this problem. Gaddi had to act

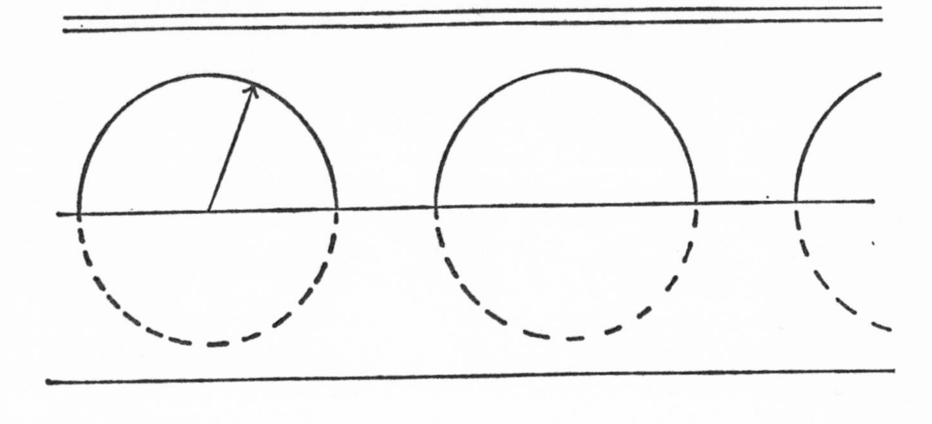

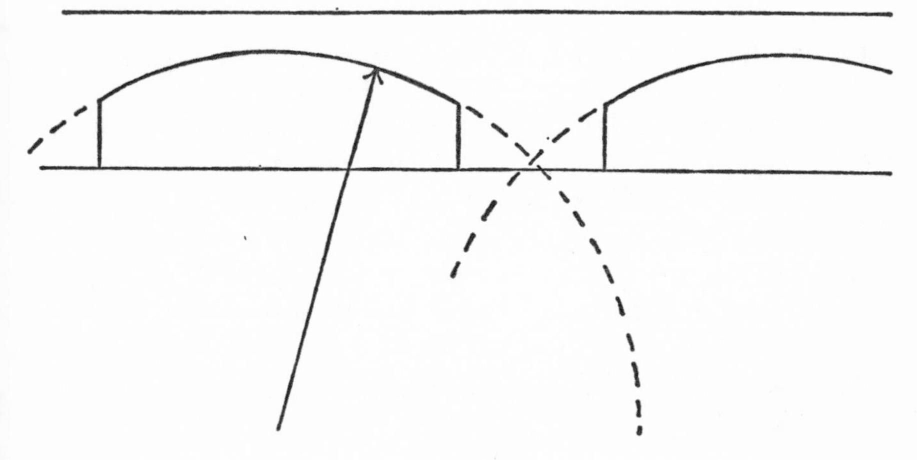

Figure 15

on intuition or experience, and of the latter he could have had very little.

The advantages of the segmental arch were obvious. In many locations the semicircular arch demanded steeply inclined roadways, while a flatter arch could keep the roadway level enough for easy wagon passage (*Figure 16*).

Requiring fewer piers in the stream than the semicircular arch, the segmental offered less obstruction to navigation and at the same time freer passage to floodwaters (*Figure 17*).

Another effect of the segmental arch is esthetic, perhaps in fourteenth-century Florence a decisive consideration. The symmetrical Ponte Vecchio (central span 100 feet, side spans 90 feet) is not only a bridge but also a two-story arcade, the upper gallery connecting the

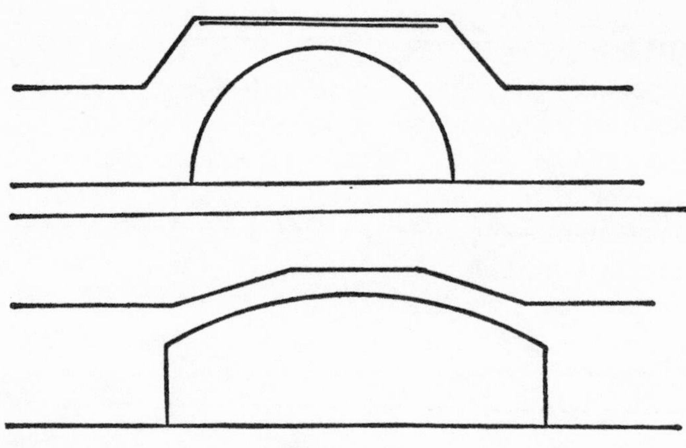

Figure 16

Pitti and Uffizi and other palaces, the lower lined with a double row of jewelers' shops. The Romans never would have thought of such an arrangement, for they had no need of it. The sudden flood of new wealth to Florence created the Renaissance juxtaposition of private palaces and precious-metal artisans.

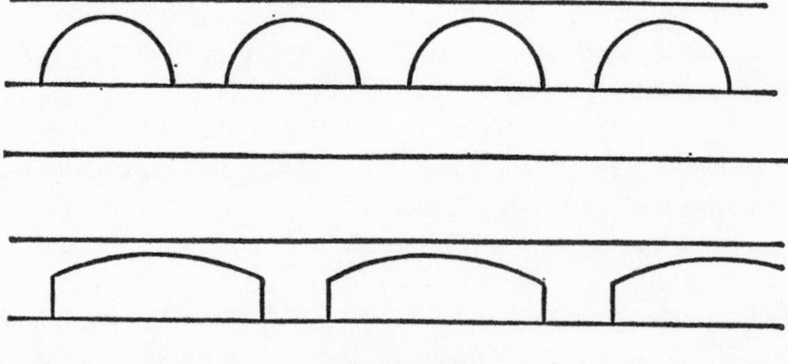

Figure 17

Still another advantage was the potential span length. This was dramatically illustrated by a remarkable single-span segmental arch over the Adda at Trezzo, in the Duchy of Milan, built in 1370–71. This arch, 236 feet, was the longest ever built in Europe, exceeding Trajan's 170-foot timber arches over the Danube. The Trezzo continued to hold the record for four centuries. A single span did have a serious weakness, however; it could readily be destroyed. This fate overtook the Trezzo in 1416. Few single-span stone arches ever were built.

Late in the fifteenth century, the adventure-bent French king Charles VIII invaded wealthy Italy, made several brilliant but ephemeral conquests, and returned to Paris empty-handed. Not quite empty-handed, however, for he brought back several Italian artists and engineers. One of these, a priest named Fra Giovanni Giocondo, who later helped to build St. Peter's in Rome, gave Paris its first stone-arch bridge. The old timber Pont Notre-Dame, built in 1413, was crowded with houses and shops that became the first in Paris to receive street numbers. By the end of the century, the bridge grew ramshackle, and the city magistrates tardily met in emergency session. Their order to evacuate arrived too late; part of the structure collapsed, causing several deaths. The new king, Louis XII, an energetic and enlightened young man, sent the dilatory magistrates to prison and ordered the bridge rebuilt in enduring stone. Fra Giocondo became the chief engineer of the bridge, which was erected in the record time of seven years (1500–1507). He introduced a new feature of design that was repeated in many later French bridges, the *corne de vache*, or cow's horn. This was a trick for extending the archivolt (the decorative exterior arch rib) outward to provide a broader deck to accommodate the houses and at the same time to facilitate passage of floodwaters by funneling the stream (*Figure 18*).

While the Pont Notre-Dame was establishing a new mark for speed in building, another great European bridge was setting a reverse record, while signaling the emergence of another city and another region of civilization. In the thirteenth century, Bohemia was an agricultural region, but in the fourteenth, precious metals were found in the Erzegebirge and the Carpathians, the mountain ranges that ringed the little country. Prague, a village on the Moldau River at its intersection with the trade route from Hamburg and north Germany to Vienna and Italy, suddenly gained importance and grew into a prosperous town. By the middle of the fourteenth century, the ambitious project of bridging the Moldau in stone was undertaken. A wooden crossing suffered the usual misfortunes of wooden bridges; damaged repeatedly by floods, it was finally swept away.

The Moldau at Prague is nearly two thousand feet wide, more than double the width of the Thames at London. The immense project was begun in 1357 by the enlightened Hapsburg emperor Karl IV, founder of the universities of Vienna and Prague. But interruptions by politics, religion, war, and finance plagued the job from the start. The rector of the University of Prague, Jan Huss, began the

Figure 18

Protestant Reformation a hundred years before Luther and became Bohemia's national martyr. The troubles accompanying the Hussite movement and subsequent fifteenth-century turmoil postponed until 1503 the completion of the bridge, which retained the name of its original promoter. The Karlsbrücke stood as the longest entirely-over-water bridge in Europe, exceeded only by the Pont d'Avignon, which rested partly on an island. Figure 19 shows a scale comparison.

Thirty statues of men and saints decorated the finished structure, including a bronze figure of St. John of Nepomuk, the martyr and patron saint of Bohemia, whose body had been thrown into the Moldau at the spot where the bridge was built. In 1620, when Prague was menaced by Imperial troops during the Thirty Years' War, St. John's image was seen fighting in the ranks of the defenders. The saint's aid was apparently of limited military value, for the Bohemian Protestants, defeated in the Battle of White Mountain, had to submit, and the heads of twenty-seven of their leaders were soon displayed on the tower of the Karlsbrücke. Twenty-eight years later, the fortunes of war having turned against the Imperialists and Catholics, Prague was threatened again, this time by Protestant Swedes. The hard-pressed defending troops succeeded in repelling the enemy

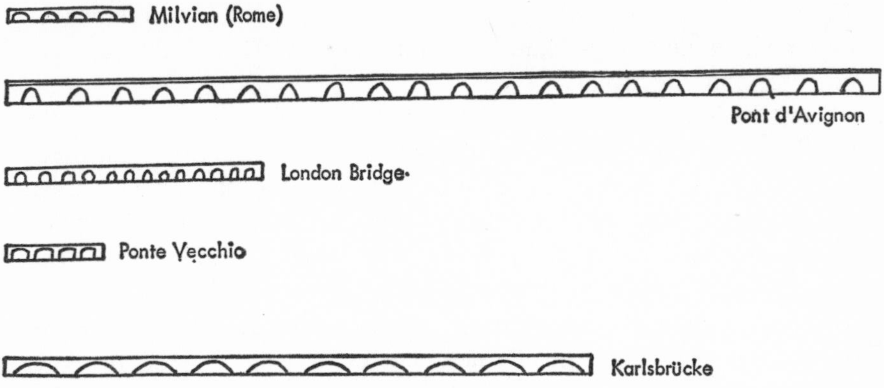

Milvian (Rome)

Pont d'Avignon

London Bridge

Ponte Vecchio

Figure 19

only with the aid of two civilian contingents from the city, one furnished by the Prague butchers, the other by the city's Jews. In recognition of their valor, the butchers were given guild status and the Jews presented with a captured Swedish flag.

The Karlsbrücke was often a place of punishment. Besides the heads, which occasionally reappeared, the gate tower had a room in its second story used for the imprisonment of "profligates." Offenders, notably bakers who gave short weight, were sometimes lowered in baskets and ducked in the Moldau.

If the fourteenth century is symbolized by the Ponte Vecchio and the fifteenth by the Karlsbrücke, the bridge of the sixteenth century is certainly the Ponte di Rialto at Venice. This is the bridge of the High Renaissance. The Renaissance, it should be remembered, was a period of intense economic activity on a more and more sophisticated level. Renaissance engineering likewise rapidly acquired new skills. The Renaissance engineers and mathematicians worked largely from practice to theory, the reverse of the modern method. They formulated such principles as those of the lever and the inclined plane from watching the ancient devices at work. The pulley, the windlass, and the block and tackle were practical answers to practical problems long before their theoretical functions were explored. The toothed gear is a typical piece of Renaissance mechanics, highly pragmatic, practically impossible to conceive theoretically.

Perhaps the most important sixteenth-century device from the point of view of bridge-building was one of the simplest: the treadwheel. A picture in the Vatican Museum in Rome shows a Renaissance building site with pulley blocks and windlasses, and a large treadwheel inside which men are walking and climbing. Simple, but cheap, trouble-free, and effective.

Most of these Renaissance inventions actually were made while the Rialto Bridge was in its prolonged planning stage. The business district in which Shylock complained that Antonio had many a time and oft rated him about his money and his usances witnessed the ceremonial opening of the world's most pictured bridge in 1591, only five years before Shakespeare wrote, but the project dated back to the beginning of the century. Together with the charm that attracted Francesco Guardi, Turner, and other painters, and the historical images it summons up of the days when Venice "held the gorgeous East in fee," the Rialto Bridge is something of an engineering mystery. When interest in engineering history developed in the eighteenth century, records of the Rialto were obscure and conflicting. There was a tradition that Michelangelo had built the bridge. Vincenzo Scamozzi, author of a notable book on engineering, half claimed credit. There were many other alleged design engineers. But nineteenth-century Italian scholars subjected these traditions to exhaustive analysis and pronounced in favor of a remarkable old man named Antonio da Ponte. Da Ponte's design climaxed a long history. The Rialto became the Wall Street of Venice because it is at the narrowest part of the Grand Canal. The town, founded amid swamps by refugees from the barbarian invasions of the late Roman Empire, profited from its position on the Adriatic as trade revived in the Middle Ages. Boats were not so much like streetcars, as a later idiom has it, as like wagons. No bridge was built over the Grand Canal till 1252, during the reign of Zeno, the forty-fourth Doge. This timber span was paid for by a toll charge that gave it its name: the Money Bridge.

Naturally the Money Bridge required more or less constant repair. It had to be completely rebuilt twice in the fifteenth century, in 1401 and 1431. In 1450 a serious accident occurred as a crowd thronged on it to witness the entry of a current celebrity, the Hapsburg emperor Frederick III. The iron rails apparently gave way, causing a number of citizens to plunge into the canal and drown. A few years later, in 1458, the bridge was enlarged and for the first time lined with shops. The rent from these displaced the toll, which no longer was charged, and the name of the bridge was changed from the Money to the Rialto (for the district—*Rivo alto,* high bank).

A STONE AGE BRIDGE

1. In what is now Somerset, England, Neolithic man dragged these huge slabs into position on boulder piers.

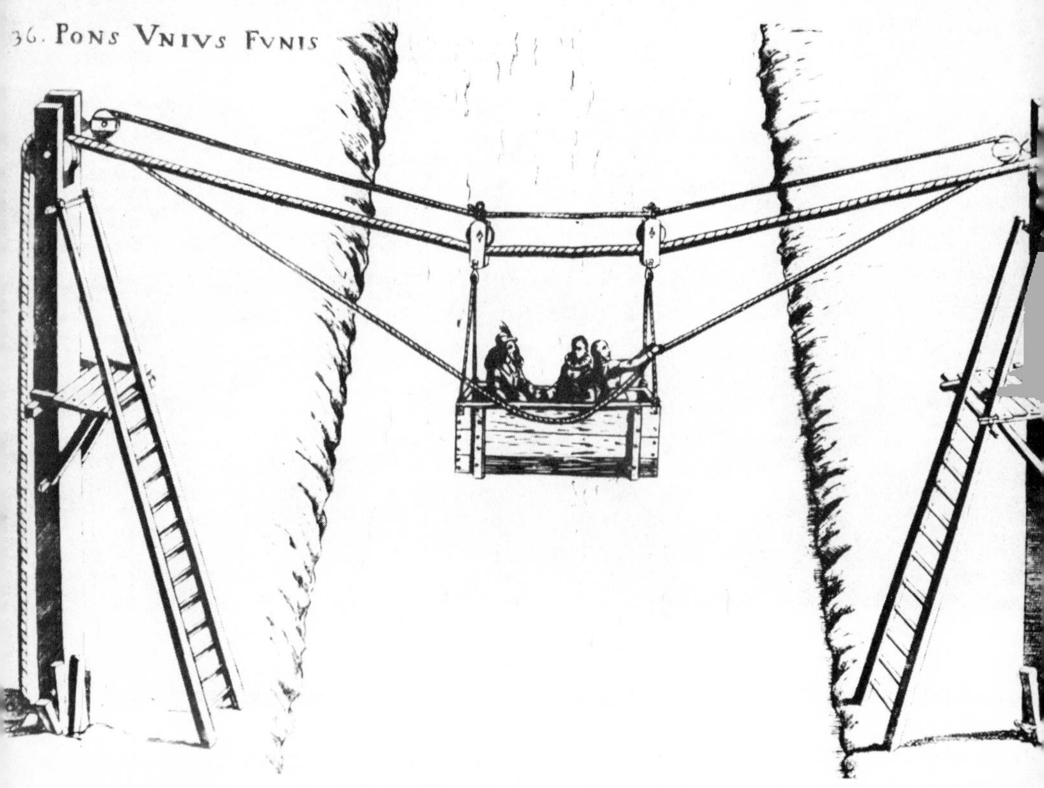

TRANSPORTER BRIDGES

2, 3. *(Above)* Natives of the Peruvian Andes pulled themselves across gorges on single cables made from fibrous plants. *(Below)* A more sophisticated version of the same device appeared in an Italian Renaissance engineering book by Fausto Veranzio.

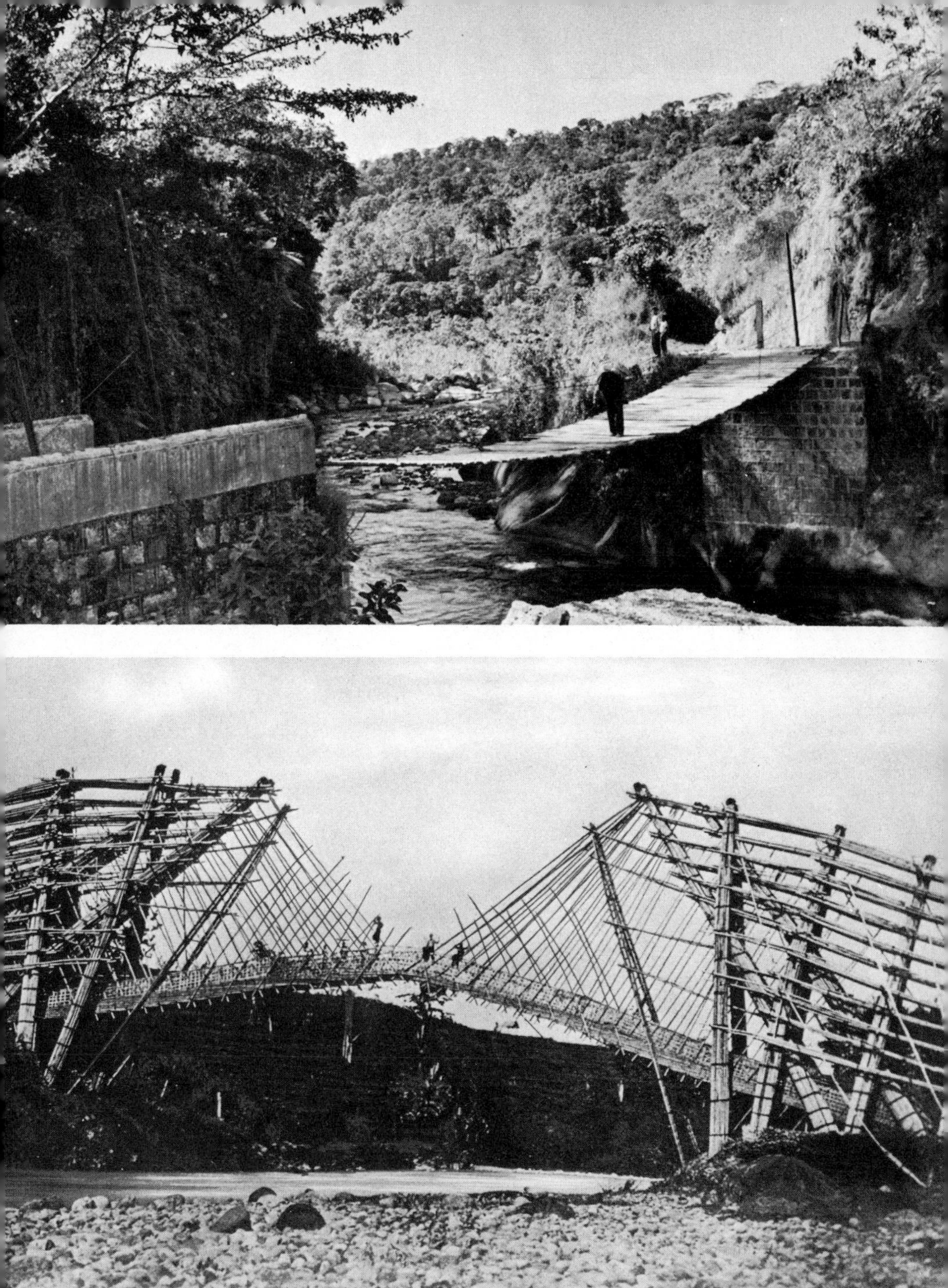

4, 5. *(Above)* Primitive suspension bridge near San Marcos in Guatemala is characterized by the principal feature of ancient suspensions: the roadway is laid directly on the cables. Similar bridges hundreds of feet long were built in the Andes and elsewhere. *(Below)* A real What-Is-It, built in Java of ancient materials and by ancient methods, and probably rebuilt many times. It still was standing in the early part of this century. It combines in one incredible crossing the four great bridge forms: suspension, cantilever, truss, and arch.

THE GRANDEUR THAT WAS ROME

6, 7. *(Above)* The Ponte Sant' Angelo was built by Hadrian in the second century to connect the city with the massive pile across the Tiber which was successively emperor's tomb, fortifieation, and Pope's castle. *(Below)* The Pont du Gard, standing in ageless majesty near Nîmes, is perhaps the most nearly immortal of all the creations of Roman engineering. Note the stone pegs projecting from pier faces which supported scaffolding and timber falsework during construction.

THE PONT D'AVIGNON

8. The Rhône flows on, past the surviving arches that St. Bénézet miraculously built eight hundred years ago, the first great medieval bridge.

TOLEDO, EL KÁNTARA

9. This medieval span over the Tagus, painted by El Greco in his *View of Toledo*, is one of several Spanish bridges called El Kántara, Arabic for "The Bridge."

MOSTAR

10. Built by the Turks in what is now Yugoslavia, the Mostar is a contemporary of Ivo Andrić's "Bridge on the Drina."

THE PONT-NEUF

11. The history of Paris and France has been written on the three-and-a-half-century-old roadway of this storied bridge... built by Henri IV, fought over by the Frondeurs, tramped by the Marseille battalion of '92. The long arm (on the left in the picture) was rebuilt by Napoleon III; the short arm to the Left Bank is virtually intact. In the foreground is another famous

The decision to build a stone arch apparently can be traced to a fire that destroyed most of the quarter on January 10, 1513, though the flames actually were stopped short of the bridge. The decision remained a dead letter; few bridges ever get built merely because an existing bridge could be improved on. What happened next is a very interesting story in the light of the modern city and its multiple engineering problems. The Rialto Bridge was not rebuilt in stone, but more urgently desired constructions took place in the vicinity; factories on one side and palaces on the other, until the canal banks were so tightly pre-empted that abutments for a stone bridge became a problem. The existing timber bridge was rebuilt in 1524 with a draw feature—two bascule spans (*Figure 20*).

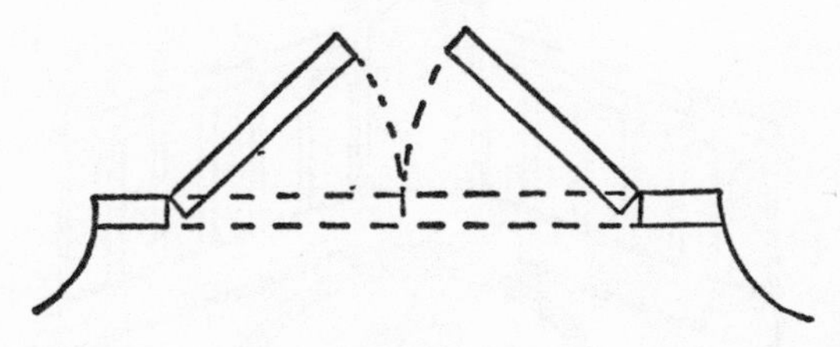

Figure 20

Through this opening passed the great ships that took part in Venice's Ascension Day procession celebrating the city's symbolic marriage with the sea.

But while the impinging buildings made construction of a stone arch more difficult, they also made it more desirable. Venice was at the height of its prosperity, a commercial republic whose ships traversed the Mediterranean, carrying European wool, metals, leather, furs, lumber, and soap to trade for the spices, perfumes, fabrics, and slaves of the Levant and the Orient. Vasco da Gama's conquest of the Cape of Good Hope route to India had not yet had its effect. As the result of a competition, the Doge and the Senate of the wealthy republic commissioned Fra Giocondo to design a permanent Rialto Bridge. The gifted brother drew his design, but it was never built and no trace of the plans remain.

The project was postponed repeatedly, and as it was postponed, projects already accepted passed into discard, changing conditions on the waterfront making them impractical. In 1570, after examination of several competitive designs, that of the celebrated Andrea Palladio was accepted, but war broke out with the Turks and the expensive plan was dropped. The Battle of Lepanto, a victory in which Venetian ships played a conspicuous role, lifted Venice to perhaps the pinnacle of her glory, though shifting trade routes already were forecasting her decline. In 1587 a new competition was held, the winner was a distinguished architect named Antonio da Ponte. Da Ponte apparently was already the grand old man of Venetian architecture, but none of his previous work has come down to us; he would remain totally unknown to posterity had he retired at sixty-five. As

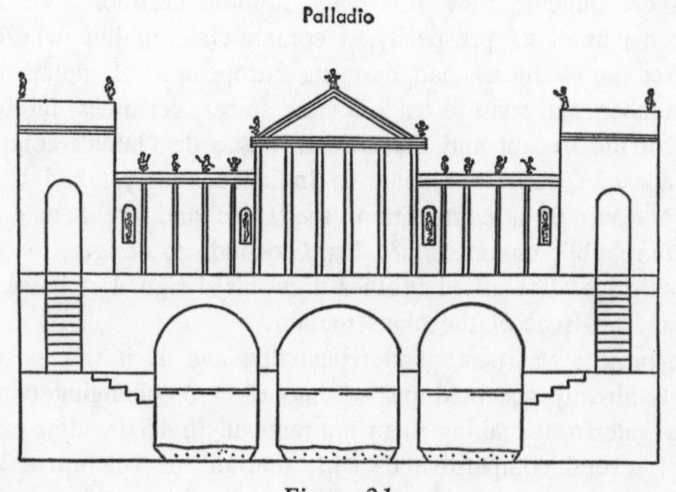

Figure 21

it was, this lively septuagenarian not only built the Rialto Bridge (we believe), but two years later also built the Bridge of Sighs.

A comparison between Da Ponte's design and Palladio's is interesting (*Figure 21*).

The lower chord of Da Ponte's bridge, as built, is only 83 feet, the height 18 feet 5 inches, the width between the balustrades a generous 66 feet. The deck is thus a broad rectangle, gently sloping upward from either side, and more than half covered by the arcaded shops. These are arranged in a unique way: four rows of tiny boutiques fronting on three roadways, the middle 18 feet 6 inches wide, the two outer promenades each 9 feet 3 inches (*Figure 22*).

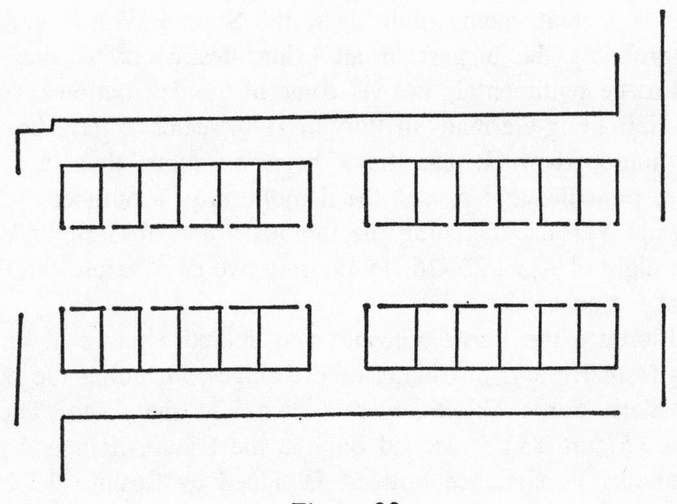

Figure 22

Work was begun in 1587 on February 1, a time when the waters of the Venetian canals were at their lowest, making it easy to construct the cofferdams, drive the piles, and build the foundations. The first stones of the arch were laid in June 1588. For its length it is perhaps the most lavishly furnished of all bridges, though Da Ponte's design was considerably more austere than some of the other plans. Its total cost, including its famous decorative sculpture, ran to the staggering figure of 250,000 ducats, approximately $375,-000 of our money. At that, Da Ponte's design was distinctly more economical than several of his competitors'. But he encountered a very expensive engineering problem in the heavily built-up canal banks, where he had to take care not to disturb the foundations of the palaces and factories. After he had driven an enormous number of piles to support the heavy masonry foundations he was building at the canal's edge, work was ordered halted by the Venetian Senate. Assertions had been made, doubtless by Da Ponte's rivals, that the abutments were not strong enough to resist the thrust of the arch. A commission of architects and contractors was convened, and they unanimously reported that Da Ponte's work had been executed with consummate prudence, a judgment vindicated by time. For three centuries his was the only bridge over the Grand Canal, and to this day the Ponte di Rialto remains the sole crossing between the Station Bridge at one extremity and the Accademia not far from the other.

War is a great enemy of bridges, the Second World War having been probably the biggest of all bridge-destroyers. Armies cannot afford to be sentimental, and yet some of the destruction carried out by the retreating Germans in Italy in 1944 seems to have been criminally unnecessary. It can have been no more than a piece of military punctilio that caused the demolition of a number of historic bridges in Verona, including the famous Ponte di Castello Vecchio, on the night of April 25–26, 1945, only two days before the German request for an armistice.

In Florence the Ponte Vecchio was spared (it is said on direct orders from Hitler), but many other bridges, including the beautiful and historic Santa Trinità, were blown into the Arno. The Santa Trinità (*Figure 23*) is second only to the Rialto, if indeed even to that, among Renaissance bridges. Designed by Cosimo de' Medici's illustrious architect, Bartolomeo Ammanati, the man who finished Brunelleschi's Pitti Palace, it is distinguished by an entirely new arch form—the ellipse. An ellipse is a flat curve, sometimes defined as the path of a point that circles two other points in such a way that the sum of the two distances separating it from the two centers remains constant (*Figure 23*).

In the Santa Trinità Bridge, Ammanati used a rise-to-span ratio of only one to seven. The lowest previous ratio had been one to four. The Trinità arch form was known as a "basket handle" from a homely resemblance to a contemporary breadbasket's handle. The beautiful Santa Trinità survived only slightly disturbed for over three hundred years, until the careful, thorough demolition job carried out by German engineers in 1944. Nevertheless, like many of its sister Renaissance bridges, the Santa Trinità stands triumphantly today exactly as

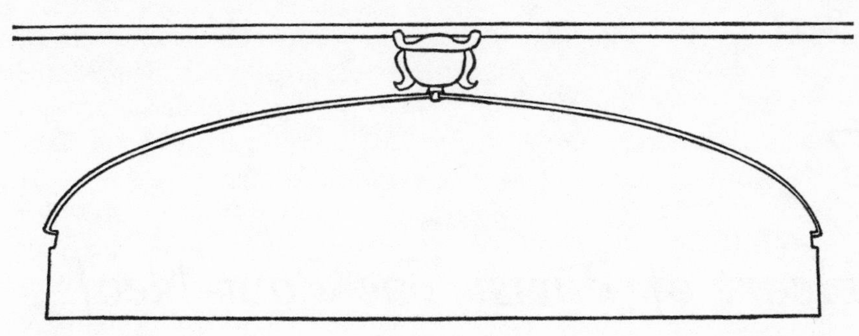

Figure 23

Bartolomeo Ammanati designed it. A painstaking labor of love and pride restored as far as possible the very stones of the original. The four famous statues, representing the four seasons, by the seventeenth-century sculptor Francavilla, which gave the Trinità its most characteristic decorative feature, were recovered virtually intact from the river. But the head of Primavera—Spring—was missing. Replace it? Abandon the original? Never! A search was conducted not only in Florence, but also throughout Italy, Germany, the world. One day in the fall of 1961 a workman on the riverfront turned up the long-lost head. Florentine papers made headlines of the discovery:

È TORNATA LA PRIMAVERA!
[Spring has returned!]

7 · Heart of Paris: The Pont-Neuf

O Pont-Neuf, belle galerie
Autrefois de moi tant chérie
Ou pour humer un peu le vent
J'allais me promener souvent,
Puisqu'en toi je voy qu'on exerce
Un si misérable commerce,
Quoique tu sois un fort beau lieu,
Cher Pont-Neuf, je te dis adieu.*

(One of the innumerable verses composed in honor of the Pont-Neuf.)

FOR forty years the Pont Notre-Dame stood in Paris without a stone-arch rival. But by the middle of the sixteenth century the town was bursting its medieval limits, spreading over both banks of the Seine, especially the Right, growing into a city of 150,000, capital of a flourishing kingdom, and developing severe traffic problems. The Ile de la Cité remained its center, with Notre-Dame hovering over the low-roofed town like an allegory of God and humanity, one of what

* O Pont-Neuf, lovely gallery
Which formerly I cherished
Where to breathe the wind a bit
I often went to walk,
Since I see carried on on you
So miserable a commerce,
Even though you're a lovely place,
Dear Pont-Neuf, I bid you farewell.

W. H. Auden calls "the Plainly Visible Churches/Men camped like tourists under their tremendous shadows." A petition requesting a bridge to connect the Ile with both banks was drawn up and presented to Henri II, a chivalrous king who died of wounds received in a tournament before he could build any bridges. His successor, François II, also enjoyed only a brief reign, after which Charles IX, decadent scion of the House of Valois, assented to Catherine de' Medici's St. Bartholomew Day Massacre, thereby embittering religious factions in France to such a degree as to interfere with works of progress for a generation. The problem meantime grew more acute. The neighboring Pont-au-Change, a timber span filled with moneylenders' stalls, was not only overcrowded, but also too weak to carry heavy wagons. Furthermore, the foundations of the Pont Notre-Dame had settled dangerously, and the royal artillery was forbidden to make use of it.

At last, under Henri III, the last Valois, a "New Bridge" (*pont neuf*) was ordered at the expense of the national treasury. A commission of prominent men was appointed to direct operations, assisted by a technical board of master masons, carpenters, and builders. The design was the creation of two men, Baptiste Ducerceau, the royal architect, and Pierre des Illes. They apparently inherited the main features of their plan from Guillaume Marchand, who had prepared a design several years earlier. Bids were asked on the masonry in 1578, and on May 31 the first stone was placed by the king in the presence of the Queen Mother, Catherine de' Medici of St. Bartholomew fame. Foundations for piers and abutments were begun shortly. All the piers on the Left Bank (short) side were founded by the end of the year.

Ducerceau's design called for a bridge resting on the Pointe de la Cité, the western end of the Ile, with a long arm of seven arches to the Right Bank and a short arm of five arches to the Left. Part of Ducerceau's final revision of the plan in 1579 consisted of widening both arms to accommodate houses or shops. Because the foundations for the piers on the short-arm side already had been built, Fra Giocondo's *corne-de-vache* was employed there; on the long-arm side the piers were built wide enough to carry the houses without the *corne-de-vache*. But the prospective tenants had to wait: the bridge was not completed for twenty-eight years.

First, the construction was interrupted by the religious wars that flared fiercely in 1588, the year the Spanish Armada was wrecked by a storm, helping to persuade European Catholics that God was not necessarily bent on murdering all Protestants. By the time peace

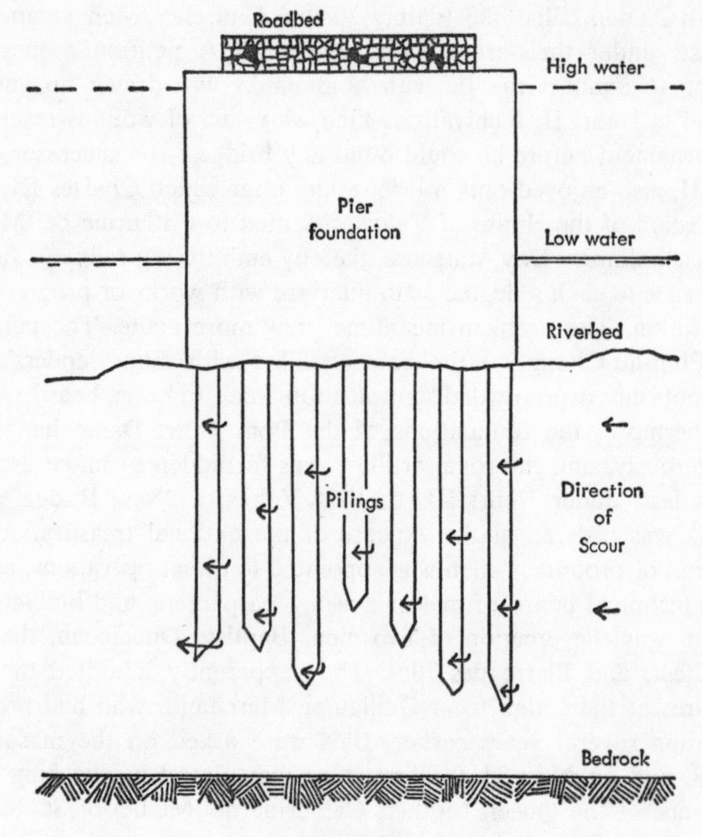

Figure 24

came to Paris with the entrance of the brilliant Bourbon prince Henri IV, victor over the Spanish-supported Catholic League, the piers of the long arm of the Pont-Neuf had suffered seriously from scour.

Scour, the abrasive action of moving sand under water, was the biggest single enemy of the medieval bridge engineer. The solidity of piers founded on piles depends largely on how far the pilings reach below the scour. In a fast-flowing stream, scour may run many feet down, especially during high water. The fifteenth- and sixteenth-century bridge-builder, with his crude cofferdams, which held out only part of the river water, and his primitive means of driving piles, usually had to stop short of foundations invulnerable to scour.

Theoretically, piles were driven to "refusal," that is, to the point at which they refused to go any deeper. In practice, this refusal was determined rather uncertainly. When a heavy weight had to be cranked up by a gang of laborers, dropped on the piling and then laboriously cranked up again for another blow, when breakdowns were frequent, and when the weight itself was limited by the strength of ropes and men, what was the refusal? In the inquiry on the Rialto Bridge, a witness testified in Da Ponte's favor that he had caused the piles to be driven till penetration was no greater than two fingers after twenty-four blows. Refusal was not absolute, and the Pont-Neuf piles must have been cut off no more than eight feet under the water's surface.

Beginning in 1602, Henri IV carried out repairs on the New Bridge's long arm and simultaneously pushed completion of the short arm to the Left Bank. In 1603 the soldierly monarch walked across a precarious temporary span, and two years later he rode his white horse over the still dangerously incomplete bridge. In 1607 the roadway was finished and the bridge opened.

Out of a combination of builders and contractors first engaged on the work, Guillaume Marchand and François Petit had, from 1584, carried on the construction. The arches and piers are of sturdy proportions, giving rise, despite their slightly doubtful foundations, to a French health simile: *"Comment vous portez-vous?" "Fort comme le Pont-Neuf."* The cornices are decorated with gargoyles, those of the long arm by Maindron and Barge, those of the short arm by Fontenelle and Lavigne. These, plus the high, angled cutwater piers, topped by bays, give the Pont-Neuf its enduring and distinctive appearance amid numerous beautiful Paris bridges.

Henri IV took a keen interest in the bridge that his rivals and predecessors had so lamely begun. He objected to its disfigurement with shops, but, cellars having already been provided over the bays, he allowed the shops to be put up. Very frequently the king crossed the bridge, on horse or by carriage, not only on royal business, but also for the pleasure of the view and the ride.

On June 29, 1610, the king who had completed the construction of the Pont-Neuf began its history. On that day the funeral procession bearing the body of Henri, assassinated by a fanatic, crossed the New Bridge on its way to Notre-Dame. Oddly, Henri IV's was not only the first, but also the last royal funeral to pass over the Pont-Neuf. No other king reached the chilly crypt of St. Denis in Notre-Dame by this route.

Among the captains and courtiers in the long cortège was an

Italian adventurer named Concini, member of the household of Marie de' Medici, widow of the illustrious Henri. Marie soon dismissed her husband's loyal lieutenant, Sully, and put Concini in his place as prime minister. The broad shopping avenue of the Pont-Neuf experienced its first major rumor, which turned to scandal, to anger, to something near insurrection. Concini added to his unpopularity by erecting on the bridge a scaffold from which to hang his enemies. By 1617 his enemies reached to within the palace, and M. de Vitry, captain of the guard, in the interest of the young Louis XIII, seized the objectionable Italian, shot him, and had him deposited in the nearby church of St. Germain l'Auxerrois, whence angry parishioners removed the body and hung it, head down, from his own gibbet on the Pont-Neuf. Not long after, Marie de' Medici herself, condemned to exile in the provinces, sadly crossed the Pont-Neuf, pursued by jeers far from polite. From an upper gallery of the Louvre, Louis XIII watched his mother's carriage till it vanished beyond the Quai des Augustins.

A few years later Henri IV returned to his bridge, in the form of a bronze equestrian statue cast in Florence, the work of sculptor Pietro Toca. The statue was shipped to France by sea, and it survived a shipwreck off Sardinia before making its way through the Straits of Gibraltar and finally up the Seine, to be installed on the tip of the Ile de la Citè, facing the middle of the bridge. In the statue's honor the little park was named Square du Vert-Galant.

In the middle of the seventeenth century, the New Bridge became a strategic as well as social center of Paris. The quarrel between Court and Parlement kindled into a succession of outbursts known as the Fronde. Parlement met on the Left Bank, across the Pont-Neuf from the Louvre. Soldiers from the palace side clashed with *frondeurs* from the Parlement side. The brothers of the Augustine monastery that gave its name to the Left Bank quai had their hands full giving last rites on active Frondist days. In 1660, Spanish princess Marie-Thérèse, bride of the new king, Louis XIV, crossed the Pont-Neuf on her way to Notre-Dame, a passage followed by scores of other princesses, princes, and foreign ambassadors.

By now the bridge was not merely an essential passageway, supplying an incomparable view of the city, but the busiest, liveliest street in town. Pompadour and Du Barry crossed the Pont-Neuf, not to mention Pascal and Voltaire. But the broad New Bridge belonged less to princes and celebrities than to plain Parisians. "The busy activity of the bourgeois," says the historian Gabriel Hanotaux, "the sprightly sauntering of the idler, the blustering vanity of the cadet, the insolence of the women of the streets, the haughtiness of the lords of high society, the haste of the courtiers passing toward the Louvre, the cavaliers, the carriages, the sedan chairs all rolled by in an endless succession. The mountebanks, fortune-tellers, quack doctors and tumblers, having established themselves there, attracted thither loafers, thieves, swindlers, pickpockets, and cutthroats." Théophile Gautier's hero, Captain Fracasse, is hardly surprised when assaulted on the Pont-Neuf just after sundown.

A Paris proverb, Hanotaux says, asserted that one never crossed the Pont-Neuf without meeting three things: a monk, a girl, and a white horse, perhaps with the implication that this center of Paris carried too many clergymen, prostitutes, and aristocrats.

The roadway was poorly maintained, Hanotaux notes, and "had more holes than paving stones." Filth piled up at the foot of the statue of Henri IV. Besides the permanent shops in the bays, dozens of tiny portable booths crowded the sidewalks, but the great diversion for the Parisian was the "Samaritaine," a hydraulic pump constructed alongside the second pier from the side of the Louvre. The Samaritaine was a far more elaborate affair than the waterwheels built by Peter Moris and his successors a few years earlier on London Bridge. Designed to supply water especially for the Louvre and Tuileries palaces, including the fountains of the Tuileries gardens, it was a little three-story jewel of a building, containing two huge waterwheels. On the top floor the pump's builder, a Flemish engineer named Jean Lintlaer, had his lodgings. The façade, facing the bridge roadway, was richly decorated, its principal motive representing Jesus at the well of Jacob in conversation with the Samaritan woman, whence the pump's popular name. There were also a clock and chimes that not only struck the hours but also played tunes. The clock's face showed not only the time of day but also the day and month of the year. For centuries the Samaritaine was a fertile reference for Parisian wit, mentioned in hundreds of political pamphlets. The carillon was rebuilt in 1712 and continued to ring its changes through the reign of Louis XV and into the Revolution.

The famous pump was finally dismantled in 1813, but a model of it survives in the Musée Carnavalet.

It was also during the eighteenth century that the provost of Paris, after numerous complaints from scandalized laundresses who washed linen under the bridge along the Left Bank, forbade boys to swim naked off the bridge piers.

"The loiterer could next stop," Hanotaux notes, "to listen to the merchants of new song, the recital of poems of the crossroads or the lotteries, or the show of the tooth-pullers who often directed regular troupes of comedians. All the oral and familiar literature of the times was connected with the Pont-Neuf, from Tabarin to Brioche, from Cormier, a rival of Molière, to Dassoucy, from *'Francion'* to the *'Roman Bourgeois.'* Good or evil, it was there the heart of popular Paris beat. . . ."

The tooth-pullers enjoyed their heyday in the eighteenth century. Dentistry was actually more or less a sideline or a promotional aspect of their real business, which was patent medicine. Like all patent-medicine men, they combined showmanship with advertising, uninhibited and unabashed. They sang, recited, played, acted, told jokes and stories, and swore that their elixirs would cure any ill. One of the most famous was a huge fellow called "*le grand Thomas*," whose powerful tooth-pulling and stentorian voice made him a center of attraction for years. He was well known to the Court, for whenever the carriage of Louis XV appeared on the bridge *le grand Thomas* shouted "*Vive le roi!*" louder than anyone else.

At the end of the eighteenth century the Pont-Neuf entered on its most dramatic days. The Revolution swirled across the no-longer New Bridge en route to the storming of the Bastille. Cannon were hauled thither to act as "alarm guns" for the city. On a June morning of 1791, their boom gave Paris its first warning of the attempted flight of the king and queen. A few months later, the statue of Henri IV was decorated for the "Feast of the Constitution" and a "Liberty Tree" was planted on the corner of the bridge facing the Quai des Orfèvres. Revolutionary pamphlets were hawked, the fiery new Republican newspapers peddled. Most popular of these latter was "*L'Ami du peuple*, whose editor, the impassioned Marat, presently provided the bridge with one of its biggest funeral processions, following his assassination by Charlotte Corday. (Marat's corpse eventually was dragged from the Pantheon by a mob, after the Thermidorean counterrevolution, and flung into a sewer, this time passing under the Pont-Neuf.)

In 1792 the foreign intervention against the Revolution resulted in stirring scenes on the great bridge. When the "nation in danger" resolution was passed by the Convention, one of the Paris recruiting stations was established on the Pont-Neuf; no fewer than 2122 volunteers enlisted there between July 22 and 24. A battalion was named for the New Bridge. That same week, five hundred Republican volunteers arrived from Marseille; halting their column on the Pont-

Neuf, they sang a song Paris never had heard before, but which every capital of Europe heard during the next years. Two cannon fired every quarter hour during these summer days of peril and emergency, but on August 10 they fell silent—they had been dragged off for the assault on the Tuileries. Three days later, the current Bourbon having been unthroned, the dynast of the line, Henri IV, was toppled from his pedestal.

During the violent years that followed, revolutionary mobs, militia of the Commune, National Guards, and troops of the regular army surged back and forth over the old bridge. Across the extreme tip of its long arm passed the tumbrils that carried royalists and revolutionaries to the guillotine. The tumbrils departed from the Conciergerie by the Pont-au-Change, and turned left down the Quai de la Mégisserie toward the Place de la Révolution. For one victim in particular the passage by the Pont-Neuf was cruel; Madame Roland could turn her eyes across the bridge and see for the last time her house across the Seine.

In the summer of 1794 the overthrown triumvirs of the Revolution—Robespierre, Couthon, and Saint-Just—were taken across the Pont-Neuf to the Conciergerie. To the curses of the crowd, the wounded Robespierre turned a look and a shrug; his colleagues remained impassive. The following day the three were taken to the scaffold via the Pont-Neuf, the only victims of the Terror to pass that way. The route was chosen because the broad roadway could be lined heavily with reliable troops.

Eight years passed, and on another summer day, Napoleon Bonaparte was proclaimed First Consul for life on the Pont-Neuf . . . and on a December day two years later still, he passed over the New Bridge en route to Notre-Dame, where he took the Imperial crown from the Pope's hands and placed it on his own head. Year after year there followed fireworks and celebrations of victories on the now two-hundred-year-old bridge, till in 1814 a carriage with the white-lily arms, bearing the sexagenarian Bourbon heir, Louis XVIII, crossed toward Notre-Dame. The great days of the Pont-Neuf were over.

Not quite; in 1830 (July again—midsummer is the time for revolution), students and workers pried up cobblestones at the Right Bank end of the Pont-Neuf for one of their major barricades.

What about the statue of Henri IV? One of the first acts of the Restoration in 1814 was the restoration of the first Bourbon to his pedestal. A leading sculptor, Mesnel, was commissioned for the job.

Mesnel, a Republican and a Bonapartist, is said to have secreted a small figure of Napoleon in the new statue's right arm. The stone for the pedestal came from the rubble of the Bastille.

The Second Empire, under which the great emperor's nephew, much-maligned Napoleon III, carried out the construction and renovating projects that created modern Paris, touched the Pont-Neuf with a heavy but enlightened hand. The foundations, chronically weakened by scour, were rebuilt completely. The seven arches of the long arm (to the Right Bank) were rebuilt and made elliptical instead of nearly semicircular, lowering the roadway. The arches of the short arm were left untouched, and despite a collapse in 1885 remain today essentially as they were when Henri IV rode his white horse across them. Faces of the crumbled piers, spandrels, cornices, and carved consoles also were redone in the 1848–55 reconstruction.

At the same time the last of the famous shops were removed. The tooth-pullers were long gone. The suppression of the portable booths during the eighteenth century had been carried out in the face of protests from the shopkeepers and apparently from the general public as well. In the nineteenth century the bays were occupied by sedate stationers and engravers, a far cry from the noisy times when an English visitor won a bet by standing on the Pont-Neuf crying, "Six-livre pieces for twenty-four sous," for two hours without exhausting his purse.

"New Bridge"—today Paris's oldest—has passed into the French language in at least three ways. From the song-pluggers who thronged it in the nineteenth century, Pont-Neuf came to be a term for familiar popular ballads. "*Au clair de la lune*" was a Pont-Neuf. The same designation was used at one time for the prostitutes who cruised the bridge.

And finally the noble old structure became a metaphor for achieving the difficult. Mme. de Sévigné wrote her daughter, "*Ma bonne, croyez-moi, ne faites point le Pont-neuf, ne forcez point la Nature*" ("Don't try to do something beyond your physical capacity").

8.

The "Flying Arch": Jean-Rodolphe Perronet

PROGRESS is an irregular series of jumps. Captain Cook sailed to the Sandwich Islands in a ship that was merely an improved version of Columbus' *Santa Maria* of almost three hundred years earlier. Then suddenly on the very eve of transocean steam navigation the clipper ship appeared—a revolution in hull-and-canvas design. In somewhat the same way the old Roman semicircular stone arch persisted for century after century and was only superseded by the flat, elliptical arch on the eve of the metal bridge. Taddeo Gaddi and Bartolomeo Ammanati had found that an arc flatter than a semicircle would stand up, but the real significance of the elliptical arch remained concealed until a momentous discovery in France in the eighteenth century. This discovery itself came at the end of a chain of developments that saw the European center of gravity shifting westward, with political, economic, military, cultural, and scientific leadership passing from Italy to France.

To trace this development we must return to the Paris of Louis XIII, which acquired its third stone arch only seven years after completion of the Pont-Neuf. The genesis of this bridge is interesting. It was undertaken by private capital as a speculative enterprise. A real-estate promoter named Christophe Marie conceived a scheme for turning two vacant islets in the Seine into a residential development. He obtained a royal charter on condition of filling in the channel between the two islets and connecting them to the Right Bank by a permanent bridge. The result is the Ile St.-Louis, in the Seine just east of the Ile de la Cité, and the Pont Marie, still standing today.

Furthermore, this early venture in bridging for profit was a success for the entrepreneur: Paris's new-rich businessmen and royal officials took advantage of the Ile St.-Louis' proximity to the Louvre and other official buildings to make their residences there. In the centuries since, they have been succeeded largely by artists and writers.

Marie built and rented houses on the bridge itself, as well as on the isle. Forty years later, on the night of March 1, 1688, an exceptionally heavy spring flood carried off two arches and the houses on them. Temporary wooden arches were hastily provided to avoid marooning the businessmen on the isle, and were eventually replaced with stone, but without the houses. The roadway was completely cleared, along with those of most other Paris bridges, in 1789. A curiosity of the Pont Marie as it stands today is that of its six arches, five are semicircular, one elliptical.

The isle was already connected to the Left Bank by a timber structure, the Pont de la Tournelle, but in the 1630s, Marie rebuilt this bridge in stone. Meantime, another stone arch was built to connect the larger Ile de la Cité with the Left Bank; this was the Pont St.-Michel, which lasted till Napoleon III's renovation time.

The St.-Michel had its special characteristic too—the roadway over its four arches rose in a steepish grade of six percent. The arches were almost, but not quite, semicircular, with the two end spans shorter (33 feet) than the two middle ones (46 feet). The St.-Michel also carried houses, sixteen on either side of the roadway. They were not removed till Napoleon I's time (1807–8), when the road to Orléans was being improved. The bridge itself was rebuilt in 1857.

Several other stone-arch bridges were built in and near Paris during the next generation. Most were simple repetitions of the established technique. But an architectural revolution was taking place in Paris during these years, and when the Pont-Royal was undertaken in 1685, its designer was the celebrated Jules-Hardouin Mansart, architect of the dome of the Invalides and uncle of the man who invented the Mansard roof (spellings were somewhat liberal in the seventeenth century). Associated with Mansart was Jacques Gabriel, an architectural contractor. They soon ran into the universal problem of stone-arch builders: the foundations. (*See Figure 24.*) A consultant was brought in: Père Romain, a late-blooming clerical engineer from Belgium. Père Romain was a foundation expert, and the method he employed for the Pont-Royal, apparently one he had experimented with before, was quite revolutionary. He sank a barge loaded with gravel, leaving a space at its center from which water was pumped. Within this space, men drove piles and laid the heavy foundation stones. Father Romain's sunken barge was the ancestor of the modern pneumatic caisson, the compressed-air chamber within which bridge and other foundations are pushed to solid rock. Reaching solid rock was beyond the aspirations of seventeenth-century engineers, but Father Romain's *caisse* made it possible to drive pilings fairly deep and cut them off evenly at a point well below the normal surface of the water.

The principal design features of the Pont-Royal however belong to Mansart. His five arches were segmental, like those of the Ponte Vecchio, and his piers each only one fifth of the arch span, providing much more clear waterway than the earlier Seine bridges. The longest (middle) span was 77 feet. The plain spandrels and the sharply pointed cutwaters capped with stepped pyramids give the Pont-Royal today a classic simplicity, befitting the age of Racine.

The Pont-Royal, a true, if late Renaissance structure, reveals how far the art of bridging with stone had advanced since medieval Europe first set foot on the path the Roman engineers had traced. The ponderous semicircular arch, half-damming the river it spanned, had been superseded by the flatter arcs of the segmental and elliptical forms. Essentially, however, this development represented a refinement rather than a change. It was a continuation in the same terms of the centuries-old search for narrowed piers that would limit navigational obstruction and reduce scour (*Figure 25*).

The possibilities of the arch had been explored in every direction—*within the limitations of the Roman engineering theory and method.* What was required for further advance was a completely new idea.

A much quoted line in French poetry is, "At last Malherbe came . . ." a salute by the poet-critic Boileau to a predecessor who brought a new sense of form to verse. One might paraphrase it aptly for the arrival of Perronet on the French engineering scene. An important task of Louis XIV, or more accurately of his able minister Colbert, was to knit France together with a first-class road system. Out of Colbert's efforts presently grew the *Corps des Ponts et Chaussées* (Bridge and Highway Force). This body, founded in 1716, was the first national engineering authority in the world. A generation later a bureau was created within the *Corps* to design the *Grandes Chaussées,* the major highway network of the realm. Out of this bureau in turn developed the *École des Ponts et Chaussées,* the world's

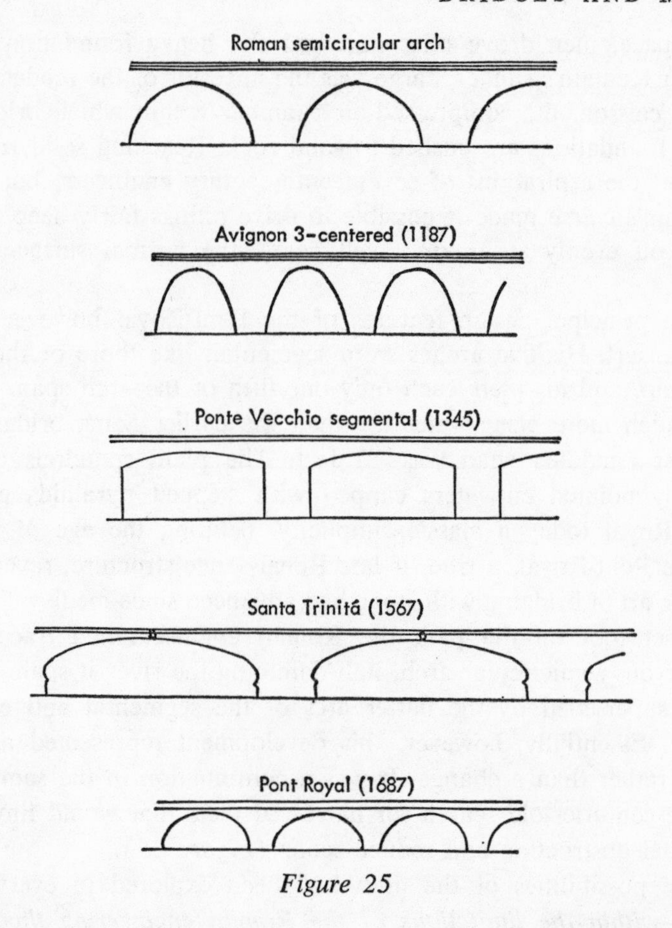

Figure 25

first engineering school (1747). The first director of this epoch-making school, which Swiss engineering historian Hans Straub notes "secured the Continent-wide supremacy of French road- and bridge-building," was Jean-Rodolphe Perronet, the most illustrious bridge-builder of the eighteenth century, which his career almost spanned.

The son of a French-Swiss army officer, Perronet was born at Surêsnes, outside Paris, in 1708, in the last years of Louis XIV. He died while completing his enduring monument, the Pont de la Concorde, in the midst of the Reign of Terror, eighty-six years later. For the last thirty years of his life he was the chief of the *Corps* itself, and *premier ingénieur* of the realm.

The first half of the eighteenth century saw many important stone-arch bridges built in the basins of the Seine and Loire. These followed the lines of the Pont-Royal; the New Bridge at Blois, for example, employed eleven segmental arches, the middle one of 86 feet, to replace a curious old London-bridge-like structure with twenty unequal, asymmetrical arches. Perronet assisted Hupeau, chief of the *Corps des Ponts et Chaussées,* on the New Bridge, and after Hupeau's death he carried to completion bridges over the Loire at Orléans and over the Seine at Mantes below Paris. During construction of the bridge at Mantes, Perronet made a momentous observation. In 1763, when the first arch was nearly complete and the second just getting under way, he noticed that the pier between them was leaning slightly toward the unfinished arch (*Figure 26*). A good many bridges with this same

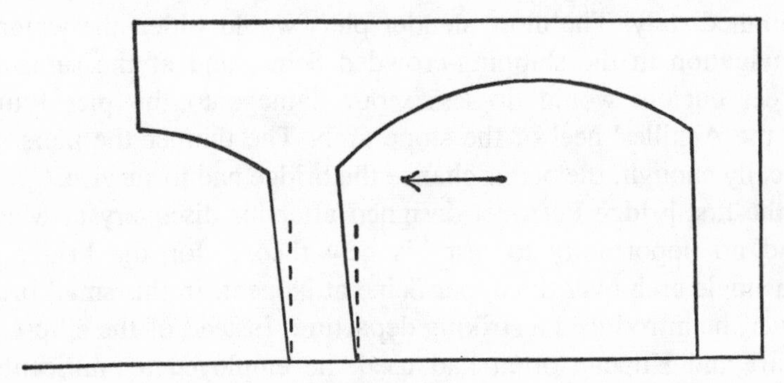

Figure 26

(1 to 5) pier-arch ratio were standing satisfactorily, so there was no cause for alarm; quite evidently as soon as the bridge was complete, it would stand safely enough. Perronet's curiosity led him further, however. If the completed arch caused the pier to lean in the absence of another completed arch on its other side, the whole grouping of arches must somehow provide mutual support. It could only be that the thrust of the arches was in part transmitted all the way to the abutments at the banks (*Figure 27*).

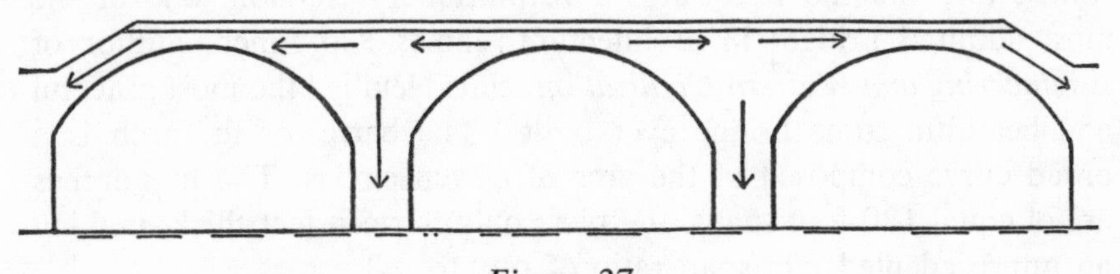

Figure 27

The Romans had known that as long as they kept their piers thick and their arches semicircular, they could safely let a single arch stand in the river all winter. Taddeo Gaddi had discovered that even if the arch was not a semicircle, piers that were thick enough would hold it up. Mansart and others had found that piers needed to be only one fifth of the arch span to be independently sustaining.

What Perronet discovered at Mantes was that in these Pont-Royal style bridges the arches were not really independent, or, more precisely, that they were barely independent. When the construction was complete, the piers did not bear as much strain as during construction because the completed bridge passed some of the thrust from arch to arch all the way to the abutments.

This being the case, why not pass more of the thrust to the abutments? Two advantages critical to stone-arch engineering would accrue immediately. The more slender piers would widen the waterway for navigation in the shipping-crowded Seine, and at the same time the freer current would do less scour damage to the pier foundations, the Achilles' heel of the stone arch. The thinner the piers, paradoxically enough, the better chance the bridge had to survive.

In the first bridge Perronet designed after his discovery at Mantes, he had no opportunity to test his new theory, for the bridge was only a single arch over the upper Seine at Nogent. In this small bridge, however, he introduced a striking departure. Instead of the ellipse that Mansart and Hupeau often had used, he employed a multicentered curve as easier for the workers to execute. In discussing this bridge later, Perronet made a significant remark: "Some engineers, finding that the arches . . . do not rise enough near their springing, have given a larger number of degrees and a larger radius to this part of the curve," but such curves "have a fault disagreeable to the eye . . . the abrupt change from a small to a large curvature." The esthetics of the arch played a role in Perronet's mind.

A few years later, Perronet was called on to build a stone arch over the Seine at Neuilly, just north of Paris. This was the chance he had waited for, and the result was a revolutionary creation, one of the most admired bridges in architecture. James Kip Finch, author of *Engineering and Western Civilization,* calls Neuilly "the most graceful and beautiful stone bridge ever built." The barrel of the arch is a broad curve composed of the arcs of eleven circles. The five arches are of equal 120-foot spans, the piers only thirteen feet thick, making an unprecedented pier-span ratio of one to 9.3.

The design triggered a storm of protest by orthodox engineers. The bridge never would stand up; the king's money was being wasted; people would be killed. Afterward, when the principle involved is well understood, such objections always seem ridiculous and irrational. But the idea of building a bridge any one of whose arches would admittedly collapse if one of its neighbors failed must have seemed to the eighteenth century no better than building a bridge of cards. Only Perronet's great reputation carried the project through, and the dire prophecies did not cease for years after its completion.

For the Neuilly cofferdams, Perronet utilized and improved the old bucket wheel operated by a paddle wheel driven by the current. With its aid the riverbed was excavated to a depth of eight feet below low-water level and piles driven to refusal by four extra-heavy drop-hammers, each weighing from 1350 to 1740 pounds. Perronet experimented with horse-driven piles and found that two horses could drive three piles a day—at considerably less than the cost of human labor. The piles were cut off at a uniform height, about ten feet below water level. An open timber grillage was laid on top, and the interstices were filled with stone and mortar. The masonry then was started on top of this solid platform. The pier foundations were considerably thicker than the piers: 21 feet. Despite all the care that went into these foundations, they were not completely satisfactory, and the finished bridge settled slightly.

The greatest effort, however, went into raising the arches. Perronet's new theory of design, involving frank dependence on the two abutments to support the major part of the thrust of the arches, demanded that all arches be completed in a single season, as the bridge could not stand incomplete and the timber centering would not survive a winter flood. At one time a total labor force of 872 men and 167 horses was engaged in transporting material and building the bridge. All the centerings were removed on September 22, 1772, in the presence of the king. The king was of course Louis XV, with whom Perronet had sometimes played as a child at Versailles, when his father had been an officer of the guard.

The Neuilly bridge withstood the floods of the Seine till 1956, when it was removed to make room for a big modern bridge—another victory for progress at the expense of history.

Perronet's next bridge represented the culmination of his architectural theory. Over the Oise at Ste.-Maixence, thirty-five miles north of Paris, it was "the most slender and daring stone arch ever built"—once more the superlative is Professor Finch's. Its three 72-foot spans had a rise of only 6 feet 5 inches, a rise-span ratio of 1 to 11. "Springing at a height of 18 feet from its tall and slender columnar piers (only 9 feet in diameter), it was truly a tour de force in stone arch construction, doubling the free waterway," in comparison with its predecessors. There is a direct connection between the low rise of the arches and the lightness of the piers, for Perronet now realized that the flatter the arches, the more horizontal their thrust. This greater horizontal thrust was met by exceptionally deep, strong voussoirs, which occupied almost all the space from the bottom of the arch to the roadway. The abutments were made extra strong. "Even with our modern methods of analysis," says Professor Finch, "we could not further refine his design."

The Ste.-Maixence piers are nearly as revolutionary as the arches. They consist of a pair of double columns connected by a lateral arch (*Figure 28*).

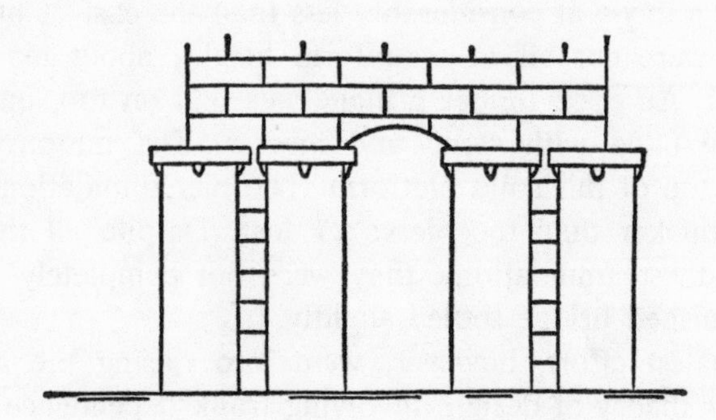

Ste.-Maixence pier: lateral view

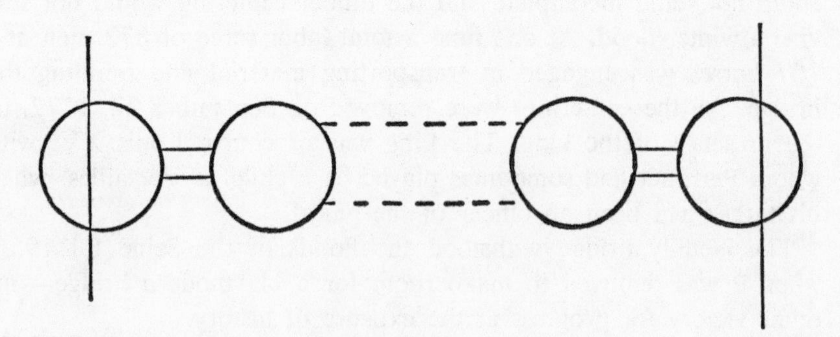

Cross section of pier

Figure 28

The outer pair of columns were connected by a bracing wall; the inner two were joined by the lateral arch. At Ste.-Maixence, Perronet used a significant new source of power for his pile driver: the river current itself. His waterwheel lifted a 2000-pound ram, and he did not consider his piles driven to refusal until twenty-five blows of this one-ton mass failed to sink the pile a "Paris line"—one-twelfth of an inch.

During Napoleon's retreat of 1814, French engineers blew up one arch, but the rest of the bridge miraculously stood and soon was repaired. But when the Germans retreated from the Marne in 1914 they did a more thorough job.

The original design for the bridge that was to become known as the Pont de la Concorde was conceived by Perronet in 1772, when he presented a plaster model to Louis XV, after whom the bridge was inevitably to be named, the great square of Paris for which it would provide a river crossing being known as the Place Louis XV. Perronet's design was attacked at once by the conservatives as too daring, and so insistent was the opposition that the great master was forced to modify his masterpiece somewhat by increasing the rise of the arches. He successfully resisted the demands for thickening of the piers, though he agreed to join the columns with a solid wall instead of a lateral arch as at Ste.-Maixence. The final result was a less slender bridge than Ste.-Maixence, but Perronet skillfully heightened the appearance of lightness by introducing a balustrade instead of the solid walls of all earlier French bridges (Labelye had given Westminster Bridge in London a balustrade).

Perronet was eighty years old when work actually was begun in 1787. The foundations were executed as at Neuilly; at one time, 1312 men, 58 horses, 11 barges and 14 small boats were at work simultaneously. The five arches in the new bridge were given unequal span lengths varying from about 70 to 90 feet.

When the construction was half done, the Revolution broke out. The turmoil of Paris did not affect the work; the old engineer had a little house built at one end of the bridge and oversaw everything in person. When the Bastille was razed, it provided him with an opportune source for his masonry. (As you walk over the Pont de la Concorde today you tread on stones that once imprisoned the Man in the Iron Mask.) Doubtless many of Perronet's laborers belonged to the military force of the Commune of Paris, the formidable "sections" that fought the National Guard, coerced the Assembly, and stormed the Tuileries. He had trouble with them only once, when they struck for more pay. They were receiving thirty sous a day, and struck for forty; Perronet settled the strike in one day by raising them to thirty-five. In every way he was a remarkably modern man.

The Revolution had one other effect on the bridge. The name of Louis XV suddenly had become unfashionable, and the famous square in which the guillotine was mounted had been renamed the Place de la Révolution. The name of the bridge at the time of Perronet's death in February 1794 was Pont de la Révolution, but, the political storms having blown over at last, square and bridge acquired their present name—one more appropriate than either of its earlier designations to this noble structure.

Genius does not operate in a vacuum; no Renaissance, no Michelangelo. This is a history of bridge engineering, so Perronet takes the front of the stage. But it should be pointed out that the eighteenth century saw extremely important advances in civil engineering in general. Buffon, best known as the author of a *Natural History,* tested the strength of iron rods and wooden beams, measuring the sag before rupture. Perronet and a military engineer named Bernard Forest de Belidor also made important studies of the strength of materials.

One of Perronet's pupils at the École des ponts, De Volgie, carried experimental engineering a step further by building a model of a stone arch and testing its effect on various sizes of abutments. De Volgie succeeded in building a bridge over the Loire near Saumur with an eighty-foot arch span and an arch rise of only eight feet. But another Perronet disciple, Lecreulx, designed an even flatter arch, with a rise-span ratio of only 1/17.

Perhaps the most distinguished graduate of the École was Emiland Gauthey, who was also one of the first. He assisted in carrying out important tests during and after the building of the Ste.-Géneviève Church (the Panthéon). Like Perronet, Gauthey was the author of an important work on bridge engineering. He developed a concrete foundation for piers, and from experiments in a stream near his home he discovered that the ideal cutwater for dividing the current was an elliptical curve circumscribed on an equilateral triangle. In two of his own bridges he carried the curve of the cutwater the full length of the piers.

Another noted graduate of the École des Ponts et Chaussées was Charles Labelye, of Westminster Bridge fame. The engineering center of gravity was now shifting westward once more, from France to England, where the abundance of coal was bringing on an industrial and engineering revolution destined to have a shattering effect on many things, among them the art of building bridges.

9.

A Scotch Farmer Boy Builds London Bridges

IN political history the eighteenth century is a century of revolution. But the biggest revolution was the invisible one that went on below the surface of political life. This revolution, very inadequately termed "industrial," transformed social and class relations by putting a sudden premium on ability. The old advantage of birth was discounted. As commerce grew, and manufacturing in turn grew to feed commerce, and basic industries, especially coal mining, grew to feed manufacturing, the rapidly expanding economic machine demanded new, quicker, better, more productive tools and techniques. This demand for talent in the practical realm was especially keen in coal-laden, manufacturing Britain.

Britain was the land of opportunity for the ordinary man. More precisely, it was the land of opportunity for the extraordinary man—the man who possessed exceptional gifts and who now at last found the way open to their use. These "extraordinary ordinary men" actually enjoyed a social advantage over their social betters. The fact that they worked with their hands and were directly involved in the economic process gave them the chance for the insight that led to creation. A squire or a duke was not likely to invent a steam engine because he was not likely ever to encounter the problem of pumping water from a coal mine.

The advent of the talented common man was marked in bridge engineering by three striking examples. All three were sons of the English-Scots border country, the cradle of the Industrial Revolution. One, George Stephenson, from the English side of the border, fits into our story a little later. The first two, John Rennie and Thomas Telford, born a few miles apart north of the border, left their native heath for the capital of the recently United Kingdom to make their fortunes, and both left behind them bridges that still are world-famous.

Rennie was the son of a simple farmer in East Lothian. When his father died in 1766, he left nine orphans, of whom John, the youngest, was only five years old. One of his brothers enlisted in the British Navy, was taken prisoner during the American Revolution, and died in Boston. Another put himself through medical school at the University of Edinburgh, became an army surgeon, and was killed in India. John Rennie was more fortunate in his adventures.

Osbert Sitwell once filled in a questionnaire by writing after the word "Education," "During the holidays from Eton." John Rennie might have put down, "While playing hookey from parish school." Between home and school, on the banks of the River Tyne, stood the millwright shop of Andrew Meikle. A millwright was an important man in any agricultural community. He built and repaired the mills that ground the flour. But the millwright, with his practically exclusive knowledge of tools and machinery, was the man above all others for whom opportunity was knocking in the new industrial age. Andrew Meikle won fame and fortune through several inventions and improvements on farm machinery. Johnnie Rennie played around in his shop every day, sometimes on his way to school, sometimes on his way from school, sometimes instead of going to school. He tinkered with everything in sight and made working models of windmills and steam engines. When he was twelve, he badgered his mother into letting him go to work as an apprentice in Meikle's shop.

Some of the family's friends felt that a lad as bright as this one ought to be pushed. At Dunbar there was a high school, and at fifteen, John Rennie was induced to go thither and study mathematics. He liked math, and at Dunbar went straight to the head of the class; after two years they wanted him to stay on as master. He preferred to go back to Andrew Meikle's shop.

In the next two years he became an expert mechanic, entrusted with repair of mills and erection of machinery. He even introduced a few innovations of his own, such as cast-iron pinions, more expensive but longer-lasting than wooden ones.

Now his friends began thinking of the University of Edinburgh, where his elder brother had studied medicine. In November 1780, when John Rennie was nineteen, he matriculated. He spent the next three winters studying under the renowned Dr. Robison. Summers—from May to October—he earned his tuition by repairing mill machinery.

In the spring of 1783 he was graduated. Few college seniors have carried so advantageous an education away from commencement. An expert mechanic, with years of practical experience, he was at the same time an accomplished mathematician. In the England of the 1780s, how could he miss resounding success?

When the average young gentleman of that day was graduated, he headed for the Continent and the Grand Tour: Paris, Geneva, Venice, Rome. John Rennie headed for Birmingham. In that bustling, dingy, machine-minded English town stood the works of Boulton & Watt, headquarters of the great James Watt.

Rennie set out on his grand tour on horseback, for in this England between two eras, with steam locomotion on the horizon, there was still no stagecoach service between Edinburgh and London. In Lancashire he stopped to study one of the celebrated engineering works of the century, Brindley's Bridgewater Canal, with its famous tunnel. Passing on, he arrived in Birmingham, and presented a letter of introduction from Dr. Robison to Watt.

By a chance less fortuitous than it seems, Watt needed an expert mechanic. He himself did not have the millwright background, and expert mechanics also equipped with theoretical knowledge were by no means common. Watt, who was also a Scot, did not immediately offer Rennie a job; he looked the young man over, let him return home, wrote to Dr. Robison at Edinburgh, and, receiving an enthusiastic reply, wrote Rennie. Although already well established near his old home as a millwright, Rennie eagerly accepted Watt's offer, packed his bag, borrowed a horse, and headed once more down the rough and muddy road for Birmingham.

Watt and his partner Boulton had an important contract in hand in London—the construction of the world's first steam-powered factory. Small wonder that he had been cautious about taking Rennie on—for it was this youngster in his twenties whom Watt sent to supervise construction of the Albion Mills. Watt's concern about Rennie was not entirely on the ground of capacity; dogged by patent infringements, the great inventor wanted to be sure Rennie could be trusted with knowledge of the Watt engine. The young Scot told the older one that he would not promise not to try to improve the steam engine, but gave his word that he would never infringe the patent. The two remained friends for life.

Built at the south end of Blackfriars Bridge, the Albion Mills was one of the engineering wonders of its day. Steam was used not only to grind the flour but also to load and unload the barges. It was extremely successful, but it was destroyed by a fire a few years after its completion.

The Albion Mills gave Rennie his start. In London he needed no more than to be known; in a few years he engaged in twenty different projects, many of a radical nature. In 1790 he installed one of Watt's engines in the hull of a small vessel, which successfully steamed up and down the Thames estuary. Rennie's boat was too slow to be economical; seventeen years later a bigger Watt engine powered Fulton's *Clermont* up the Hudson.

Canals were the inland transportation queens of the day, and consequently the principal field for civil engineers. Rennie was soon off digging canals, and on one of them he built his first bridge—a matter-of-fact, according-to-the-book stone aqueduct of five 75-foot semicircular arches, to carry the canal over a river. He was also engaged in drainage work, for the rising industrial population of England was creating a demand for more wheatland. The marshy fens of Lincoln and Cambridge had dread reputations as breeders of disease, and Rennie's drainage work gained him the nickname of "slayer of dragons."

In 1799, Rennie designed his first important bridge, across the Tweed, near his own country, at Kelso. His arches were elliptical but distinctly conservative, with piers a sixth of the arch span. All the same, with this project Rennie became at one stroke a bridge engineer; he plunged into the geometry of the arch, developing theories in arguments with Dr. Robison. The doctor was preparing an article on "mechanics"—civil engineering—for the *Encyclopaedia Britannica,* and soon found himself relying on Rennie for all his bridge information.

Rennie theorized about arches and voussoirs in the evening, and during working days he paid close attention to the practical problems. Nearly all the bridges on British high roads still were steeply inclined; a horse and heavy wagon barely could struggle over many of them. Rennie perceived the practical wisdom of taking trouble with the approaches, and pioneered level bridge roadways. This radical departure won almost, but not quite, universal approbation. Samuel Smiles reports that a Scots farmer, asked how he liked the new Rennie-built bridge over the Esk on the high road to Edinburgh, replied, "Brig!

It's nae brig ava! Ye neither ken whan ye're on't, nor whan y're aff't!"

In 1803, Rennie undertook one of the biggest hydraulic-engineering projects of the epoch—the new London and East India docks. A compelling reason for building new docks in the Thames lay in the fantastic amount of theft that went on under the system of "lighterage." Cargoes were taken off big ships by small open vessels (lighters) and piled helter-skelter on open quays. Sugar hogsheads, barrels, tubs, baskets, boxes, and bales vanished into the London night. Many shippers partly recovered their losses by using the chaotic arrangement to dodge customs duties. Rennie built huge floating docks that rose and fell with the tide, enabling ships to discharge cargoes directly to receivers. Further, the docks were enclosed by high walls that shut in vessel and cargo.

Dock-building is of course an underwater operation, and at the London and East India, Rennie gained invaluable experience both in underwater work and in the special peculiarities of the Thames. During the next fifteen years he built a succession of bridges in many parts of England. He had married, and had two sons, whom he brought up as bridge engineers—a not uncommon family habit among bridge engineers, as we shall see. John Rennie II often accompanied his father on his trips of inspection. On one of these, in 1812, the two had a narrow escape. They were visiting Newton Stewart, where a bridge over the Cree was in progress. Arriving during a violent thunderstorm, they found the ferry service interrupted. After waiting several hours, the elder Rennie decided to try crossing the swollen river on the bridge falsework, which was topped by a narrow two-plank scaffolding. With the senior Rennie in the lead, the two men made their way from the first pier to the second. As the elder Rennie was about to step onto the planking leading to the third pier, his son saw the framework tremble. Seizing his father by the coat, he pulled him back just in time; a moment later the whole gangway collapsed into the river with a tremendous crash. Luckily the scaffolding back to the first pier remained intact, and the Rennies made their way to the south shore safely. The Cree bridge was finished and opened two years later.

Old London Bridge had been supplemented after six hundred years by two additional Thames crossings—Westminster Bridge, built by Labelye in the middle of the eighteenth century, and Blackfriars Bridge, built a few years later. When a private company prepared to build a fourth bridge in the heart of London, at the end of the Strand, they submitted the proposed design to Rennie. Recognizing it as a copy of Perronet's Neuilly design, Rennie roundly criticized it on somewhat specious grounds, citing the settling of the Neuilly foundations. Rennie's report impressed the company's directors as well as the Parliamentary committee that presently sat. In the end, Rennie was asked to design the bridge. He offered two designs, one for a seven-arch, the other for a nine-arch bridge. The company chose the more conservative nine-arch.

Rennie took extreme care with his foundations, having a wholly new chart of the river bottom executed, then driving his cofferdam piles to an exceptional depth with a steam hammer and cementing and iron-clamping them together. Inside this very strong enclosure, he pushed his piles several feet deeper than Peter of Colechurch had succeeded in doing. The erection of the superstructure was marked by one notable advance on Perronet's method. Perronet had withdrawn his timber centerings all at once, slowly and evenly, but all in one day. Rennie first drove his main wedges back two inches, then let the arches stand for ten days. Another six inches, and another ten-day wait, after which the wedges were hammered clear of the arches. The arches settled only two or three inches.

But the most surprising thing about the bridge—eventually named Waterloo in honor of the Duke of Wellington—was its beauty. John Rennie, that stolid Scots mechanic, struggling with such problems as economical construction and foundation settling, created a bridge that so endeared itself to British art-lovers that a hundred and twenty years later its demolition to meet modern traffic requirements stirred eloquent protests.

While the work on Waterloo Bridge was going forward, Rennie was engaged in a host of other enterprises—harbor works at Hull, Holyhead, Southampton, and other ports, the Plymouth breakwater, which Napoleon admired en route to St. Helena, and Southwark Bridge in London, one of the first in which iron was used for the arch spans. But John Rennie's enduring monument was one that he did not live to see—New London Bridge.

The incredible old nineteen-arch ruin built by Peter of Colechurch still stood, more or less by a miracle, the tottering houses at last stripped from its deck, but its culvert-like openings still cursed by every boatman in London. Patching the roadway and shoring up the piers cost a round £3500 a year, and in 1821 the Corporation of London (which 150 years earlier had bribed Charles II to veto a second bridge) sought the advice of a committee of experts on repairs for its beloved old wreck. The committee recommended removal of eight arches and the substitution of four, an expanded version of Labelye's alteration of the previous century. The plan was studied and argued and referred to a second committee, of which Rennie was the active member. Now sixty years old, the foremost engineer of England, he was as always deliberate in his approach. He personally examined the ancient piers down to the foundations, and had new soundings and studies of the river made, including borings of the bed. He concluded that the rejuvenation plan was practical from an engineering standpoint, but recommended that the whole venerable structure be replaced. A modern bridge with elliptical arches would permit coastal vessels, even colliers, to pass under if provided with "striking masts" (hinged masts, easily lowered). The freer waterway would facilitate the flow of the tidal current, reducing flood damage all along the Thames shores.

Rennie's report, thoroughly debated in Parliament and public, ended by convincing nearly everyone. The Corporation applied to Parliament in 1821. Rennie's testimony in Committee overcame the last resistance. During the progress of the bill through the two houses, Rennie designed a bridge: only five arches, a center span of 150 feet, soffits thirty feet above Trinity high-water mark. London boatmen must have been dazzled by so much good fortune. Some thirty other designs were submitted, but Rennie's was a foregone certainty as the choice. By the time construction was authorized, in 1823, the old engineer was dead, but his son, young John Rennie, his father's apprentice and namesake, was appointed to fill the commission.

The younger Rennie eventually accepted the knighthood his father had turned down, which was reasonable enough; a knighthood seemed appropriate to the son of a distinguished engineer whereas it had not suited a simple peasant's son.

Once, on a journey into Scotland to visit the Earl of Eglinton, the elder John Rennie was traveling in a stagecoach. It broke an axletree on a lonely road over the moor, without a house in sight. Rennie asked the coachman if there was a blacksmith anywhere near. He was told the nearest was a mile or so off. "Well then, help me carry the parts of the axle there, and I'll see to its being mended," said the engineer, and with a couple of others helping, they set off. Arrived at the smithy, they found the smith away. Rennie peeled off his coat, lighted the forge, blew the bellows, and with the clumsy assistance of his fellow passengers welded the axle. The part was carried back to the coach, restored to place, and the journey resumed. But Rennie's fellow passengers, formerly communicative, suddenly turned silent and chilly, like those of Boule-de-Suif in Maupassant's story. They were above conversing with a blacksmith. Rennie made no effort to correct their impression. Next morning one of the same passengers called at Eglinton Castle and, entering hat in hand, discovered to his mortification the presumed blacksmith breakfasting with the earl.

But if John Rennie scorned pretension, he knew his worth in harder terms. Commissioned to do a job for the Army Ordnance Department, he charged his usual fee of seven guineas a day (perhaps a hundred dollars of today's United States currency). The general receiving the bill exclaimed, "Why, this will never do. Seven guineas a day! Why, it is equal to the pay of a field marshal!" "Well," Rennie replied, "I am a field marshal in my profession, and if a field marshal in your line had answered your purpose, I suppose you would not have sent for me."

"Then you refuse any abatement?" asked the general.

"Not a penny," Rennie assured him, and the bill was paid.

10.

Thomas Telford Spans the Menai Strait

THOMAS TELFORD was a native of the same Sir Walter Scott border country as John Rennie. His family background was even a notch humbler; his father was a shepherd. Telford was orphaned younger than Rennie, his father dying while little Tom, the first child, was still a babe in arms. As usual with the poor, relatives and friends rallied to the widow's help. Despite their poverty, Tom was sent to school, profiting from the same democratic Scottish educational system that had helped Rennie get his start.

But Tom Telford could hardly aspire to go further after parish school, and he also missed John Rennie's lucky connection with a millwright shop. When he was fourteen, the family-and-friends council deliberated his future and arranged to have him apprenticed to a stonemason.

This was an ancient and honorable profession. It was also, as the youngster's advisers realized, a flourishing one in the lowland Scotland of the 1770s, thanks to rapidly expanding industry. They may even have foreseen that energetic, intelligent, good-natured Laughing Tam, as the boy was called, would make a first-rate success. What they could hardly have guessed was that stonemasonry could lead this bright and active boy to building, fifty years later, the world's first great metal bridge. Today, when engineers train for their specialty and then go out to practice it, the ready versatility of their eighteenth-century forebears is breath-taking. Tom Telford worked hard and became a proficient stonecutter, learning a good bit about the art of building at the same time. In 1780 he left his native

Eskdale for Edinburgh, where he spent a profitable year amid a building boom. He returned home in 1781, but only to visit his mother and friends before taking off for a more distant place—London.

London was not merely the capital; it was the only really big city in Britain. Its population, already over a million, was expanding rapidly. Twenty-four years old, full of confidence in his ability, unafraid of hard work, armed with letters of introduction to London connections of his Scottish friends and relatives, Telford set out in February 1782. John Rennie was completing his education at the University of Edinburgh; Telford now completed his in the school of experience. With the aid of his connections, especially Sir William Pulteney, a Scot who had married an English heiress, he found work, and his own talent, plus his unfailing good humor, won him advancement.

Telford's letters home from London give an interesting insight into the psychology of the new working class. There were clearly two distinct types from the start, Telford exemplifying one, and most of his fellow masons on the building jobs around London the other. These men struck him as a competent enough lot, but they lacked purpose to their lives. They worked for their week's pay and their chance for a bit of fun off the job. Telford, on the other hand, was consciously building a career. He never married, though he was a sociable, gregarious, and popular man all his life. That he was married to his work is obvious.

In 1784, Telford left London for Portsmouth to work on a Navy construction job. Within a year he was made general superintendent. This not only was a splendid advancement, but also gave him a great opportunity to study harbor engineering.

When Sir William Pulteney got Telford appointed county surveyor of public works for Salop (Shropshire), the young builder completed his transition to civil engineering. He designed his first bridge—a three-arch span in stone over the Severn at Montford which still stands. A few years later, heavy floods having destroyed another span over the Severn at Buildwas, Telford recommended to the county authorities that it be rebuilt in iron.

Behind Telford's proposal lay an interesting history. Shropshire was the scene of a growing iron industry, centered at Coalbrookdale. Back in 1777 the two leading ironmasters, John Wilkinson and Abraham Darby, had built an iron bridge over the Severn to replace the town ferry. This bridge, designed by an architect named Thomas

Pritchard, consisted of a single 140-foot semicircular arch made up of five arch ribs, each cast in two 70-foot halves. This Coalbrookdale bridge, the first ever erected in iron (an iron bridge assembled in France a few years earlier was never erected), recently has been retired from active service to be preserved as a British national monument.

At the time, the remarkable Coalbrookdale construction did not attract great attention. Although an iron arch was demonstrably cheaper than a stone arch, imitation came slowly. More than fifteen years passed before a bridge-builder undertook to use the new material. This daring engineer was none other than Tom Paine, the versatile author of *Common Sense,* who designed a tremendous 400-foot iron arch for the Schuylkill at Philadelphia. Paine went to England to supervise the casting of his arch ribs at Rotherham, in Yorkshire, another iron center. But his American financial backer failed and Paine himself became engrossed in the French Revolution. His iron ribs, exhibited in London, were reclaimed by the manufacturer and presently sold for a bridge over the little River Wear. Coincidentally, Telford proposed his iron bridge at Buildwas, which was thus the third iron bridge ever constructed.

In his memoirs, Telford observes that the Coalbrookdale ironmasters "deserve great credit for introducing a new material . . . but they had not disengaged their ideas from the usual masonry arch, the form of which in iron is not graceful; nor does it offer sufficient resistance against the pressure of earth behind the abutments, which has pushed them forward, and thus raised the iron arch in the middle." This defect in the Coalbrookdale bridge may be noted in illustration 16.

For the Buildwas bridge, Telford used the segment of a large circle as his arch. The ribs were cast by the Coalbrookdale ironmasters in 1796. The span was only 130 feet, less than that built simultaneously over the Wear with Tom Paine's iron, and much less than the Schuylkill arch that Paine had planned. The main importance of the Buildwas, in fact, was that it gave Telford confidence in iron as a bridge material. In the next several years he built four more small iron bridges. "Telford," says his biographer, Sir Alexander Gibb, "if not the inventor of iron bridges, was certainly the chief pioneer of their general adoption. . . . He first recognized that the real advantage iron offered was that it allowed the introduction of a much flatter arch"—thereby reducing the foundation weight as well as producing, as Telford himself noted, a more graceful bridge.

Soon after, the question of replacing London Bridge coming up, Telford submitted a daring plan for an iron bridge—a plan that actually was accepted, but the continuing debate on this interminably discussed project, and political conditions—the French Revolution—caused an indefinite postponement. Telford turned to other things.

But the Buildwas achieved what the Coalbrookdale had failed to do: it demonstrated the great advantages of iron over stone as an economical bridge material. Many iron bridges were built in England during the next two decades, including two major Thames crossings, the Vauxhall and the Southwark, the latter, a triple arch, containing the enormous weight of six thousand tons of iron. In France too, iron bridges were built—notably two over the Seine, the Pont du Louvre and the Pont d'Austerlitz (since replaced in stone). Telford had launched the metal bridge on its tremendous career, and a little later he was to contribute an even more revolutionary advance. Meantime, he was preoccupied with several major non-bridge projects, notably the Caledonian Canal which eliminated the laborious and perilous voyage around the north cape of Scotland.

In 1810–11, Telford was engaged for the Holyhead Road Survey, a major communications reform aimed at improving the wretched connection between London and Ireland by developing a good road west across the Welsh Island of Anglesey to Holyhead, where a harbor on the Irish Sea would be provided. The great problem of the road was the Menai Strait, between Anglesey and the mainland. Rennie examined the site and suggested an iron bridge, either a single 450-foot arch or three smaller arches. The heavy shipping traffic demanded a very high bridge, and Rennie's cost estimates, running from £260,000 to £290,000, were discouraging. It was decided to keep the old ferry, subject to the whims of wind and tide.

Meantime, Telford was consulted on a proposed crossing of the Mersey at Runcorn in Cheshire for the new London-to-Liverpool road. "I recommended a bridge of wrought iron, upon the suspension principle," is the surprisingly calm statement recorded in his memoirs.

As with the iron bridge itself, Telford was not inventing. The suspension principle was a very old one, known to primitive man. Suspension bridges hung from iron chains had been built in India, China, and western Europe as early as the sixteenth century. They were all notoriously flexible and flimsy, and only the most recent ones, built by Judge James Finley in America, had had a level floor and were meant to carry serious traffic. One of Finley's bridges collapsed under a drove of cattle, another under snow and ice. The suspension principle was simple and the suspension bridge cheap, but the form was treacherous, more so than any engineer of 1820, including Thomas Telford, realized.

Telford embarked on a series of experiments on the strength of wrought iron at Brunton's Patent Chain Cable Manufactory, where he made the acquaintance of Captain Samuel Brown. This naval officer also had become interested in suspension bridges and had invented a new kind of flat iron link, which he believed capable of sustaining heavy loading. Telford and Brown, who might have become rivals and enemies, hit it off excellently and became close friends and collaborators, exchanging ideas to their mutual profit.

In the end, Telford's suspension bridge over the Mersey never was built, being considered too expensive, but Telford emerged from the project profoundly enriched. He lost no time in recommending a solution to the Menai Strait problem—a tremendous suspension bridge with a main span of nearly six hundred feet.

Quite a proposal: a new kind of bridge, depending on cables made of a new material—iron links—with a span length unheard of for any kind of bridge ever built.

Despite Telford's stature, it is remarkable that his proposal was accepted by Parliament. The acceptance probably reflected the pressure the committee was receiving for a bridge—any bridge—over the Menai Strait as much as it does the confidence of the committee in Telford's suspension plan.

In 1817, Telford received a definite go-ahead, and early in 1818 his design was ready. He chose as his site a point with the unpronounceable Welsh name of Ynys-y-moch, where the strait was 300 yards wide at high tide, 160 at low. On the Anglesey side there was a splendid above-water rock on which the west pier could be founded; on the Wales side, it was necessary to go six feet below low water to get a firm rock foundation. But this presented no difficulties. The two great towers would rise 153 feet above high water, with the roadway 100 feet above high water. The deck was designed to carry two carriageways, each twelve feet wide, with a four-foot-wide footpath between.

In the spring of 1818, Parliament voted £20,000, and on July 8, carpenters began building workshops. The opposition, which had fought the bridge before, reappeared in more virulent force than ever. The Marquis of Anglesey, lord of the island of Anglesey, and Mr. Asheton Smith, leader of the "Carnarvon interest" on the mainland, created legal difficulties. But a new Act of Parliament finally disposed of these, and work began in earnest in 1819. The island of Anglesey itself supplied the hard gray limestone for the towers, the first stone of which was laid (on the Anglesey side) on August 10.

Through 1820, 1821, and 1822, the work on the foundations and piers (towers) was carried on side by side with another, quite new type of bridge work—testing iron bars, 935 of which would compose each of the bridge's sixteen chain cables. According to Telford's experiments, bars of the dimensions used were capable of withstanding 87 tons' tension. But at half this strain they showed elongation, so Telford fixed on 35 tons as his maximum tension. Every iron bar was proved with strictest care, to insure maximum uniformity. Telford was proud of the way the huge chains were fixed in the rock at Anglesey, and in his memoirs urged its inspection by every visitor "who feels no dread at entering by a side-drain into a cavern in the rock, containing gigantic ironwork, and productive of feelings of superhuman agency."

The two great suspension towers were raised to thirty feet above the roadway level. The carriageways, narrowed to nine feet, passed through the towers, which were completed in the spring of 1824, with cast-iron plates and saddles fixed on their tops. The rest of the year was spent in final preparations for the critical act of suspending the first cable. The chains on the Carnarvon side were brought over the tower and down the sea face to high-water level; there the mass of iron was laid on a barge, or timber float. Meantime on the Anglesey side, capstans capable of pulling fifty tons were installed.

"Every necessary preparation having been made," Telford records, "about the middle of April, 1825, I left London for Bangor; and having satisfied myself that every due precaution had been taken, it was resolved to raise the first chain on the twenty-fifth of that month. Accordingly, on that day, at half-past two o'clock in the afternoon, about an hour before high-water, the raft was cast off, and floated into position between the piers, where being moored, one end of the chain, which lay upon it, was joined to that which hung down the face of the Carnarvon pier; the other end was attached to ropes connected with the Anglesey-side capstans, and the said ropes passed, by means of blocks, over the top of the pyramid of the Anglesey pier. Then the workmen who manned the capstans moved at a steady trot, and in one hour and thirty-five minutes after they commenced hoisting, the chain was raised to its proper curvature, and fastened to the portion of chain previously placed at the top of the Anglesey pyramid.

"I then ascended, and satisfied myself that by this juncture had been formed a continuous and safe chain from the Carnarvon fastening in the rock to that in Anglesey. Having announced this fact, a loud and general shout of exultation arose from the workmen and the numerous spectators who had assembled to witness this novel operation."

From other sources come added fillips to Telford's description of the memorable day. The men turning the capstan worked to the rhythm of a Welsh fife band, and after the task was completed (perhaps this was the reason for the cheer), ale was distributed to the workmen in generous portions. Two men, in fact, became so enthusiastic over the day's feat that they mounted the tower and crossed to the Wales side by clinging like monkeys to the solitary chain cable.

Within six weeks the last of the sixteen chains was raised into place. In each chain Telford placed four adjusting links to assure proper curvature. He made certain by experiment that any part of any chain could be replaced without endangering the bridge. In August and September the roadway was laid—two thicknesses of fir plank, with felt between the layers, a third layer of planking, on felt, for each carriageway. The side railings, the tollhouses, and the gates were installed by the end of the year, and on Monday morning, January 30, 1826, the London mail coach, occupied by Telford's assistant engineers, the mail coach superintendent, "and anyone who could find a place to stand or hang by," crossed the world's first bridge over ocean waters. All day long, carriages, horsemen, and people on foot crossed; that evening the workmen—all who had helped build the bridge—"were regaled with a joyous festival."

The bridge took 2000 tons of wrought iron—a considerable amount, but a notable advantage for the suspension design when contrasted with the 6000 tons of iron required for the Vauxhall iron arch over the Thames.

A week after the opening, a terrific gale blew up in the strait. A very disturbing observation was made: the chains undulated in an uneven manner, causing the carriageway to lurch and jump alarmingly. Telford dealt with this perplexing problem by installing transverse bracings—that is, by fastening the chain cables to each other at intervals. The measure was successful until another violent storm ten years later, in January 1836, broke six of the iron rods by which the roadway was suspended. Three years later, in January 1839, the biggest hurricane of all hit the bridge, wrecking the roadway and breaking more than a third of the 444 suspending rods.

The engineers who investigated the bridge strengthened the roadway and made a significant addition—installation of four "strong trussed railings," two for each carriageway. This was one of several embryonic versions of the future stiffening truss, the indispensable reinforcement of every modern suspension bridge. The railings preserved the bridge for a hundred years; in 1939 its sixteen old wrought-iron cables were replaced with steel, and it carries automobile traffic to this day.

The Menai Strait Bridge, Telford's great memorial, secures his place in engineering history. But though he was nearly seventy at its completion, he continued his active career virtually to his death at seventy-seven. The list of his works after 1821 is staggering—bridges and aqueducts by the score, roads (he was Macadam's chief rival), harbors, canals, and several railroads. In addition he became the first President of the Institution of Civil Engineers. Formed by a band of younger men in London, the Institution invited Telford to lend his prestige and his practical assistance by accepting its highest office. He at once introduced the recording of minutes, assuring the Institution's usefulness by creating a rich body of material for engineering discussion and for historians. In 1828 he succeeded in obtaining a Royal Charter for the group, assuring its success. Finally he insisted on strict examination of candidates for membership, thereby assuring its importance.

Another of Telford's interests late in life was the automobile. Most people believe the automobile to have been invented around 1900; actually James Watt patented a "steam carriage" as far back as 1784. For four months in 1831 a regular steam bus service operated between Cheltenham and Worcester, four times a day, carrying some three thousand passengers at a speed of from 10 to 15 mph. But the privately financed Turnpike Trusts objected to the new vehicles, which they foresaw would ultimately reduce their revenue, and obtained permission to charge them prohibitive tolls. Telford took part in a test run of a steam bus from London to Birmingham in 1833, but despite his favorable testimony before a Parliamentary Committee, mechanical transport was postponed till the arrival of the gasoline engine.

In Telford's day an engineer was an engineer, innocent of specialization and expected to be able to build or repair any structure, machine, or man-made work. A delightfully comic incident occurred during Telford's time as county surveyor in Shropshire. The parishioners of the church at St. Chad's, a small town near Shrewsbury, called on Telford to give an opinion on their leaky roof. Telford made a thorough examination and found that the leaky roof was the least of the church's defects: the walls, undermined by age and the proximity of graves in the churchyard, were in a most alarming condition. He delivered his report to the wardens and appeared at a meeting in the church to discuss it. But sentiment hardly favored an extensive remodeling of the building. Several elderly vestrymen declared that the threatening fissures Telford had observed had been there "since time immemorial." Several voiced the suspicion that Telford was merely seeking a commission. Telford thereupon rose and proposed that the discussion be adjourned to another place, on the grounds that the church where they were sitting might fall in on them at any moment. With this parting shot, he left, amid a chorus of outraged jeers. "I gave myself no disturbance about it," wrote Telford to a friend, "when lo & behold on the Morning of the 9th inst the very parts I had pointed out, gave way—and down tumbled the mighty mass forming a very remarkable, magnificent Ruin, while the astonished and surprised inhabitants were roused from their delirium—tho' they have not yet recovered from the shock."

Telford's lively writing style is a good indication of his personality. He wrote hundreds of letters to his friends in Scotland all through his life. His letters to his mother, which he continued faithfully until her death, were printed in block capitals for easier reading. In his youth he indulged in poetry, some of which evidently was inspired by his compatriot Robert Burns, to whom one of his poems was addressed. One stanza reflects Telford's own career, as well as the careers of Watt, Rennie, and other self-made Scottish engineers of the day:

> Nor pass the tentie curious lad,
> Who o'er the ingle hangs his head,
> And begs of neighbours books to read;
> For hence arise
> Thy country's sons, who far are spread,
> Baith bold and wise.

Like many other British poets, if not engineers, Telford was attracted by the democratic idealism of the French Revolution. He learned, however, to restrain the expression of his feelings after one nearly disastrous episode. In 1791 he sent a piece of subversive literature to some friends in Langholm, under the frank of his patron, Sir William Pulteney. The pamphlet caused a great stir, and Sir William was seriously vexed. The pamphlet? *The Rights of Man,* by Thomas Paine. Telford was shocked by the later excesses of the Revolution, according to his close friend and editor of his memoirs, Rickman, but as Rickman himself was a deep-dyed Tory—he refers to *The Rights of Man* as "some of the political trash of the day"—he may have read a good bit of his own political views into Telford's tactful silences in discussion.

Long before his death, Telford's fame had spread well beyond British shores. He was invited to Sweden by Charles XIV, Napoleon's former Marshal Bernadotte, to advise on the great Göta Canal linking the North Sea and the Baltic. Telford and his two companions made the voyage in six days, but evidently were prepared for a considerably longer time at sea. Their ample provision for the journey included four dozen bottles of port and Madeira, three dozen bottles of cider, six dozen bottles of porter, and a half dozen bottles each of gin and brandy. Telford had a congenial attitude toward the pleasures of the bottle. Southey, the Poet Laureate, and one of his closest friends, noted the extraordinary affection with which he was welcomed at Highland inns.

Like all successful men, Telford was besieged chronically by improvident friends, relatives, and former workmen. A man who worked for him on the Caledonian Canal wrote to Rickman that "numerous applications were incessantly made to him; I never knew an instance of unkind rejection. The possession of any talent, literary, scientific or mechanical, I always observed was an irresistible passport to his bounty."

As we have noted, Telford had one lifelong economy; he never married, and in all his letters a single reference to a woman occurs, an actress whose talent he had admired. The explanation given by Rickman is: "He lived as a soldier; always in active service."

Telford had expressed a desire to be buried in the parish church of St. Margaret, Westminster, but the Institution of Civil Engineers successfully urged the propriety of burying him in Westminster Abbey. John Rennie had been buried in St. Paul's; thus the two Scots farm lads from the border country lie in England's two most august crypts. Both men would have laughed at the pomp and ostentation; both, however, would have accepted the compliment for their profession and their generation.

11.

The Yankee Bridge

We crossed this river by a wooden bridge, roofed and covered in on all sides, and nearly a mile in length. It was profoundly dark; perplexed, with great beams crossing and recrossing it at every possible angle; and through the broad chinks and crevices of the floor the rapid river gleamed, far down below, like a legion of eyes. We had no lamps; and as the horses stumbled and floundered through this place, towards the distant speck of dying light, it seemed interminable. I really could not at first persuade myself, as we rumbled heavily on, filling the bridge with hollow noises, and I held down my head to save it from the rafters above, but that I was in a painful dream; for I have often dreamed of toiling through such places, and as often argued, even at the time, "this cannot be reality."

—Charles Dickens, on crossing the Susquehanna River, 1842.

BRITAIN was not the only country bursting with activity as the eighteenth century drew to a close. Across the sea the United States of America was multiplying in population and wealth, spreading across the mountains, its towns turning into cities, its villages into towns, and every road-river intersection demanding a bridge. Stone bridges were too expensive for transportation-hungry, timber-rich America; bridges had to be made of wood. The curious thing is that suddenly for the first time the question was raised seriously: how do you build a wooden bridge?

Of course, innumerable timber beam and pile-trestle bridges had been built. But how did you bridge deep, broad rivers, such as those that cut the American coast from Maine to Florida? The question had received intermittent attention in Europe, and just recently a spectacular series of long-span timber-arch bridges had been built by the Grubermann brothers of Switzerland. Yet the real solution was only half realized, and it was a set of Yankee carpenters from New England and a German emigrant to Pennsylvania who in the course of a single generation pragmatically created a major new bridge form—the truss.

The origins of the truss go nearly as far back in history as those of the arch. But the basic principle is so simple that the truss must have been developed in many ancient countries to support roofs. Sometime, somewhere, the same inverted V was used to hold up a log bridge (*Figure 29*).

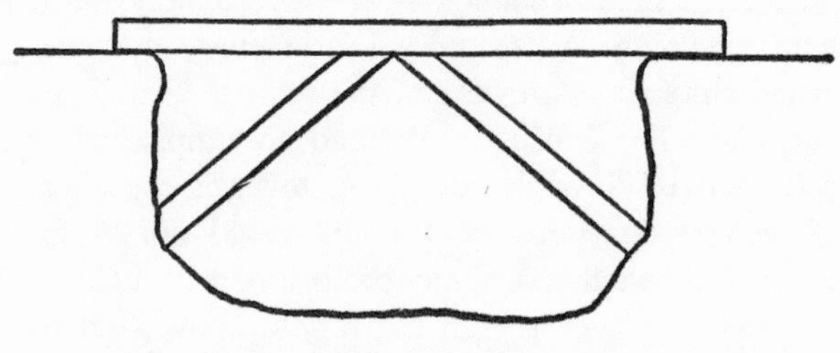

Figure 29

Some time later, the next step was taken: a horizontal member was inserted across the bottom of the inverted V (*Figure 30a*). This was presently followed by the addition of a short central vertical member (*Figure 30b*).

What the primitive bridge-builder had achieved was an absolutely stable geometric structure. It was based on the triangle, a linear form with a unique value in construction: *a triangle cannot be distorted.* In this it is utterly different from a square or rectangle.

The enormous importance of this simple truth to a carpenter or architect can be appreciated if you take seven pieces of wood, nail

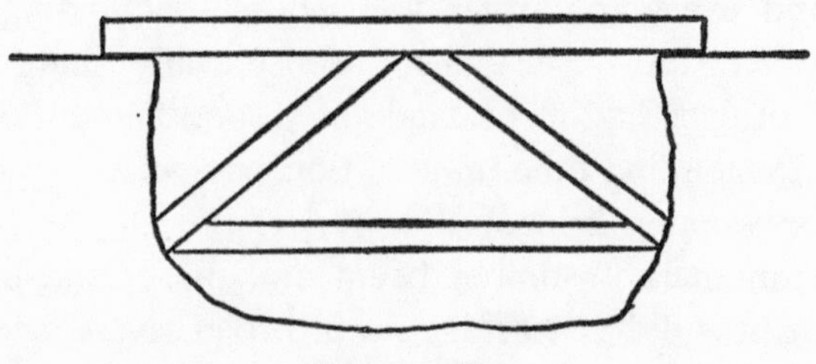

Figure 30a

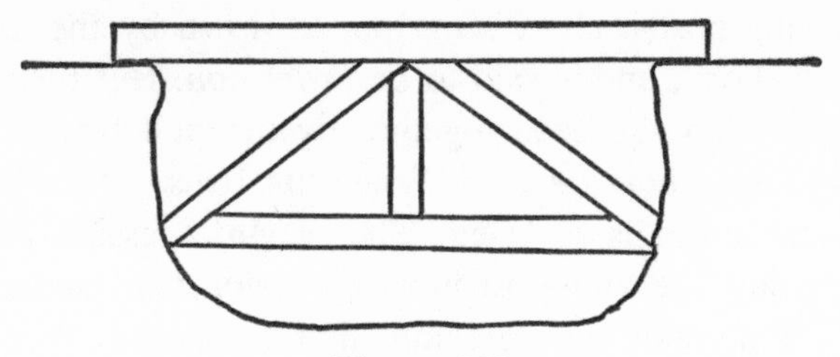

Figure 30b

four of them together and nail the remaining three together. The four can be pushed about into different quadrilaterals with ease; the three will only break, never distort, under pressure (*Figure 31*).

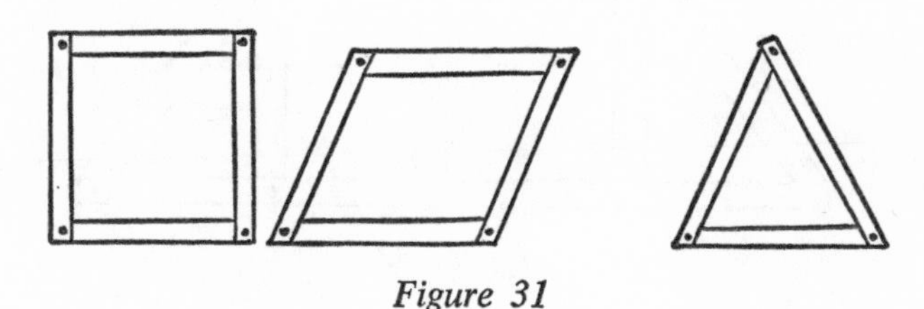

Figure 31

The basic design of two triangles sharing a side is known as a king-post truss, the king-post being the vertical member forming the common side of the supporting right triangles. Two king-post trusses can carry a roadway and a considerable live load. They may support the roadway from below, but serve the same purpose, and can be more easily erected, if built above the deck (*Figure 32*).

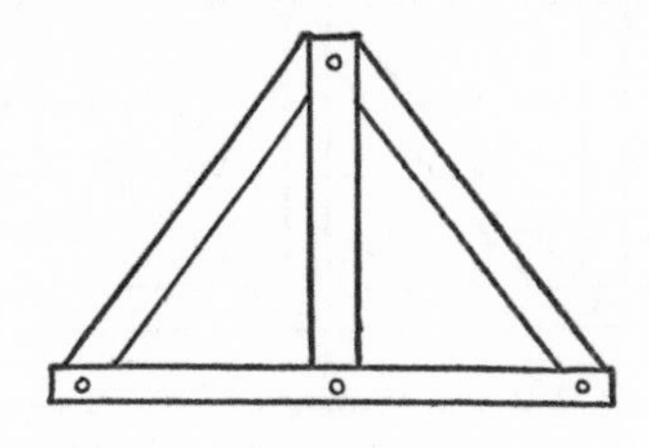

Figure 32

The king-post forms the common side of the two right triangles. The second side is formed by the horizontal beam called the lower chord. The hypotenuses are the diagonal members. There is a very interesting difference in the functions of the members of a king-post above and a king-post below the roadway. When the king-post is above, the king-post itself is being pulled down by the load pressing on the lower chord, and is said to be *in tension.* But the diagonals in this case are being squeezed together by the pull from the top, and are said to be *in compression.* When the truss is built below the bridge, the situation is reversed. The weight pressing down on the lower chord puts the king-post in *compression,* and at the same time subjects the diagonals to stretching, that is, *tension.* We shall come back to this a little later. The next step was to lengthen the span, which was achieved quite simply, again by anonymous European builders (*Figure 33*).

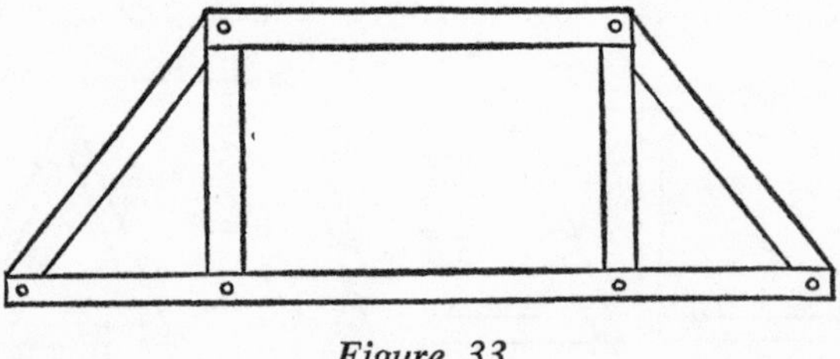

Figure 33

A horizontal crosspiece (usually braced) was made to connect two triangles. The result was named the queen-post. The queen-post doubled, or more than doubled, the length of span that could safely be built. Yet there was a limit to the span length; the farther apart the triangles were placed the less support they gave to the center of the bridge. But once more, the next step is natural (*Figure 34*).

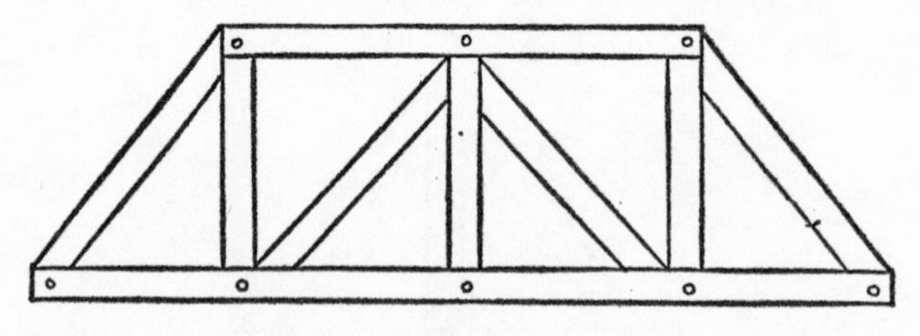

Figure 34

This chain of triangles was called a multiple king-post. A more general name for it is a truss. As early as the thirteenth century the form was known, for the sketchbook of the famous cathedral master-builder Villard de Honnecourt contains what Hans Straub describes as "a kind of truss bridge." By the sixteenth century it had been brought to the point of sophistication. Four truss designs were included by Palladio in his *Treatise on Architecture,* a four-volume engineering classic published in 1570. Palladio ascribes his four types to German bridge-builders (*Figure 35*).

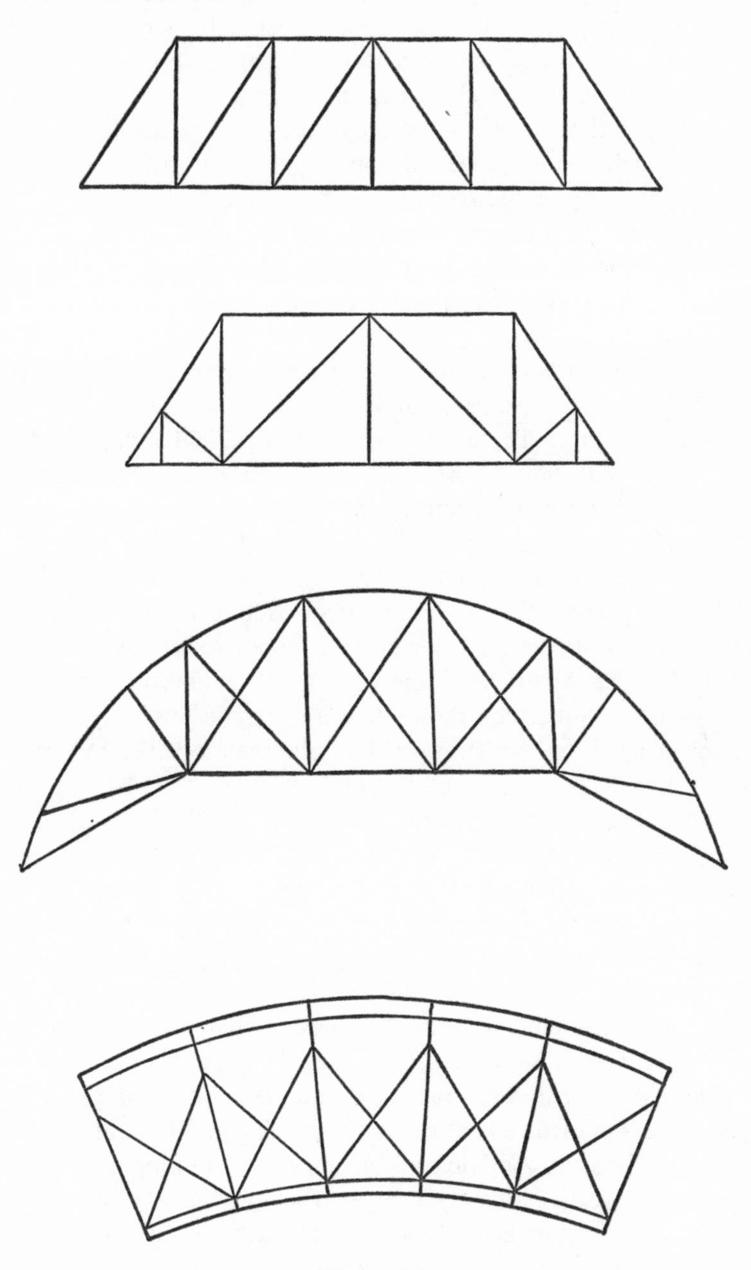

Figure 35

Palladio himself built a few truss bridges, including a 108-foot span over the Cismone at Bassano (not to be confused with the covered bridge of a later day over the Brenta, at Bassano del Grappa, subject of a popular Italian song). Two even more famous timber bridges mounted on timber piles, with partial truss construction, are the Swiss Kapellbrücke and Spreuerbrücke at Lucerne. Like the Bassano del Grappa bridge, the Lucerne bridges were covered, and the coverings are their most noteworthy feature. The inside of the roof of the Kappell bears a series of one hundred and twelve paintings in the triangular spaces between the roof and the crossbeams, depicting the history of the town of Lucerne and the lives of its two patron saints. The Spreuer has an even more celebrated gallery, The Dance of Death, a macabre suite painted by Kasper Meglinger from 1626 to 1636.

More important in an engineering sense were the bridges of the Swiss Grubermann brothers, over the Rhine and elsewhere, in the eighteenth century. These were of considerable length, the first to give a real indication of what could be done with the truss form. Their longest, over the Limmat in Baden, had a clear opening of 390 feet, an amazing piece of daring. Built in 1758, it stood till 1800, when it was destroyed by French troops. Possibly the Grubermanns have been overpraised, as two American engineers, Robert Fletcher and J. P. Snow, asserted in a paper reviewing early timber bridges for the American Society of Civil Engineers. The Grubermann constructions, they thought, were "ponderous . . . a maze of timbers, scarfed, bolted, strapped and clamped together to form nondescript trusses . . . stretched-out and awkward . . . lacking the appearance of adequate strength," and "not worthy of consideration from an engineering standpoint."

Some national feeling is involved here. British bridge historians and doubtless other Europeans have been sublimely unaware of the American covered bridge, and American engineers are exasperated, understandably, as beyond question, whatever the truss bridge's European antecedents, it was in America that with an astonishing suddenness it grew into one of the world's great bridge forms.

Palladio's *Treatise* was translated into English in 1742. Whether anybody in America read it or not is uncertain. The real question is whether anybody in America *had* to read it. The king-post truss was universally known. Not only every carpenter, but also every farmer knew how to support a mill floor or a barn by a king-post truss. To hold up a bridge by the same means was an obvious enough idea.

We know little about this important development in American engineering, for the men who built the first truss bridges on this continent over the creeks and streams of early America were much concerned with making things work and little with making them remembered.

The first glimmer that we have is of a bridge built at Norwich, Connecticut, by a "curious mechanic" named John Bliss. All we know for sure is that this bridge was 124 feet long and required no intermediate supports. Doubtless it was an arch. Another famous early American timber bridge, built by Enoch Hale at Bellows Falls, Vermont, apparently was a truss arch; records of it are untrustworthy. But the man who made the truss bridge a successful reality, not merely as an engineering technique but also as a commercial proposition, was a big New England Yankee with a Roman nose. In 1792, Timothy Palmer of Newburyport, Massachusetts, a millwright like John Rennie, built a bridge consisting of two trussed arches meeting on Deer Island in the middle of the Merrimac, and bearing a suspicious resemblance to one of Palladio's four truss designs. The longer of Palmer's two arches was 160 feet, and he soon exceeded this when he built a bridge over the Piscataqua in New Hampshire that contained a trussed arch of 244 feet.

Timothy Palmer patented his arch-truss and built it repeatedly, not only in New England but also farther south, over the Delaware, the Schuylkill, and the Potomac. His 550-foot, three-arch "Permanent Bridge" over the Schuylkill, built in 1806, was the solution to the Philadelphia bridge problem which Tom Paine had thought of solving with an iron arch. A truss, incidentally, may be regarded as a simple beam with unnecessary pieces removed (*Figure 36*).

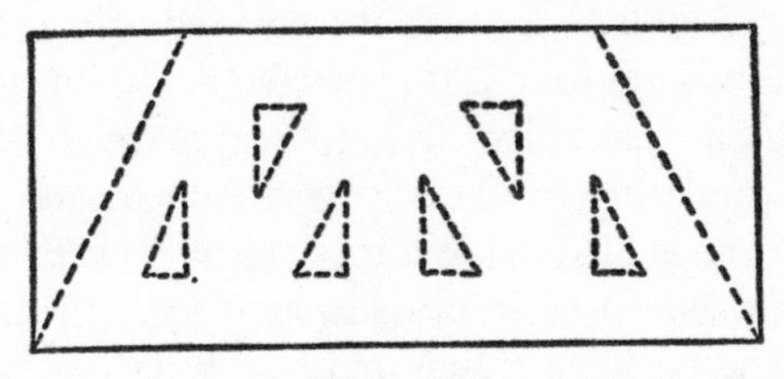

Figure 36

Timothy Palmer's "Permanent Bridge" was completed before Judge Richard Peters, of the bridge company, made the suggestion that gave America's timber truss bridges their characteristic appearance and name. Judge Peters reasoned that a covering would make the Permanent Bridge a little more permanent by preserving the principal members from rot. Wood will survive indefinitely fully submerged in water, but alternations of wet and dry soon destroy it.

The idea was of course not new, as witness the Kapellbrücke and Spreuerbrücke. For that matter, it had long been a common practice in America to build housings over the trusses of king-posts and queen-posts (*Figure 37*).

Figure 37

Palmer went further even than the European builders, however. He added sidings as well as roof, completely enclosing his bridge. The covering proved its value by preserving the bridge for nearly seventy years. It was finally destroyed in 1875, not by weather but by fire. He repeated this technique in his next bridge, over the Delaware at Easton, Pennsylvania, and America's distinctive covered-bridge form was established. Once the covered bridge got started, all sorts of advantages were found. It protected the wood not only against wet but also against excessive drying in summer. It kept too much snow from accumulating on the roadway—uncovered bridges sometimes collapsed under blizzard loadings. (But New England tollkeepers had to "snow-pave" their bridges in winter, because everybody used sleighs.) The barnlike siding and roof were reassuring to horses and cows, who often did not like to venture out over rushing water. The exterior provided excellent space for both religious and secular messages: "The wages of sin is death" competed with "Dr. Parker's Indian Oil for Ills of Man and Beast." The covered bridge soon became the place to take one's girl in the rig, and simultaneously the place to hide in the roof rafters to watch the occupants of the rig. It became part of the American language as well as the American landscape; a Vermont sarcasm if someone failed to close a door promptly was, "Were you born in a covered bridge?"

Six years after Timothy Palmer's "Permanent Bridge," an even more spectacular covered bridge was built across the same Schuylkill River a few miles downstream, at Fairmount, Pennsylvania. This bridge, built by German immigrant Lewis Wernwag, was an arch-truss with a clear span of 340 feet—a truly remarkable feat, meriting, for its technical virtuosity, the applause and attention it won for its size and beauty. The covered arch, painted white, rose in a long gentle arc, the siding pierced by a row of small windows, resembling, in the words of a contemporary, "a white scarf thrown across the stream." The interior of Wernwag's structure was even more interesting than its picturesque exterior. Two arches, framing a truss, carried the roadway, which rose in an arc of greater magnitude. Thus the roadway did not present as steep a hill to the wagon driver as the bridge, seen from the outside, indicated. The truss itself was strictly a reinforcement, consisting of heavy verticals and light diagonals. But it was remarkable for another reason—the light diagonals were iron rods, the first time iron was used in a long-span bridge (*Figure 38*).

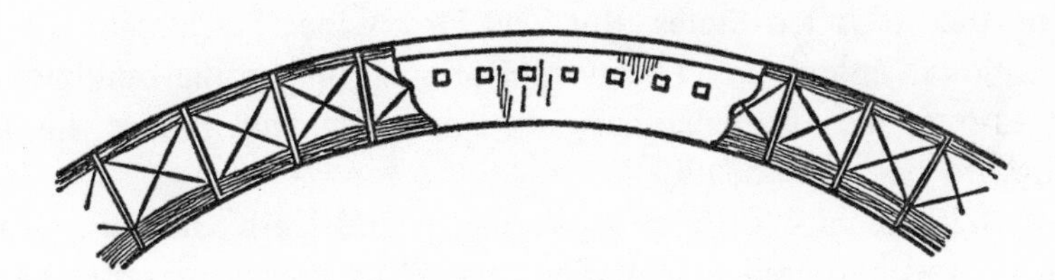

Wernwag's arch truss

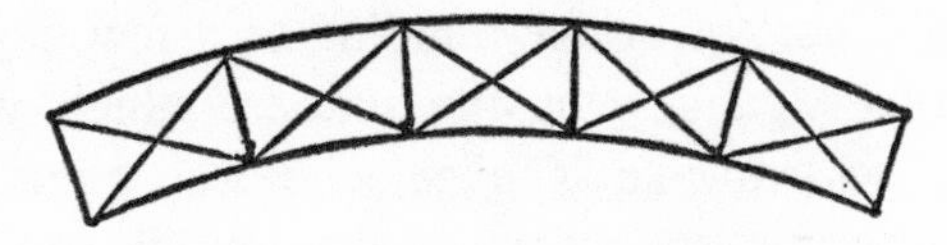

Palladio's arch truss

Figure 38

Wernwag's bridge, known in its time as "The Colossus," doubtless would have lasted longer than it did but for fire, the great enemy of covered bridges, which cut short its life in 1838. The conflagration, as esthetically memorable as the bridge itself, was described by an eyewitness as "sublime."

Meantime, another New England carpenter-mechanic was discovering Palladio. Theodore Burr of Torrington, Connecticut, boldly based a new design directly on Palladio's king-post truss. When it proved unstable under moving loads, Burr strengthened it with an arch. His design was usually known as the Burr arch-truss, but it was significant that the arch was added to the truss rather than the other way around (*Figure 39*).

Figure 39

The Burr arch-truss became for a time the most popular of all timber-bridge forms, repeated hundreds of times, especially throughout the northeast United States. But alas for engineering inspiration and promotional enterprise; Theodore Burr, at one point building five bridges over the Susquehanna, ended as a financial failure, his ruin leading to his early death.

By 1820, thanks to Palmer, Wernwag, and Burr, the truss principle was well explored in America, and if its theory was still hardly understood, its practicality was tested. In that year a New Haven architect named Ithiel Town took out a patent for a new kind of truss which reduced the cost of bridge-building to a few days' labor by an ordinary carpenter's gang, plus the timber, which was universally cheap. Town, a wide-awake Yankee who was already ranging the whole country putting up churches and public buildings, got his bridge brainstorm in North Carolina. He named it the "Town Lattice Mode" (*Figure 40*).

Town substituted a number of light planks, pinned together with "trunnels"—wooden pegs, that is, "treenails"—for the heavy web members of a Palmer or Burr truss. He did not build the "Lattice Mode," he peddled it. His advertising claimed it could be "built by

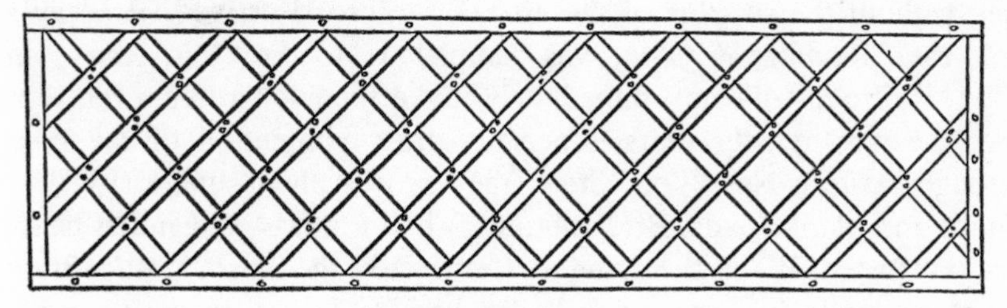

Figure 40

the mile and cut off by the yard." It was phenomenally successful, for it solved every cost problem: cheap material, cheap preparation of material, cheap construction, cheap maintenance. Town collected a dollar a foot for every bridge built under his patent, and charged a genial two dollars a foot if somebody built a lattice bridge without asking his permission. By doubling the planking and the wooden pins, he even made his truss serve the early railroads.

The Town Lattice was sometimes constructed in conjunction with a wooden arch, but the arch was not essential. With the Town Lattice the truss really had arrived. Another panel truss quickly followed. In 1830 an army engineer named Colonel Stephen H. Long, returning home to Hopkinton, New Hampshire, produced an attractive little model of his new design which could be carried about in a wooden box. In the 1830s, Colonel Long's traveling bridge salesmen gave vigorous and profitable competition to Ithiel Town's. In these years the sprawling, muscular young republic was pushing its roads westward and multiplying its river crossings in every direction on both sides of the Appalachian spine.

Colonel Long's design was a multiple king-post (*Figure 41*).

Figure 41

At this point arose one of the remarkable coincidences of history, which very often are not coincidences at all but confluences of simultaneously stirred forces. Just as the truss rose to stand on its own feet, without the support of the arch, the railroad arrived. America's first, the Baltimore & Ohio, was completed (to the Ohio River) in 1833. Railroads did not immediately make their advantages felt, but over the next twenty years, especially after completion of the lines through western New York State, they proved their superiority over canals and plank roads. Bridge-builders had a new—and much heavier—customer. While the Long and especially the Town Lattice truss could be made to serve, they had a serious weakness deriving not from their form, but from the material itself. Wood, while a fine compression member, is weak in tension—it can be pulled apart, especially if bolted at the joints.

It will be recalled that Lewis Wernwag had used iron diagonals in the Colossus over the Schuylkill. Wernwag's iron rods had played only a small part in carrying the loading of his bridge. Now another inventive Massachusetts Yankee came forward with a proposal to give iron the principal—tension—role in a bridge. This was William Howe, of Spencer, Massachusetts, whose brother Tyler invented a bedspring and whose nephew Elias presently invented a sewing machine. What William Howe did was take the Long truss and supply it with a wrought-iron vertical. The wooden compression members could be single diagonals or Xs, as the strength required. The iron uprights were formed of cylindrical rods with screw ends, running through top and bottom chords, and held by nuts and washers. The ends of the timber braces (the diagonals or Xs) were secured by abutting them against cast-iron joint boxes (*Figure 42*).

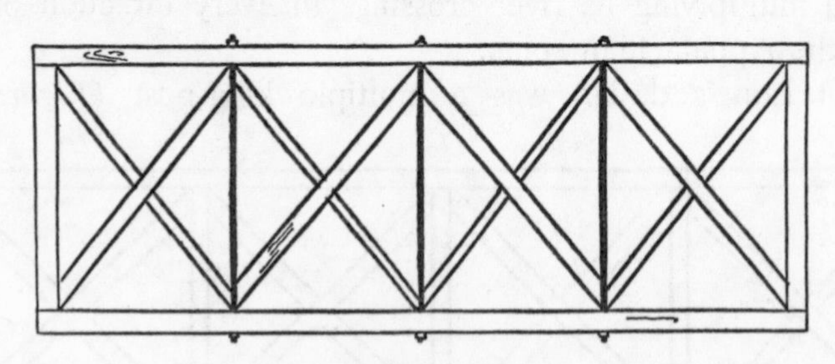

Figure 42

There were several advantages to the Howe idea. One was mass production. The iron parts, easy to manufacture and simple to assemble, could be loaded on railroad cars and shipped to a bridge site; in fact, all the parts, iron and wood, of a Howe truss, could be prefabricated and shipped. Also, some flexibility in design was introduced—as many iron rods could be inserted at a given point as the stress was believed to require. Finally, a turnbuckle arrangement made it possible to tighten the joints where they became loosened by passage of loads. In the preriveting age this passed for an exceptionally secure arrangement.

Howe introduced a more advanced mechanics into bridge-building. He did not, any more than Colonel Long or Theodore Burr or Timothy Palmer, introduce science. They were carpenters; Howe was a carpenter-mechanic. Among them all, with their hewed timber and trunnels, their iron rods and turnbuckles, they built thousands of bridges that stood up, carried loads, and made money. But soon after William Howe presented his wood-and-iron design for both highway and railroad bridges the theoretical problems of bridge-loading came under scrutiny. In 1847 the first American treatise appeared: *A Work on Bridge-Building* by Squire Whipple of Utica, New York. Whipple was not a country gentleman; his first name just happened to be Squire. In his book he analyzed the stresses in a truss design, observing among other things that the tensile strength of cast iron did not greatly exceed that of wood. Putting theory into practice, Squire Whipple built iron bridges with wrought-iron tension and cast-iron compression members. His initial form was the bowstring truss (*Figure 43*).

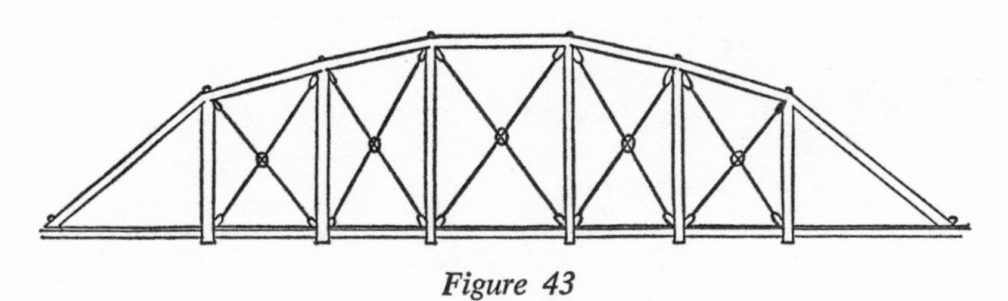

Figure 43

The curved upper chord, like any arch, was in compression and so could be made of the cheaper cast iron. The bottom chord was in tension—the load was pushing down on, and so stretching it—and was of wrought iron, as were the intermediate members. The bowstring form itself was not original with Whipple, having been developed in France some years earlier.

"Cast iron will resist a greater crushing force than any other substance whose cost will admit of its being used as a building material," Squire Whipple noted. "Steel has a greater power of resistance, but its cost precludes its use as a material for building. Wrought iron resists nearly equally with cast iron, but its cost is twice as great, which gives cast iron the advantage. On the other hand, wrought iron resists a tensile force nearly four times as well as cast iron, and twelve to fifteen times as well as wood, bulk for bulk."

Actually the greatest weakness of wood was the difficulty of joining it strongly; the tensile strength of a wooden beam always exceeded the tensile strength of its joint.

Other attempts were made to solve the problem of the insufficient strength of the tensile members of a truss. None was very successful. In Squire Whipple's thoughtful words about the relation between the strength and cost of the various materials lay the great bridge problem of the railroad age, and the failure of this and the next generation to solve it satisfactorily brought disaster, tragedy, and national scandal.

On March 4, 1840, High Rock Bridge, a Town Lattice over the Catskill Creek, New York, fell apart and dropped a train of boxcars into the water. One man was killed. It was America's first railroad-bridge fatality, an ominous note hardly heeded at the time.

The railroad, in fact, was about to strike bridge engineering with such devastating impact that we may profitably turn back a little to examine its arrival in some detail.

12.

The Stephensons Invent the Railroad and the Railroad Bridge

FOR twenty centuries the essential problem of bridge-building was to build spans that would stand up. The Roman semicircular stone arch stood up; its later improvements and modifications, in the direction of a longer and flatter arch form, were aimed at providing better navigation room below rather than more carrying capacity on top. As long as a stone arch bridge would stand at all, it would carry a man, or a man and a horse, or a horse and wagon. Even the shops and buildings that crowded the roadways of London Bridge, the Pont-Neuf, and the Ponte Vecchio made only a modest addition to the ponderous "dead loading" of the structure itself.

Now suddenly, within a few decades, if not actually a few years, two major changes came. Bridges were asked to carry really heavy burdens—and burdens which, unlike the five-story houses on London Bridge, moved. Though trains could be slowed down for bridge crossings, the strain they imposed was terrific, far exceeding anything bridges ever had experienced before.

At the same time the railroad created an utterly unparalleled demand for new bridges. At the time of the introduction of railroads, some thirty thousand bridges of all kinds and all ages existed in Britain. Twenty years later the number had doubled. The story in America and in Continental Europe was the same. Most of the new bridges were built quite simply; most were merely the result of the railroad's finicky and characteristic need for an almost absolutely flat roadway. But where railroad met river a very serious bridging problem arose. To see this problem develop and to witness its solution, we must return to England, the land of coal—and so the land of steam and iron—of the early nineteenth century.

We must, in fact, visit Newcastle, on the Tyne River, in the north of England just below the Scottish border, the town whose name was a synonym for coal all over the world in days when the mines of Pennsylvania, Ohio, Illinois, the Ruhr, the Saar, the Donetz, never had been heard of. Coal was mined at Newcastle in Elizabethan days, when Londoners, having cut and burned their neighboring forests, needed fuel to heat their homes. The advantages of Newcastle's coal for manufacturing rapidly founded a whole set of English industries, notably glass and cutlery. As demands for coal grew and Newcastle owners coined money, a difficulty arose; the mines filled with water at a certain depth and had to be pumped out by man or horse power. The deeper the mine went, the more water had to be pumped. Another problem: the farther the pits strayed from the Tyne docks, the more expensive the transport became. Out of this situation grew a steam engine for water-pumping and iron rails for hauling.

Both these two elements of the future railroad were in regular use at the Newcastle pits when George Stephenson was born in 1781. The steam engine was still the slow-acting "atmospheric" Newcomen engine, though James Watt had already developed his crucial improvement, the separate condenser, which made it possible to turn wheels by steam piston. The rails were used for wagons hauled by horses and mules.

The steam railroad was shuffling impatiently in the wings, and its offstage noises already could be heard. Back in 1769 a French army officer had even built a steam-driven vehicle that had knocked down a wall in the Luxembourg Gardens—the first locomotive, the first automobile, or the first army tank.

Geordie Stephenson's father worked in the Newcastle pits. He was not a miner, or "pitman," but fireman of a Newcomen pumping engine. Geordie went to work without ever going to school—driving a widow's cows home, holding gentleman's horses, leading horses to plowing, hoeing turnips, and finally going into the mines as a "picker" to help clear coal of stones—pay, sixpence a day.

Through his teen years Geordie worked and advanced—to eight pence a day as a "gin horse driver," then as fireman assistant to his father, and eventually fireman, at twelve pence a day, a raise that caused him to exclaim, "I'm a made man for life!"

News of Napoleon's sensational campaign in Italy stirred George Stephenson's curiosity about newspapers; at the age of nineteen he enrolled in a night school and learned to read and write. Pleased with his success, he took up arithmetic. An athletic and ambitious youth, he also pushed ahead in the expanding mines. As a result of pushing himself into the important job of brakeman, he got into a fight with a bully, whom he thrashed. It was just like Horatio Alger.

One day in late November 1802, Newcastle residents were edified by the spectacle of a young man and woman riding through town on a single horse, the girl behind, her arms clasped round the man's waist. It was George Stephenson and his bride. He had signed the marriage register for both, his wife, a farmer's hired girl, not having had his recent educational advantages.

His financial responsibilities increased by marriage, (and presently by the arrival of a son) Stephenson took to working outside as well as in the pits. He got a mechanic friend, William Fairbairn, to take over his engine for a few hours at a time so that he could heave ballast out of ships' holds for extra money. He also learned to repair shoes, to fix clocks, even to cut clothes for the miners' wives to sew for their husbands. After his young wife's sudden death in 1804, he took a job in Montrose, Scotland, superintending a spinning works powered by a Boulton-Watt steam engine. He hiked to the job, his kit on his back, saved £28 from a year's salary, and walked home again. This thrift was rewarded a year later, when his number was drawn for the militia—Napoleon was threatening invasion. Patriotic fever did not run very high in Britain in 1805; the war was unpopular, especially among the poor. Borrowing an additional £6, Stephenson used his savings to hire a substitute. Had he been able to raise a few more pounds, he would have emigrated to America.

But within a few years things took a turn for the better for the hard-working mechanic. With two other brakemen, Stephenson contracted for braking two pumping engines, whose efficiency he soon succeeded in improving. One day he heard of a Newcomen engine that was failing to pump adequately at Killingworth High Pit nearby. He hiked over to take a look.

"Weel, George, what do you mak' o' her? Do you think you could do anything to improve her?" he was asked.

"Man, I could alter her and make her draw," our hero replied confidently. "In a week's time I could send you to the bottom"—that is, make the mine dry and workable. He was given the chance. He called in his own comrades to assist, figuring that the local mechanics, who already had failed on the job, would obstruct rather than help.

In less than a week he had the engine running like a charm and the miners went down.

Not long after, the engine-wright (chief mechanic) at Killingworth High Pit was killed in an accident—no uncommon occurrence. The proprietors gave the job to the man who had fixed the Newcomen engine; salary, £100 a year, which probably put George Stephenson in the top ten percent of income-earners in Great Britain. Although now thirty years old, he still kept after his education, working doggedly at arithmetic in his spare moments, keeping a slate, solving problems in chalk on the sides of wagons while on the job. One of his transient arithmetic teachers taught him some drawing, an art that he grasped quickly.

His boss, the manager of Killingworth, sometimes invited Stephenson to stop in the village pub for a glass of ale. One noon the boss extended the usual invitation, and this paragon of Alger heroes replied: "No sir, you must excuse me; I have made a resolution to drink no more." Well—truth compels us to give the quotation in full: "I have made a resolution to drink no more at this time of day."

He married a second time—a respectable farmer's daughter, Samuel Smiles assures us, in fact a lady whose social antecedents apparently were a little above his own. From his first marriage he had had one child, a son, Robert. Rarely have father and son enjoyed as congenial a relationship. Robert took to machinery as Mozart took to the piano. George taught him to read plans and drawings, bought him a donkey, and sent him to a school in Newcastle to learn mathematics. When Robert came home from school every night, the two bent over the lessons together, both learning.

Robert, who combined the scientific spirit with a touch of Tom Sawyer, repeated Franklin's kite experiment: with his electrified wire, he made the neighbor's cows skip about the field and gave George's horse a shock, causing his father to emerge from the house and call him a "mischievous *scoondrel.*" Together, with infinite pains, father and son constructed a sundial and made it operate accurately for the latitude of Killingworth.

One day in 1813, George Stephenson visited a neighboring colliery for a look at the latest mechanical wonder—"Blenkinsop's steam boiler on wheels." Actually Blenkinsop was not the first man to build a successful steam engine to run on rails; an erratic genius named Richard Trevithick had done it with complete success several years earlier. Blenkinsop's invention, moreover, suffered from a fatal defect; in the belief that a heavy steam boiler could not gain traction on smooth wooden rails, it was operated by a ratchet wheel running on a cogged third rail. It drew seventy tons at three mph, but frequently broke down as the ratchet wheel pulled the rails apart.

Stephenson thought he could do better. He talked the matter over with Lord Ravensworth, the principal partner of Killingworth Colliery. Lord Ravensworth, a forward-looking man with a keen appreciation of both Stephenson's ability and the economic potential of an engine that could pull several carloads of coal at a time from a pithead, backed his engine-wright with money for experimentation.

Stephenson convinced himself after a few trials that a steam engine could be made to run on rails without the cumbersome ratchet wheel. On July 25, 1814, his own engine, the "Blücher," drew eight loaded wagons carrying thirty tons' weight at four mph. Not satisfied, Stephenson sought a means of improving his locomotive's power, and soon hit on it. The "steam blast," a simple trick by which the draft was greatly enhanced, made the locomotive truly practical. The new device was patented on February 28, 1815.

The birth of the most momentous invention in transportation history was inconspicuous. During the next several years, Stephenson built more locomotives for Killingworth and for other collieries. Then, in 1821, he heard of a scheme to build a railroad, with horse-drawn wagons, from Stockton to Darlington, to facilitate exploitation of a rich vein of coal lying a little distance from the coast. Riding over to Darlington, Stephenson told Edward Pease, the promoter, that his engine could pull fifty times what horses could draw on rails.

Pease was impressed, as much by Stephenson's solid confidence as by his arguments. A few days later he sent a messenger to Killingworth with a letter. The messenger asked in town for "George Stephenson, Esquire." None of the villagers had heard of such a person; the messenger was on the point of giving up when a happy thought struck a collier's wife—it must be "Geordie the engine-wright" the man wanted.

History was made at last. On September 27, 1825, ten years after Stephenson's successful steam-blast locomotive, the first engine ran from Darlington to Stockton, preceded by a man on horse carrying a flag reading *"Periculum privatum utilitas publica"* (The private danger is the public good). When the horseman had got out of the way, Stephenson opened the throttle and pulled his train of wagons, carrying 450 persons, at the breathtaking speed of fifteen mph. However, when the line was inaugurated, the lone passenger car was horse-drawn; the locomotive pulled only the "goods wagon."

But the line was an immediate success, and a demand arose from the business communities of those two up-and-coming towns, Liverpool and Manchester, for a connecting railroad across Lancashire.

Naturally, Stephenson was called in. He was now almost famous, though he owed his reputation perhaps more to a mine-safety lamp that he had invented than to the railroad, but he was the single notable authority on the dazzling new form of transportation. Dazzling and alarming—he soon discovered that the enthusiasm of his Manchester and Liverpool backers was matched only by the violent hostility of practically everybody in the forty miles between—farmers, landowners, stagecoach people, innkeepers, and canal-promoters. The Duke of Bridgewater, Britain's biggest canal-builder, had his agents out spreading word that, among other things, the railroad would ruin horses and consequently the market for oats and that it would destroy the game with its smoke. Squires and farmers went forth with shotguns and pitchforks, and Stephenson had to carry on his survey work after dark, on moonlit nights. Sometimes he sent a few men around to fire shots on a distant corner of a farm or estate; when the landowner's people went after the "poachers," Stephenson and his surveyors sneaked through with their transits.

In the teeth of a skillful barrage of propaganda, which pictured cows refusing to give milk and women miscarrying at sight and sound of the smoke-belching monster, the Liverpool & Manchester bill was approved by Parliament, and the line laid. A competition among steam locomotives followed; Stephenson won against three rivals, including John Ericsson, future inventor of the "Monitor" ironclad. For a short stretch Stephenson's "Rocket" traveled at thirty-six mph.

The railroad was fairly born, and suddenly Geordie Stephenson, miner's son from Newcastle, hard-working mechanic who had had to learn his letters when a full-grown lad of nineteen, and who had once built a "perpetual-motion machine" because of his total ignorance of well-known scientific principles, was sitting on top of the engineering world, the acknowledged master of an awesome, revolutionary new force.

The Manchester-Liverpool line was quickly succeeded by one from London to Birmingham, though the bill for the new road was held up a session in the House of Lords till an adequate bribe—a round half million pounds sterling—was added to the price of the sequestered lands, the first but far from the last such maneuver.

From this point, the railroad grew by fifty- and hundred-mile leaps in every direction, all over Britain. It sprang across the Channel to Continental Europe on one side and across the Atlantic to the United States on the other. Steam boilers and iron rails could carry anything in the way of freight or passengers and could go anywhere, with one important qualification, the grade. From the beginning to the present time the mighty iron horse has been under the handicap of its demand for a nearly level road. A grade of as much as three percent—three feet of rise in a hundred—makes virtually any regular rail line uneconomical. The consequence, immediately felt by George Stephenson and his colleagues, was an unprecedented demand for bridges and tunnels, especially bridges—England being richer in streams and valleys than in mountains.

Furthermore, the problem had to be solved within strict limits: "The railway engineer could not [Samuel Smiles points out], like the ordinary road engineer, divert his road and make choice of the best point for crossing a river or a valley. He must take such ground as lay in the line of his railway, be it bog, or mud, or shifting sand. Navigable rivers and crowded thoroughfares had to be crossed without interruption to the existing traffic, sometimes by bridges at right angles to the river or road, sometimes by arches more or less oblique. . . . In executing these extraordinary works, iron has been throughout the sheet anchor of the engineer. . . . By its skillful use the railway architect was enabled to achieve results which thirty years since would scarcely have been thought possible."

George Stephenson used two bridge forms. For short spans, such as canal crossings or street crossings in cities, he employed a simple beam of cast iron. For bigger spans he used the arch, very strong in cast iron, especially the bowstring girder or arched beam. Gradually his son Robert took over the bridge-building, along with the rest of the booming railroad work, and it was Robert who built the two most famous Stephenson bridges, the High Level Bridge at Newcastle and the Britannia over the Menai Strait, the former of which was finished and the latter begun in 1849, the year of George Stephenson's death.

Robert Stephenson, though less of an original type than his father, was equally gifted. Profiting from the educational advantages that George had not enjoyed—including even a stint at the University of Edinburgh—he nevertheless remained, like the senior Stephenson, essentially a mechanic, pragmatic, experimental, persevering, and by the same token ready to look at problems with a fresh eye and to consider solutions a book theorist would rule out.

Born in 1803 (he never knew whether in October, November, or December, George Stephenson having neglected to record the date), Robert was his father's closest companion and collaborator from the days when they put their heads together over school books and drawings at Killingworth. He helped assemble the *Rocket;* he carried the transit on moonlit nights across the estates of the Tory landlords of Lancashire; he helped lay out the London & Birmingham. Between times, he voyaged to South America to install and operate steam pumps for mines in Colombia. By 1840 he was ready to take his father's place as England's leading railroad man.

In building the Newcastle & Berwick line, to connect the great coal center with the port to the north, Robert Stephenson had to bridge two good-sized rivers, the Tyne and the Tweed. The Tyne flows through a deep ravine at Newcastle, and the city authorities had long desired a high-level highway bridge; they now seized the opportunity to press for a combination span. Robert designed a cast-iron "bowstring girder," of six arches, with the railway on top of the arches and the carriageway suspended beneath by wrought-iron vertical rods, 120 feet above the water. Each arch was cast in five segments, and bolted together. Each comprised four main ribs in two pairs. For the foundation work, Robert was able to exploit a new tool, the steam hammer. Previously, piles had been driven into the riverbed inside the cofferdams by a heavy weight laboriously raised by capstan and horse power. The steam hammer delivered one blow a second under steam pressure and shoved the pile thirty-two feet deep in the mud in four minutes. Sometimes the heat of the blows caused the pile-head to burst into flame. In the deepest part of the river, quicksand was encountered; after some experimentation, the spot was filled in with cement.

The Newcastle High Level Bridge was opened on August 15, 1849, and a few days later Queen Victoria's train was halted on it to permit Her Majesty to admire the view.

Over the Tweed, at Berwick, Robert Stephenson built an entirely different bridge—a stone-arch viaduct. No fewer than twenty-eight semicircular arches carried the roadway high above the river; the steam hammer once more performed its pile-driving prodigies.

Before the Newcastle and Berwick bridges were finished, Robert Stephenson had begun work on his masterpiece at Menai Strait. Thomas Telford had solved the problem of bridging this arm of the Irish Sea for wagons and carriages by the novel expedient of a suspension bridge. A short suspension bridge built for the Stockton

& Darlington by Sir Samuel Brown, Telford's friend, had bent disconcertingly under the strain of a locomotive and cars, and after a few years' precarious service it had gone to pieces. An iron arch at Menai was ruled out by navigation considerations; the Admiralty refused even to allow the strait to be obstructed by the temporary timber centering.

Thinking in terms of rigidity, Robert Stephenson tried to picture an iron span that would be strong enough to support a locomotive's weight. Over hundreds of British streams, canals, gulleys, and city streets, his father had built short bridges supported by cast-iron beams stretching across the full span. Robert Stephenson imagined an enormous iron beam, that could reach out across the Menai Strait. Of course, such a massive iron bar could not be cast, and would take a million or so tons of iron. . . .

But suppose the beam were hollow? Suppose one built a succession of rectangular iron boxes open at both ends, riveted together end to end, *through* which trains could run? Certainly the result would be an exceptionally firm span, one that might cross even the Menai Strait. Bracing could be supplied by an intermediate pier on Britannia Rock in the middle of the strait. Stephenson began to picture a complex of four rectangular iron tubes, arranged in two pairs meeting over Britannia Rock.

But would such a structure really withstand the loading of steam trains? Stephenson doubted it, even if it were braced further with chains. He considered diagonal struts inside the tube, but if he used struts, his trains would have to run on top of the tubes instead of through them, greatly augmenting the strain, especially in a wind.

In his dilemma, Robert Stephenson turned to his father. Old Geordie was now enjoying retirement, entertaining friends at what he called "crowdie nights," not from the crowd of people present, but from a Newcastle oatmeal concoction with which he regaled them. Hale and frolicsome, the sexagenarian inventor frequently challenged his guests to a footrace or wrestling match, and enjoyed singing his favorite songs, especially "John Anderson." One of his regular visitors was William Fairbairn, the man who in the old days had taken over his pumping engine while Geordie went to the Tyne docks to earn extra pence by heaving ship's ballast. Fairbairn himself was now an engineer and even a scientist of distinction. Old Geordie considered Robert's tubular-bridge idea and thought it good; Fairbairn suggested experimenting with wrought-iron sheets to ascertain the strength of various weights and forms. Robert Stephenson readily agreed, and in the next few months of 1845 Fairbairn carried out a series of tests.

Fairbairn's conclusion was that a rectangular-shaped tube, while offering more resistance to the wind than a cylindrical shape, nonetheless could sustain railroad loadings in the spans necessary for Menai Strait. Furthermore, he maintained that the tubes needed no auxiliary chain bracing. The advantage of the rectangular form was that it was far easier to make. Stephenson had Fairbairn's conclusions checked and retested, and then determined to plunge ahead. "I stood on the verge of a responsibility from which I confess I had nearly shrunk," he wrote later.

Iron plates were brought by ship from Liverpool, Anglesey marble from Penmon on the island, and red sandstone from Cheshire. Fifteen hundred men were soon at work on the mainland, on the Anglesey shore, on Britannia Island, and on boats and barges in the waterways. The central tower, "Great Britannia," rose 230 feet high on the rocky isle in the strait. The two shore towers were a little shorter.

Simultaneously, Robert Stephenson was building another bridge, over the Conway, part of the same (Chester & Holyhead) railway, on the same tubular principle and by the same method. The Conway was only 400 feet wide; two 400-foot tubes, side by side, sufficed. The Conway position being ready before the Menai, Robert Stephenson supervised the positioning of the tubes on their pontoons in March 1848. On April 8 the lifting began. The giant tube was raised eight feet—two inches a minute—by steam power. In eight days it was in position. The rails were laid the next day, and the day after that (April 18) Stephenson passed through on a locomotive. The second tube was in place the following January.

Meantime, the work at Menai was pushed; in June 1849 the first of the four tubes was ready to be lifted. At low tide it was hauled to the water's edge. As the tide came in, the big square tube, closed at both ends, was gradually set afloat. Tugs pushed and pulled it into its designated position. Robert Stephenson mounted the top of the iron monster and gave hand signals to Captain Claxton, in charge of a corps of sailors manning the pontoon boats. A sailor in each boat held a distinguishing letter aloft. Captain Claxton, armed with a speaking trumpet, bellowed Stephenson's instructions to each capstan by letter. The men turned the capstans, the hydraulic presses on top of the towers strained, the heavy chains attached to the tube creaked, and the mass began to lift. Thousands of spectators lined both shores.

But at the outset a capstan gave way, and the work was postponed to the next morning. After a day of repair, preparation, and pulling, the great tube was out of the water by evening. At this critical moment another capstan broke, the men working it were knocked down by the crazily spinning arm, and some of them were hurled into the water. Charles Rolfe, in charge of the broken capstan, shouted for help. The end of the line was paid out into the crowd on shore; men, women, and children laid hold, and the tube's fall was checked. By midnight the pontoons were clear and the mighty tube hung suspended between Britannia Rock and Anglesey, its ends resting on ledges cut in the rocky abutments. The calculations had been precise; only three quarters of an inch of room was left on either ledge.

Next morning the labor of raising the tube to its place a hundred feet above the channel began. Robert Stephenson was cautious. Although once the raising started, the tube could have been lifted to position in a day or two, he very prudently insisted that it be provided with timbering support at every lift. When one of the other three tubes was going up, this foresight proved providential: the bottom of a hydraulic press gave way and the tremendous mass of iron fell, but only nine inches, reducing potential catastrophe to a minor setback. The workmen built a stone cairn to commemorate the averted disaster.

On March 5, 1850, Robert Stephenson drove home the last of the two million rivets that held the vast cylinders together (that rivet is painted white to this day), and a short while later rode through the completed bridge at the head of a train of three locomotives pulling a thousand persons. Later, on the inaugural day, a freight train loaded with two hundred tons of coal was stopped in the center of the Wales land tube to test for deflection. The tube sank only four tenths of an inch.

Finally the main tubes were tested for deflection; under a fifty-ton load left standing all day, they sagged nine inches. The same load was then left throughout the night and the deflection measured again in the morning. To the amazement of that scientifically unsophisticated age, it was found that it actually had diminished during the night by five eighths of an inch. The iron, of course, had cooled and contracted.

The Britannia Bridge, which stands today, was named with accidental aptness. Samuel Smiles, who wrote of it as a contemporary American writer might describe a flight to the moon, awarded the credit to the whole mid-nineteenth-century mechanical and industrial progress of Great Britain. "But for the perfection of our tools, and the ability of our mechanics to use them to the greatest advantage—but for the matured powers of the steam-engine—but for the improvements in iron manufacture [making possible] plates and bars of immense size—but for these, the Britannia Bridge would have been designed in vain. Thus it was not the product of the genius of the railway engineer alone, but of the collective mechanical genius of the English nation."

Old Geordie Stephenson had died in 1849. Robert Stephenson died somewhat prematurely in 1859 after building several more tubular bridges—two across the Nile, one over the St. Lawrence at Montreal. The elder Stephenson was buried modestly in Trinity Church, Chesterfield, where he spent his last years; the younger received the pomp of Westminster Abbey, where by his request he lies next to Thomas Telford.

Nothing ever happens quickly in history, and no one or two men can be much more than important symbols of change. The Stephensons, father and son, did not invent the locomotive or the railroad, but they married the two successfully and solved the difficult problems that the marriage created. Unluckily their successors lacked something of the Stephensons' sagacity and caution. Once it was clear that the railroad was a money-making proposition, the laissez-faire spirit of competition and greed drove engineers to recklessness and disaster. That is another story, another chapter, but very much a part of bridge history.

13.

The Age of Disaster

But oh! how much of sorrow,
  And oh! how much of pain
Awaited those who journeyed
  On that fated railroad train.

—*"The Chatsworth Wreck," 1887.*

ROBERT STEPHENSON'S tubular iron bridge had only one fault: it took a lot of iron. A railroad promoter could reap magnificent profits by building a roadway and laying track across a hundred miles of countryside that a locomotive could somehow traverse while pulling a few light cars. Nothing had to be very good—the roadway, the tracks, the locomotive, or the cars. The Britannia Bridge cost six hundred thousand pounds—three million dollars, in U.S. currency of the same period. Compare that with the cost of Theodore Burr's long covered bridge over the Delaware at Camden: $18,000. In America no railroad-promoter could afford to consider an iron tubular bridge. An iron arch, while not as expensive as an iron tube (or a stone arch), was far from being the cheapest possible bridge. The cheapest was a wood-and-iron truss, provided that it would support a railroad loading, and the next cheapest was an all-iron truss.

The truss, not surprisingly, was what the rail lines settled on, each choosing its own. The Howe was one of the most popular. The Howe patent did not belong to William Howe. He had sold it in 1841, a year after taking it out, to Amasa Stone, another Massachusetts Yankee, who joined with a partner and formed the bridge-building company of Stone & Boomer.

But as railroad loadings grew heavier in the late 1850s and early 1860s, Howe trusses began breaking down. Meantime, Amasa Stone himself became president of a railroad—the Lake Shore & Southern Michigan. In 1865 he faced the problem of replacing an important bridge at Ashtabula, Ohio. The stream was only Ashtabula Creek, narrow and shallow, but it ran at the bottom of a gorge 700 feet wide and 75 feet deep, with steep, cliff-like banks. The existing bridge was a series of Howe trusses in wood, supported by trestles. The railroad company had gradually built an earth embankment out from either side of the gorge, and in 1865 all that was needed for a thoroughly secure crossing was a span of about 150 feet over the creek itself. A special bridge, in form a modified Howe truss, but made entirely of iron, was built. It was 157 feet long and cost $75,000, and it represented a new approach to railroad bridge work. There was, it later developed, some disagreement about the design. The original was drawn by John Towlinson, a Canadian engineer, and modified by Amasa Stone. Manufactured in the company's own carshops, it was found to be too short, and had to be lengthened. As finally erected, it stood 69 feet above the creek.

It stood for eleven years. Then on the night of December 29, 1876, in a blinding snowstorm, the Pacific Express, a westbound eleven-car train with doubleheader locomotive, started across it at fifteen miles per hour. Halfway over, Dan McGuire, engineer of the lead locomotive, felt a drag, as if he were "running up hill." To this alarming sensation he reacted by throwing the throttle wide open. His engine surged forward, and as it did something happened behind. He heard a grinding sound, which was his tender sideswiping the bridge abutment on the left (the express was using the south—left-hand—track of the two-track bridge). Next moment there was a terrific crash—the second locomotive was smashing head-on into the abutment. At approximately the same instant, or just before, the drawbar coupling the lead tender to the second locomotive broke. McGuire's engine raced ahead, off the bridge. He brought it to a halt a few moments later and backed up. By the time he jumped down and ran to the edge of the embankment, a ghastly illumination was growing swiftly. The Pacific Express' eleven cars, their pot-bellied wood stoves upset, their wooden hulks blazing, lay strewn in snow, broken ice, and water. Out of the roofs of some coaches hands and arms were thrust upward. A few demoralized figures were clambering up the embankment, others staggering free of the fire.

Of 123 passengers on board, 65 died that night, four more later. Eleven trainmen—conductors, brakemen, firemen—also perished, though miraculously the engineer of the second locomotive survived. Altogether, eighty dead—the worst rail disaster America had seen.

Newspapers from coast to coast burst into headlines—and editorials. Railroads already had acquired notoriety, partly through the financial-political scandals of the 1870s, partly through the appalling number of accidents, bridge and other. "Disasters . . . grew into a national scandal in the fifties," Stewart Holbrook notes in *The Story of American Railroads.* In the 1860s "they were thrown into deep shadow by the other and greater tragedy," but "with railroad expansion in the seventies, accidents increased in proportion and possibly in deadly effects."

As usual, the question of causation resolved itself in the minds of the public and the newspaper editors into whom to blame. As usual, too, a great deal of ignorance was apparent in the outcry. *Harper's Weekly,* declaring that the traveling public was anxiously inquiring "What was the cause?" put these questions:

> Was it improperly constructed? Was the iron of inferior quality? After eleven years of service, had it *suddenly* lost its strength? Or had a *gradual* weakness grown upon it unperceived? Might that weakness have been discovered by frequent and proper examination? Or was the breakage the sudden effect of the intense cold? If so, why had it not happened before in yet more severe weather? Is there *no* method of making iron bridges of assured safety? . . . Was the bridge, when made, the *best* of its kind, or the *cheapest* of its kind?

The idea that iron could lose its strength through long use or repeated strains was a popular misconception; iron still was a remarkably mysterious metal, by no means completely understood by engineers. The suspicion that the bridge was cheaply built was unfounded: for its size it was an exceptionally expensive structure. The Ohio legislative committee that investigated the disaster found that "frequent and proper" examination had been carried out under the conscientious supervision of fifty-one-year-old Charles Collins, chief engineer of the line. Collins was a resident of Ashtabula, and had himself been a passenger on the smoker (last car) of the wrecked train. He could hazard no reason for the bridge's failure, and at both the coroner's inquest and the legislative committee's investigation, he appeared badly shaken. Very unfairly, Collins, who had had nothing to do with the bridge's design, was made a scapegoat by the press, along with Amasa Stone, especially by James Gordon Bennett's *New York Herald*. Collins, a sensitive, gentle man, suffered agony and finally committed suicide, an act that sobered a great deal of the criticism. Amasa Stone, a tougher species, stoutly defended himself and his bridge design.

An explanation for the tragedy was advanced by *The Engineering News* on January 6. The authoritative organ of the profession pointed out that the bridge had been tested by a train of six locomotives soon after its erection, that two trains had occupied it simultaneously innumerable times, including once shortly before the disaster, and that these facts precluded the idea "of its falling from any intrinsic weakness of the structure itself." The idea of the bridge's being weakened by "low temperatures or from crystallization or disintegration of the structure of the iron from repeated strains," the *News* dismissed as unworthy of serious consideration. The publication also answered a more sophisticated question. A Howe truss, held together by the grip of brace ends against angle blocks, might indeed become weakened in its joints by repeated strain. But Engineer McGuire testified at the inquiry that he had been between fifty and a hundred feet from the western end of the bridge when he felt the drag that first had signaled something wrong. In other words, the lead engine was near the middle of the span, the No. 2 locomotive not much more than on the bridge, and most of the cars still on the mole leading from the gorge.

Engineering News offered a theory that represented a consensus of leading members of the engineering profession: some of the wheels or trucks of the first tender, the second locomotive, the second tender, or the first car must have become derailed in the deep snow east of the bridge. On hitting the crossties of the bridge the derailed car smashed or piled up several, and struck the floor beams. As these gave way under the unintended strain of moving wheels (especially locomotive wheels), the second locomotive and the following cars began sinking through the left side of the bridge flooring. This created a terrific pull on the right-side truss, the upper chord of which buckled inward, and the whole bridge quickly crumpled.

A surviving woman passenger in a sleeping car gave vivid supporting evidence for this theory. She had experienced a double sensation: first, violent thumping, "like the wheels going over logs," second, a sensation of "going down, down, down," though the light in her

12. No other bridge in history was the subject of designs by so many talented engineers and artists. The unique form in which it was finally erected is credited to a remarkable septuagenarian named Antonio da Ponte, who afterward also built the Bridge of Sighs. For centuries the Rialto remained the solitary crossing of Venice's Grand Canal.

THE PONTE VECCHIO

13. The "segmental" arch form of this celebrated bridge, based on a small arc of a large circle, represented a dramatic advance from the semicircular arch of the Romans. Alone among the famous Florentine bridges, the Ponte Vecchio was spared by the retreating Germans in 1945.

EIGHTEENTH-CENTURY BRIDGE-BUILDING

14, 15. Jean-Rodolphe Perronet, first director of the world's first engineering school, completed the Pont d'Orléans *(above)* and built the Pont de Neuilly *(below)*. The top picture reveals the real problem of bridge engineering through all the early centuries—the underwater foundations. The cofferdam was driven a few feet into the riverbed and "dewatered"—note the hand pump, right foreground, and the water-powered "trough pump," discernible in center of picture.

The boldly flattened arches of Perronet's Pont de Neuilly *(below)*, "the most graceful stone bridge ever built," resulted in a highly functional design, giving maximum freedom to floodwaters.

16. The world's first iron bridge. During the American Revolution, at Coalbrookdale, Shropshire, two pioneer British ironmasters erected this arch as a demonstration of what could be done with iron. It is preserved today as a British national monument.

17. New London Bridge. Built in the 1820s to replace the tottering and picturesque Old London Bridge, this stone-arch span designed by Scots farmer boy John Rennie is today a treasured London landmark. Photo shows bridge about 1900.

THOMAS TELFORD'S SUSPENSION BRIDGES

18, 19. *(Above)* The Menai Strait Bridge, 580 feet in span—a world's record—was opened to traffic on January 30, 1826. Repeatedly shaken by storms, it provided valuable lessons for engineers and survives to this day, carrying automobile loading far in excess of the wagon-and-carriage traffic shown in the nineteenth-century photo. Note in background Robert Stephenson's Tubular Railroad Bridge. *(Below)* Telford, who began life as an apprentice stonemason, designed the suspension towers for his bridge over the Conway to match those of old Conway Castle.

20. John Roebling's Niagara Railroad Bridge was built in an age when suspension bridges were collapsing under wind, marching troops, even droves of cattle. This tremendous (822-foot) doubledecked span endured gale winds and increasing loadings for forty years before it was dismantled to make room for a double-track bridge. Note stays running upward from shores to roadway and truss webbing between the two decks.

21. A circus artist named Dixon traversed his own Niagara bridge in 1890, in the shadow of C. C. Schneider's pioneer cantilever. A generation earlier, the celebrated Blondin performed a whole series of tightwire acrobatics near John Roebling's bridge.

THE TAY DISASTER

22, 23. *(Above)* A contemporary engraving preserves Sir Thomas Bouch's fatally defective design. The train in the drawing is coming south, toward Edinburgh. When the tragedy occurred, the northbound mail train that entered the bridge on the stormy Sunday night of December 29, 1879, was in the "High Girders," the section of the span in which the truss is elevated above the roadway. *(Below) Harper's Weekly* depicts, somewhat inaccurately, a dramatic moment in the Tay story: James Roberts crawls out from the Dundee side to the broken end of the bridge.

THE OLD COVERED BRIDGE

24. Once a functional and nearly universal part of the American landscape, then a nostalgic and rapidly vanishing curiosity, the covered bridge is being preserved as an object of historical importance. What the roof and siding covered was the ingenious truss designs that, repeated in steel, carry the whole world's railroad traffic to this day. The bridge above is over the Cheat River near Erwin, West Virginia.

upper berth had been extinguished. Other passengers also testified to the rearmost cars being off the rails seconds before the plunge into the gorge. The bridge itself was protected against derailments by "guard rails"—extra iron strips, three and a half inches outside the real rails, designed to hold on the ties cars that might jump the tracks after entering the bridge. Further, the recovered fragments of the bridge flooring showed it to be in good condition.

The Lake Shore & Southern Michigan was already somewhat notorious for track-jumping, owing to its having used "compromise cars" for a number of years. These were coaches whose wheels were built wide enough to cover an inch and a half discrepancy in gauge between the Lake Shore and connecting roads. Track-jumping by rolling stock hardly needed any explanation anyway—coaches left the rails of all lines at all sorts of places. In the coroner's inquest over another disaster, a couple of years later, William Sooy Smith, C. Shaler Smith, Henry Flad, and various other leading engineers all agreed that derailment of coaches was the most common cause of railroad-bridge accidents. Hundreds of railroad bridges had the rails spiked directly to the wooden stringers without any ties, a method virtually inviting derailment and disaster. But even where ties were used, a car's wheels hitting the ties were likely to pile them up in front of it, and the car, pulling the car behind it in the same direction was likely to crash right or left, putting sudden undesigned strains on wooden stringers, cross-bracing pieces of wood or iron, and finally one of the trusses. Two years before Ashtabula, another Lake Shore & Southern Michigan train, the New York Express, had lost its last two cars just before crossing Big Sisters Creek west of Buffalo, wrecking the bridge and killing forty-nine passengers.

Ashtabula focused public attention on railroads and railroad bridges. So severe was the storm, in fact, that the engineering profession, which at first had tended to defend Stone's bridge design, turned sharply and, at a meeting of the American Society of Civil Engineers in New York, roundly condemned not only the design but also Stone personally. General Gouverneur K. Warren asserted that Stone should have called in Squire Whipple, Albert Fink, or J. H. Linville to design the bridge for him, overlooking the fact that in 1865 these famous engineers had had little more experience with heavy railroad bridges than had Stone himself. A bewildering variety of defects was ascribed to the design. C. Shaler Smith declared that "the construction of the truss violated every canon of our standard practice," again overlooking the fact that in 1865 one could hardly speak of "standard practice" in railroad-truss building.

Certainly there were a lot of worse-built bridges than Ashtabula. Two years later a bridge at Tariffville, Connecticut, fell under an excursion train, killing seventeen. There was no derailment; the bridge, a wood-and-iron Howe truss, simply gave way. The train was returning from a revival meeting, and many outraged New Englanders asked when people *were* safe if not coming home from a revival meeting?

The answer was that they were never very safe traveling on railroads or crossing bridges. No fewer than forty bridges a year fell in the '70s—one for every four built. Half of the forty were timber highway spans. One over the Merrimac at Groveland, Massachusetts, collapsed under a single team of horses and a light snow. The majority even of the railroad bridges that fell were wooden. In 1876 practically all New England railroad bridges still were wooden.

The iron bridge failures made the headlines. They were the biggest bridges and their failures cost the most lives. In the decade after Ashtabula, two hundred bridges fell, including several involving major loss of life. In 1887 a toll exceeding Ashtabula—eighty-four—was recorded at Chatsworth, Illinois, in a very similar accident. The lead locomotive of a fifteen-car excursion train bound for Niagara Falls made it across a stream, but the No. 2 locomotive and all the cars broke through the bridge, piled up, and burned. A lugubrious ballad called "The Chatsworth Wreck" achieved considerable popularity.

Highway bridge failures were far more frequent than railroad. Most local highway bridges were contracted for by county officials who combined a lack of technical knowledge with a pressing commitment to economy. Bridge-promoters and salesmen sold low cost virtually to the exclusion of other considerations. Fly-by-night operators sold wherever and however they could, threw together a bridge, and moved on in a hurry. The more established firms were pressured into dangerous economies by the competition. Graft frequently entered into contract negotiations, and was also rife in state legislatures, where bills for railroad safety were introduced constantly and as regularly blocked or withdrawn.

The Ashtabula failure actually reflected less discredit on the officials and engineers involved than did scores of other bridge failures that by mere good fortune happened to be bloodless or nearly so.

In February 1879, a Chicago & Alton bridge at Wilmington fell under a load of empty coal cars, a shocking reflection on the construction and maintenance of the bridge, but one that provoked no comment because nobody was killed.

The American Society of Civil Engineers recommended appointment of state bridge inspectors, adequately paid and approved by the A.S.C.E. Some members of the committee went further, recommending that standards laid down by the A.S.C.E. be written into the law and that all bridge specifications be checked by the A.S.C.E. Eventually, state laws and state inspectors did come to the aid of bridge safety, but it was not an easy reform to put through. The rich and powerful railroad industry could very nearly defy the Federal government to reform it, and practically snapped its fingers at the state legislatures. Although many states created Railroad Commissions after Ashtabula, fully half of the two hundred bridges that fell in the next ten years were in states with commissions. To get obsolete railroad bridges replaced was beyond the capacity of most of the states, and rickety old Howe trusses continued to carry railroad loadings in many places. Richard Sanders Allen, leading authority on covered bridges, records a case of a covered bridge wrecked by a gang of boys who mischievously loosened the turnbuckles that secured the bracing guys before a heavy freight locomotive entered it.

The best solution to the local highway-bridge problem was the adoption and enforcement of state standards of construction. Given such standards, and given adequate inspection and maintenance, bridges to carry horse-and-wagon traffic could be made safe and long-lasting, that is, economical.

But the railroad bridges were another story. Here the problem was technical. Some railroad lines or bridge-promoters might cut corners in the interests of false economy, but Amasa Stone's $75,000 Ashtabula Bridge did not represent such cutting. Yet the Ohio legislative committee estimated the safety factor of the Ashtabula at between 1.2 and 1.6. The bridge was strong enough to carry from twenty to sixty percent more loading than the maximum to which it might actually be subjected at any time. That is scarcely a reassuring safety factor, yet it was far from unusual. Still another failure at about the same time—of a Bollman truss at Zanesville, Ohio—underlines this. Built twenty years earlier to carry a loading of one ton per lineal foot, the Zanesville bridge failed under the weight of a locomotive weighing one and a half tons per lineal foot.

Two things could be done in the realm of design to make railroad bridges safer. One was to cut down on derailment failures by strengthening bridge floorings and by taking steps to reduce derailments themselves. The second was to strengthen joints to prevent their weakening under repeated strains (the initial break in the Ashtabula truss apparently came at one of the angle blocks).

The real trouble with the Ashtabula, General Warren to the contrary, was that it was made of iron. Cast iron used for compression members in this as in most iron bridges, was extremely liable to fail by flexure, that is, to buckle when pulled inward or pushed outward by an undesigned strain. Cast iron also was susceptible to defects in the iron itself, though the Ashtabula iron was found to be sound. For a time the all-wrought-iron bridge, which achieved a record span length of 515 feet over the Ohio River in 1876, seemed to be the answer to the railroad-bridge problem. But railroad loadings were shooting up at a rate that soon made even wrought iron inadequate.

Because of the size of the United States and consequent enormous scope of the national railroad-building program, American engineers were confronted with a more severe demand for economy. Thus American bridges kept to their weak pin connections and angle-block joints long after British and European engineers had adopted riveted joints. In 1876 one United States railroad, the New York Central, was experimenting with rivet work.

Yet American engineers were by no means alone in their dilemma, nor American railroad passengers in their peril. Three years to the day after Ashtabula, Great Britain, the leading industrial and engineering nation of the world, was rocked by a disaster whose extraordinarily dramatic circumstances make it to this day the most memorable of all bridge tragedies.

14.

The Mystery of the Firth of Tay

Beautiful Railway Bridge of the Silvery Tay!
With your numerous arches and pillars in so grand array,
And your central girders, which seem to the eye
To be almost towering to the sky.
The greatest wonder of the day,
And a great beautification to the River Tay.

Beautiful Railway Bridge of the Silvery Tay!
I hope that God will protect all passengers
By night and by day,
And that no accident will befall them while crossing
The Bridge of the Silvery Tay.

—From a poem of William McGonagall, of Dundee, 1877.

Beautiful Railway Bridge of the Silv'ry Tay!
Alas! I am very sorry to say
That ninety lives have been taken away
On the last Sabbath day of 1879,
Which will be remembered for a very long time.

—Poem of William McGonagall, 1880.

Beautiful new railway bridge of the Silvery Tay,
With your strong brick piers and buttresses in so gray array,
And your thirteen central girders, which seem to my eye
Strong enough all windy storms to defy.
And as I gaze upon thee my heart feels gay,
Because thou are the greatest railway bridge of the present day.

—Poem of William McGonagall, 1887.

IT WAS war to the death in Scotland. The Caledonian Railroad was slowly but surely strangling its rival, the North British. The directors of the North British, sitting around a conference table in London, listened hopefully to a scheme that would redress their fortunes at a stroke. The scheme was based on a peculiarity of the map of Scotland (*Figure 44*).

Figure 44

The two great estuaries, the firths of Tay and Forth, cut deep into the coastline, barring direct rail connection between Edinburgh and northeast Scotland. Passengers and freight had to be loaded on ferries, shipped across the Forth, reloaded on cars, carried to the Tay, again transferred to ferries, and once more put on cars. The forty-six-mile journey from Edinburgh to Dundee took three hours and twelve minutes. Furthermore, the ferry crossings were unpredictably interrupted by storms, and were hardly a pleasure even when the ferries were running. If the North British could bridge the two firths, it would gain a tremendous advantage over its enemy, the Caledonian. The directors approved the attempt, and the railroad's chief engineer, Thomas Bouch, designed a bridge to span the Tay, the northernmost of the two estuaries. Bouch was a disciple of Robert Stephenson and a thoroughly experienced bridge-builder. He had no especially long spans to his credit, but the three hundred miles of railroad line he had built included dozens of short and medium spans. (He had also designed the ferries for the two firths.) The Tay, wide but shallow, did not call for a long span, but for a great number of short spans. The shore-to-shore distance was a bit over a mile, but because of the southern approach along the shore, the bridge had to describe a sweeping curve, making its total length nearly two miles.

Bouch designed a viaduct of eighty-five spans of lengths varying from 200 to 285 feet. The trusses were 27 feet deep. In the middle of the channel, fourteen spans mounted on piers driven to bedrock were given a distinctive character. While most of the single-track, twenty-foot roadway was to be carried on top of the truss, there, over the deep water, it was placed inside the truss (*Figure 45*).

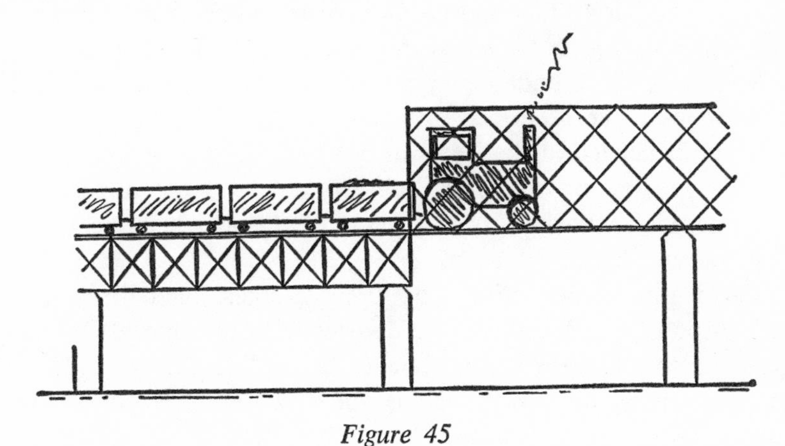

Figure 45

This arrangement represented an eleventh-hour change to accommodate the all-but-irreconcilable opposition of the shipping interests at Perth, up the Tay. There was nothing radical or inherently dangerous in it; a truss may run above or below the roadway. Yet these "High Girders," as the central truss spans became known, lacked firm and cohesive connection with their neighbors. In the course of construction it was discovered that the geological soundings had erred, and that bedrock did not extend across the channel floor. Bouch designed new piers, mounted on cast-iron piles driven into the riverbed, and reduced the number of High Girders to thirteen—a number long remembered in superstitious Scotland.

A recent British writer, John Prebble, has delved into the Tay

Bridge mystery. His narrative, *The High Girders* (in the United States *Disaster at Dundee*), gives a fascinating insight into the engineering environment of the Victorian age, and even casts a few shadows on our own science-and-engineering-based society. The Tay work was begun in a spirit of invincible complacence. Although the bridge was extraordinary in length—in fact the "biggest bridge in the world"—it was disarmingly commonplace in every other respect. To Victorian engineering and to the Victorian world in general, progress appeared to consist largely in doing the same thing over in an ever bigger way.

Not a feature of technique was new. Each big iron-lattice girder was riveted together on the south shore, floated out on heavy barges, and raised by hydraulic jacks, twenty feet a day, until, just before the turn of the tide, it reached a position higher than the piers it was to join. The barges then moved directly under the piers, so that as the tide fell the big girder lowered to position on the pier heads.

Several of the foundations required sinking by pneumatic caisson, a technique to be described in detail later on. The amount of compressed air needed at the Tay was not great, and caisson disease, the terrible scourge of compressed-air workers, did not appear. There was one accident when the caisson suddenly and inexplicably blew, trapping and killing six men.

"But it was the Victorian age," Prebble notes, "and life and death had Purpose. There could be no disaster without a moral. Writing to the Dundee *Advertiser* a gentleman of Fifeshire discovered such a moral: 'Life is not lost which is spent or sacrificed in the grand enterprises of useful industry.'"

Another accident involving smaller loss of life sounded a more foreboding note for the future. One of the treacherous storms for which the Firth of Tay was noted came boiling down with little warning. In five minutes the barometer dropped an inch, and Albert Groethe, the foreman, ran out shouting orders to secure pontoons and send the tug to bring the men off the High Girders. The tugboat, standing off the High Girders in the blackness, heard three sounds like cannon shots, then a screaming grinding of metal followed by a tremendous splash, and a huge wave nearly capsized the tug. It was hours before the men could be taken off, and it was found that by good luck only one had been blown to his death. The others had all gone down to the lower beams of the girders and hung on for dear life. The last two girders, numbers Twelve and Thirteen from the south shore, in which no workmen had taken refuge, had blown down. The crack and fall of these two masses of iron was what the tug crew had heard at the height of the storm.

The two spans were replaced and the lower girders of the north span erected to meet them. The completed bridge, of which photographs are rare, was a long, spidery curve reaching out from the south shore on slender stilts, the truss cage appearing light and fragile, the High Girders rising capriciously in midstream. One cannot resist comparing its appearance with that of two of its great contemporaries, the stalwart arches of the Eads Bridge at St. Louis and the majestically solid suspension span of the Brooklyn Bridge.

Its appearance evidently inspired a few pangs of doubt among some observers, for in the meretricious panegyric of local poet William McGonagall a hope was expressed that God would protect the passengers against accident.

On September 26, 1877, the inaugural train carrying the directors of the bridge companies and of the railroad crept out over the sparkling water behind a pilot engine at whose throttle Thomas Bouch himself stood. Thousands watched from the shores and dozens of boats gathered in the Firth below as the little string of coaches snaked around the long curve. The crossing took fifteen minutes; the train ran at about ten mph.

The following winter the official inspection was made by Major General Hutchinson of the Royal Engineers, inspector for the all-powerful Board of Trade. Accompanied by Thomas Bouch, the general went over the bridge with painstaking care for three whole days. He ran six heavy ballast engines across at various speeds, making observations from several different points. At the highest speed tested, forty mph, the engines raced through the thirteen High Girders in fifty-two seconds.

In his report, General Hutchinson made some minor recommendations and criticisms, and suggested that trains be restricted to a maximum speed of twenty-five miles per hour. Then almost at the very end of the report he dropped in a solitary, casual reference to the wind: "When again visiting the spot, I should wish, if possible, to have an opportunity of observing the effects of a high wind when a train of carriages is running over the bridge."

General Hutchinson fell ill not long after, and the final inspection of railway connections with the bridge was made by another officer. Nobody ever observed "the effects of a high wind when a train of carriages is running over the bridge."

No one considered this deficiency of any importance the following May when passenger service was opened with a suitably florid ceremonial. The chairman of the company made a speech. "The Tay Bridge," he declared, "is a structure worthy of this enlightened age!"

A little over a year later, in June 1879, the bridge was the recipient of an even greater ceremonial honor. Queen Victoria was at Balmoral, and the directors of the railroad were turning over the delicate question of inviting Her Majesty to return to Windsor Castle by way of the Tay Bridge when suddenly an engine pulling the empty royal coach appeared on the line. It was promptly signaled through and came down to the bridge, crept cautiously across, turned around and went back. This was the last test the bridge underwent. Soon the royal train returned with the sovereign herself aboard. The chubby little widow, still dressed in black seventeen years after her bereavement, was hailed with reverent "God Bless Your Majesty" 's all along the way. Graciously she halted for seven minutes at Tay Bridge Station to receive an address of welcome and the leading officials, including Thomas Bouch.

At this moment it certainly seemed as if all was not only well, but even perfect for the gentlemen who had put their money and their hopes into the Tay Bridge. The North British Railway had gained the dominant position in eastern Scotland. Traffic between Dundee and Fifeshire doubled; both passenger and freight revenues paid splendidly; North British stock rose thirty percent.

And Thomas Bouch was busy with his even bigger Firth of Forth Bridge, which, when complete, would give the North British a solid rail line uninterrupted by ferries right into Edinburgh. The two great bridges would do something else; they would make Thomas Bouch the most renowned of living engineers. As such he merited the traditional reward, and on June 27, 1879, he received it. Along with Henry Bessemer, the inventor of the method for converting iron into steel, he received his knighthood at Windsor Castle.

There were small disturbing notes. Some passengers reported an odd effect on their ears when passing through the High Girders in a strong wind. Others complained that the trains were running over the bridge too fast. Some commuters took to timing either the whole crossing or the passage through the High Girders, and asserted that the trains were exceeding by as much as 17 mph the 25 mph speed limit imposed by General Hutchinson. A cautious few even went back to riding the ferries.

Painters found a number of bolts rusting through on the ironwork. And they experienced a good deal of vibration when they were painting the High Girders as a train passed through. At least one painter noticed sizeable cracks in the iron of the piers below the High Girders. The railway's bridge inspector, Henry Hoble, discovered some vertical cracks in the cement portion of the piers. On Sir Thomas Bouch's instructions these were braced with wrought-iron hoops.

And here and there the voices of ministers were raised to criticize the railroad for running trains on the Sabbath, a desecration they foresaw would draw stern retaliation from on high.

In Scotland the winter sun sets early. It was already nearly dark when the storm of Sunday, December 28, 1879, struck Dundee, at about four o'clock. At first it was merely a steady rain, with a swift drop of the barometer. Then, at about five o'clock, the wind began to blow, west-south-west, broadside onto the Tay Bridge. As so often in the Firth, the gale hit all at once. Experienced naval men estimated it as Force 10 to 11, the highest gale force on the scale being 12. Three coal gondolas weighing ten tons each were blown several feet on an upgrade. A couple of hours later, the storm still going full blast, a small turret was blown from a Dundee church.

And a few minutes after that, at twelve minutes past seven, the mail train from Burntisland—the ferry landing across the Firth of Forth from Edinburgh—arrived at Tayport. It did not stop, but slowed down to three miles an hour, in accord with regulations, to receive the signal of clearance, in the form of a baton.

Thomas Barclay, the signalman, handed up the baton; it was taken by the fireman. The train moved on, and Barclay, glancing at some of the faces in the passing coaches, hastened back to his cabin out of the storm. There he sent the wire signal over the bridge to the north shore signalman, who gave the reply.

John Watt, a railroad employee who had come in to join Barclay for a cup of tea, watched the train's lights move off over the bridge. A spray of sparks from the wheels blurred into a steady flame blown eastward by the gale. Then Watt saw three distinct flashes, then one big flash. Then he could no longer see the tail lights.

Puzzled, he said, "There is something wrong with the train."

Barclay, who was raking the fire, arose and looked. "Nothing has happened to the train, John," he said impatiently. Watt pointed out that the tail lights had disappeared, and Barclay said of course they had. The bridge dipped a little on the north side, and at a certain point a train's lights were temporarily invisible. "We'll see her again soon," Barclay said, and taking the scuttle went to fetch coal. When he returned, Watt was still at the window. No lights had reappeared on the far side.

Barclay rang the bell signaling the north shore. There was no answering ring. He tried his speaking tube, and got no reply.

The two men looked at each other, then opened the door and ran down the steps into the gale. They started out across the bridge, but after twenty yards were on their hands and knees, in peril of being blown into the river. Making their way back, they climbed and slid down the long bank to a point under the bridge at the water's edge, and stared out into the blackness. They shouted at each other, but could not hear their own words.

Incredibly, the moon came out, and to their horrified eyes revealed a paralyzing sight: the whole center section of the great bridge —the thirteen High Girders—was gone. Only the stumps of the piers remained.

The two men turned and scrambled madly up the bank. Running through the darkness they called the news to everyone they met: "The bridge is doon!"

Across the firth, in Dundee, the same shocked phrase had been shouted several moments earlier. People in Dundee often watched trains cross the bridge, and a number of eyes had seen flashes—some said two, some three—and columns of white spray leaping up from the black water. Two men who had seen spray ran to the signalman's cabin. The signalman, Somerville, had waited vainly for the train, and finally had left his cabin to go to stare in perplexity into the darkness. "Is there a train due on the bridge?" someone shouted to him. He nodded. "Then I am afraid it is in the river!"

A locomotive foreman from the Tay Bridge Station, James Roberts, pluckily crawled out on hands and knees on the wickedly vibrating bridge, yard by yard, for half a mile, occasional snatches of moonlight illuminating the big waves far below him. Suddenly the moon showed him something else—directly in front of him stretched emptiness, and far below, twelve clouds of spray marked the pier stumps. The water pipe that ran overhead was torn off, and from the jagged end the water sprayed down on him. He reached ahead and felt the very ends of the splintered wood and torn iron. Then he pivoted around on his belly and crawled back.

A tense crowd already had gathered. The harbor master was sought and was found emerging from evening church service. A ferryboat was ordered out. Before she returned, a message came from down the river . . . mailbags had washed ashore. The crowd was angry, and semihysterical; many had relatives or friends on the train. The ferry returned after midnight; a boat, lowered in the heavy seas at great risk, had courageously reconnoitered the pier stumps in a vain search for survivors.

The police cordoned off the harbor and the crowd slowly dispersed. But its anger was not gone; it was spreading. The news was being sent to London by telegraph, and the next day it was told to the whole shocked world.

What caused the disaster? Two points of view developed immediately. The religious extremists blamed the railroad for running trains on Sunday.

"If there is one voice louder than others in this terrible event [an Edinburgh minister said], it is the voice of God determined to guard his Sabbath with jealous care."

"The fall of the Tay Bridge [another minister asserted] can be classed with the wars in Afghanistan and Zululand as a token of God's displeasure. God has been speaking to us, and now he is speaking by the voice of events near to every one of us."

For the less Sabbatarian branch of the Protestant church, and perhaps more especially for the business community, the London *Times* replied:

It will be felt that they exhibit in a peculiar light at once the credulity and illogical ruthlessness of these persons, for they must believe that if the railway company abolishes Sunday trains it will be needless to make the bridge stronger.

And the Reverend Mr. Macrae of Dundee took the liberal position that the bridge's fall might be God's judgment, but if it were, it should lead to the building of a better bridge.

The more natural and universal response to the disaster was that somebody must be to blame. That somebody was not hard to seek. It was, of course, the man who had built the bridge.

Thomas Bouch, now by exquisite irony Sir Thomas Bouch, was notified by telegraph the night of the disaster. He came to the scene immediately, and contributed a check for £250 to the fund being raised for the survivors. From the moment he arrived at the Royal Hotel, Dundee, he felt the hostility of the atmosphere, but, striving to keep his dignity as the nation's leading engineer, he at first refused to talk to the press. A few days later, the Board of Directors of the

North British met in Edinburgh and resolved that the Tay Bridge would be rebuilt, and that the Forth Bridge would be built on a new design, that is, without the participation of Thomas Bouch. Doubtless suffering agonies in his lonely suite at the Royal, Sir Thomas gave an interview to a reporter for the Dundee *Advertiser*. He tried to demonstrate that the bridge's fall had resulted from inconceivably unusual circumstances. The *Advertiser's* editor brushed this notion aside. Instead of an interview, what appeared was a reference in an editorial, far from favorable:

> Sir Thomas Bouch is anxious to show that the circumstances in which the bridge broke down were entirely exceptional. The public, however, will require very strong guarantees for the security of the restored bridge.

The public required first of all that the restored bridge be built by another engineer.

An investigation was conducted by a three-man court appointed by the Board of Trade, and begun on the spot in Dundee, as divers searched the Tay for bodies. (They brought back practically everything else, and every kind of pathetic flotsam was washed ashore—a child's sock, a woman's purse, a conductor's cap—but bodies were recovered only very slowly. Nearly four months after the catastrophe, the forty-sixth body was recovered. The other twenty-nine remain buried in the Tay. The Court consisted of Her Majesty's Wreck Commissioner, Henry Cadogan Rothery, Colonel Yolland, Chief Inspector of Railways for the Board of Trade, and William Henry Barlow, President of the Institute of Civil Engineers. They interrogated dozens of witnesses in Dundee and London, listening to the facts, explanations, and theories of everyone from the commuters who had been frightened by the speed of trains crossing the bridge to Sir Thomas Bouch. Several interesting and damning things emerged. The cast iron in the piers and girders was hardly perfect. Its production had been left entirely to the iron-foundry foreman, who had allowed holes in the castings to be filled with a mixture of iron filings and beeswax called "Beaumont Egg." The inspector responsible for the maintenance of the bridge was inexperienced and incompetent. The locomotive engineers often raced across the bridge to overtake the ferry. Various other pieces of carelessness were uncovered. But the most appalling discovery was that Thomas Bouch scarcely had considered the problem of wind pressure in designing a bridge for the windswept, storm-ridden Firth of Tay. In a paper specially prepared in his defense by his assistant engineers, the bridge was said to have been made to withstand a pressure of twenty pounds per square foot. This calculation was based on the tables prepared by John Smeaton, Britain's "founder of civil engineering"—in 1759—a hundred and twenty years earlier. Smeaton's tables gave the following wind forces:

High winds 6 lbs. per sq. ft.
Very high winds 8 to 9 lbs. per sq. ft.
Tempest 12 lbs. per sq. ft.

These wind forces were not inaccurate. As far as bridge construction was concerned they simply were based on a misconception. The iron pier columns that Thomas Bouch had designed, while probably strong enough against a uniformly applied wind force (and unquestionably strong enough to support the bridge loading) lacked strength against erratic storm-wind pressures.

No one in 1879 questioned Smeaton's tables, and not a word in the compendious, closely printed minutes of the Inquiry suggests that the 120-year-old theory might have been out of date. Besides, in the third year of construction, while he was preparing his design for the Forth Bridge, Bouch had called on the Astronomer Royal, Sir George Airy, for advice on the Forth, and Sir George, a spry and self-confident septuagenarian, had pronounced that "the greatest wind pressure to which a plane surface like that of the bridge will be subjected on its whole extent is ten pounds per square foot."

Elsewhere in the inquiry it was established that a wind force of forty pounds per square foot would have been necessary to overturn the bridge, and as this would have meant a wind of over a hundred miles per hour, even above Gale Force 11, the investigators concluded that something more than the wind force alone was involved.

Sir Thomas, worn out by the shock and the terrible public opprobrium, offered his own explanation. It was a plausible one in view of then-recent bridge-disaster history. Sir Thomas declared that the second-last car must somehow have jumped the track and struck the end of one "girder" (the girders being what a modern engineer would call "framed trusses"). Bouch believed that the truss was jarred loose, causing it to fall and in turn wreck its neighbors. The fact that the locomotive throttle was found on forward speed rather than reverse made the Court skeptical of this explanation. If a car had jumped the track, would not the engineer have reversed speed to brake?

Albert Groethe, the superintendent, had a more complicated explanation. One of the girders, already shaken by the hurricane, had up-ended slightly as the train ran onto its neighbor. The gale had blown the sprung member loose, and it had fallen, dragging the rest of the High Girders with it. The theory accords with the position of the train, located by the divers inside High Girders Four and Five, numbering from the south shore. In other words, it had reached a point about a third of the way through the High Girders when the break came.

In their report, the members of the Court parted company, at least formally. The two engineers, Colonel Yolland and William Henry Barlow, refused to attach blame to any individual. There was, however, no doubt of their real opinion. Rothery, the Wreck Commissioner, wrote, "I do not understand my colleagues to differ from me in thinking that the chief blame for this casualty rests with Sir Thomas Bouch, but they consider that it is not for us to say so."

Rothery himself had no compunctions about spelling out the blame: "The conclusion . . . is that this bridge was badly designed, badly constructed, and badly maintained, and that its downfall was due to inherent defects in the structure which must sooner or later have brought it down. Sir Thomas Bouch is, in our opinion, mainly to blame." In the question of wind pressure, Rothery nailed the vague and confusing testimony of Sir Thomas, the Astronomer Royal, and the rest with a devastating fact: in contrast to the ten pounds per square foot Sir George Airy had named, "engineers in France made an allowance of fifty-five pounds per square foot for wind pressure, and in the United States an allowance of fifty pounds." And Sir George Airy himself presently wrote a paper suggesting one hundred and twenty-pounds per square foot as a proper wind pressure to assume for bridges!

The Board of Trade and the public agreed with Rothery's summation; a specification of fifty-six pounds per square foot was shortly laid down for British bridges.

Rothery believed that the bridge had been strained by previous gales and by trains running through at excessive speeds. He pictured the six-column pier structures, loosened by this strain, subjected to "a racking motion" by the storm of December 28. This would augment the strain on the piers still further, to near the breaking point. The train, weighing 120 tons, moving at an accelerating speed, and slammed broadside by Force 11 winds, came onto this shuddering mass of bolted-together iron, and something gave. In a few grinding, clashing seconds, a pier came apart, a girder nosed downward; then girder after girder, pier after pier, and in the middle of them the locomotive, the cars, the people, plunged eighty-eight feet down into the Tay.

This writer has submitted the problem of the Tay disaster to a distinguished present-day American civil engineer. The engineer, Dr. Jacob Feld of New York, generally sustains the opinion of the Board of Trade investigators and explains why the wind calculations were so misleading. The wind acting on a bridge during a gale is not a single pressure, but a series of gusts. These "directional gusts" would have a considerably more dangerous overturning effect than the more measurable pressure of a Force 11 gale would indicate. The two trusses and the solid plank flooring, even without a train on the bridge, would give a sufficiently large exposure to such gusts to account for the collapse, in view of the insufficient lateral strength of the piers. The significant effect of the train was to present a bigger surface for the gusts to act on.

As for Thomas Bouch's explanation, Dr. Feld, like the contemporary investigators, is skeptical, pointing out that the length of the fallen "High Girders" greatly exceeded the length of the train. Had the failure occurred in the manner Sir Thomas suggested, it seems far more probable that only a part of the High Girders would have been carried down.

Sir Thomas Bouch paid the full price for his blunders. By a painful irony, he had inherited a large block of stock in Hopkins, Gilkes & Co., the bridge contractors, just before the bridge's completion, and the company since had gone bankrupt, leaving him liable for a large sum. Because of rumors connected with this, he had had to return to the witness stand a last time to explain. He had been treated gently and excused, and had gone home to the house he shared with his wife.

Throughout his ordeal he had maintained an air of impassivity which broke slightly on his second appearance at the Court. What that air had cost him became evident a few weeks after Rothery's devastating report. "His reason went so quietly from him," Prebble says, "that its passing was scarcely noticed." That fall he caught pneumonia, and within a few days was dead. He was only fifty-eight.

"Thomas Bouch was a little man on stilts," Prebble says. "His century, his country, arrogant and upward-reaching, was full of such men, and life tolerantly permitted most of them to totter through to natural death. But the Great Storm of December 28 blew the stilts from beneath Thomas Bouch, as cynically as it plucked the stilts from beneath his bridge."

The Tay Bridge was a turning point as well as a dramatic climax. Bridge engineers had climbed the rugged hill of innovation and arrived on the treacherous plateau of self-assurance. A generation earlier, Robert Stephenson had worried, calculated, discussed, questioned, as he conceived and executed his twin tubes over Britannia Isle. Thomas Bouch had experienced no such hours and weeks of intellectual torment. He knew perfectly well how to build a bridge over the Firth of Tay.

His failure shook the British engineering world as nothing before or since has shaken it. The almost traumatic reaction is expressed in the extraordinary decisions made in connection with bridging the Firth of Forth. Some four or five thousand tons of iron had gone into the Tay Bridge. The Forth design called for more than *forty thousand tons* of steel.

Steel. . . . Here is the final irony of the Tay. Poor, smug, reserved, very British Thomas Bouch received the accolade of knighthood from Queen Victoria, it will be remembered, side by side with Henry Bessemer. But Thomas Bouch, even had he so desired, could not have used Bessemer's new product in his bridge. It was against the law. In 1878, the year after the High Girders were joined, the year before its Court of Inquiry condemned and killed Thomas Bouch, the august Board of Trade admitted steel as a structural material for bridges.

In America there was no Board of Trade, no restrictive government agency to lay down unnecessarily narrow rules about what could be built and what could not. America's transportation safety record was appalling, of course. Perhaps a Board of Trade would have helped. But in democratic, federal, decentralized America, the two great bridge-engineering problems, comparable to Britain's problems of the firths of Tay and Forth, were approached and hammered out in a spirit of hardheaded rationalism. The result was two truly revolutionary creations—the St. Louis and Brooklyn bridges—both completed in the face of apprehensive and skeptical opposition, before the completion of the Tay Bridge, and both still standing.

15.

James Eads Falls in Love with the Mississippi

THE story of the St. Louis Bridge, the first steel bridge, the biggest bridge built up to its time, in many ways the most remarkable engineering job in bridge history, is also the story of a very remarkable man. James Buchanan Eads is an authentic—and neglected—American hero. His achievements in war and peace, climaxed by his towering masterpiece, the Bridge, entitle him to be ranked with his friends and contemporaries, Farragut, Grant, and Sherman; certainly his name should be far better known than that of the cousin for whom he was named and who became a disastrously mediocre president of the United States.

James Eads arrived in St. Louis in 1833, on a steamboat that caught fire as it neared the dock and barely succeeded in discharging its passengers. He was thirteen years old; his father, Colonel Thomas Eads, a bit of a Micawber, was moving his family from Louisville in search of business opportunity in the booming West. While the colonel sought his opportunity, the more practical Mrs. Eads opened a boarding house and young James sold apples on the street. Not long after, he got a regular job as "boy" at a dry-goods shop, which gave him an opportunity to acquire an education from his boss's collection of books in the loft. In 1839, eighteen years old, the books all read, he emerged from the shop and headed for the river. No Missouri boy (even one born in Indiana) could resist the river. "When I was a boy," Mark Twain said, "there was but one permanent ambition among my comrades in our village; that was to be a steam-boatman." Mark Twain succeeded in getting taken on as a cub pilot by the immortal Mr. Bixby; James Eads was fortunate enough to land a berth as "mud clerk." The mud clerk was so called because he had to do such legwork along the muddy waterfronts as collecting freight bills and bargaining for fuel. He also had to keep an eye on the riffraff crew and the barrels of whiskey in the cargo, to make sure that the two did not mix. It was endless work, sleepless days and nights, deadly routine, but it was life on the Mississippi, and James Eads would not have traded places with a clerk in a city office for a thousand dollars. Late in his first winter his vessel, an elderly steamboat named the *Knickerbocker,* hit a snag in the dawn hours as she turned into the Ohio. A splintering rip, and the *Knickerbocker* was sinking. By a good stroke of luck, a flatboat flotilla was passing and took off the half-dressed passengers and crew.

Those famous river steamboats were not only picturesque and exciting; they were also about as hazardous a means of transportation as America ever has seen. Extremely vulnerable to fire, with their primitive wood-burning boilers and all-timber construction, they had thin hulls that were easily torn open by the hidden, shifting snags that lay in wait around every bend. Storms, floods, pier fires, ice floes added to the toll. What became of the wrecks? They lay on the bottom, adding further hazards to navigation.

In his three years as a mud clerk, James Eads gave the wrecks a lot of thought. Most had salvageable cargoes, if you could figure out a way to locate them and lift them from the river bottom. One morning in 1842 he walked into the office of Calvin Case and William Nelson, St. Louis boat-builders, with a scheme. Although their caller was only twenty-two years old, the two businessmen listened with increasing interest and respect. Eads had designed a twin-hulled boat equipped with derricks and pumps which he called the *Submarine,* a word designating its function rather than its character as a vessel. Case and Nelson agreed to build the boat in return for a partnership in the enterprise, and started work at once.

While Eads was waiting for his *Submarine,* a salvage offer came in to the newly formed company from near Keokuk, up the river. Not wishing to pass up his very first job, Eads hired a professional Great Lakes diver from Chicago to go down and fasten a line to the lead pigs (bars) of the cargo. But the strong Mississippi current was too much for the laker. Eads promptly demonstrated the characteristics that marked him all his life: determination, courage, and a genius for improvisation. Buying a whiskey barrel in Keokuk, he fashioned it into a rude diving bell, dropped to the river bottom in it, felt his way to the cargo hold, and began sending up lead pigs. As soon as he had proved the efficiency and safety of his device, he let the Lakes diver take over and finish the job.

His *Submarine* launched, Eads lost no time in going out on the river. There was no lack of business; not only did the insurance companies knock at the door with the wrecks of the past five years, but also numerous older wrecks could be located and, the legal time limit for recovery by the owners having expired, Eads and his partners could acquire the whole cargo.

It was good, but by no means easy, work. Eads took his *Submarine* to the approximate site of a wreck, climbed over the side in his diving bell, sank to the bottom, and began feeling his way over the wreck to the hold. There he fastened a line to a pig of lead or iron, a crate or a barrel, and signaled by a tug on the line. Eads kept his craft and crew busy as long as there was a wreck ahead; up and down the Mississippi, the Missouri, the Ohio, and its Tennessee and Cumberland tributaries, the *Submarine* worked its way. Sometimes there were strange surprises. The *Neptune,* an old wreck for which Eads searched three miles of river bottom below Cairo, Illinois, for two months, yielded a fine cargo including a jar of butter still in a good state of preservation. And at Plum Point, a hundred miles below the Ohio mouth, he salvaged the cargo of the *America.* This wreck was a regular saga of the Mississippi. After its sinking, the current had piled brush and sediment against the decks and smokestacks until an island had been formed on which willows grew; the willows helped hold still more sediment and were replaced by cottonwoods; twenty years after the boat went down, a farm was being tilled on the island and cordwood sold for fuel to passing steamboats. Meantime the royally unpredictable current edged the streambed westward. The island, at first near the Arkansas shore, gradually reached midchannel. Then a succession of floods ripped it, destroying the farm buildings, uprooting trees, tearing shreds from the shoal itself, till the superstructure of the long-lost *America* became visible to passing steamboats. Later yet, Eads recovered the cargo from forty feet down.

In 1845 Eads quit the river bottom for a shore business. The reason was most unbusinesslike. He had fallen in love with the beautiful daughter of a certain Colonel Dillon, a distant relation, who was shortsighted enough to regard the young salvager as a poor catch for his daughter. Martha Dillon viewed the matter differently. "Do not use this pen," she wrote with a Victorian flourish, "until you have occasion to write to her whom you have selected for your companion as you journey through this vale of life."

They were married at the Cathedral Church of St. Louis de France, October 21, 1845, and the Captain, as he was now known up and down the river, went into the glass business. The idea was not bad, but the timing was ill-starred; the outbreak of war with Mexico suddenly made all sorts of businesses boom, except glass. By 1848 the Captain was broke and back on the bottom of the Mississippi. The salvage business was better than ever. Steamboats were building at a breakneck pace, and almost as rapidly were blowing up, ripping open on snags, or otherwise finding their way to the riverbed. Eads designed and his partners built three new *Submarines,* the third of which was a remarkable advance on her sisters, equipped with centrifugal pumps to rid a sunken hull of water and sand and with hoisting apparatus powerful enough to raise the pumped-out hull to the surface.

When *Submarine No. 4* made her first cruise, with Captain Eads directing navigation, walking the bottom, attaching the pump lines, and hauling cables, the whole river world hailed the inventor. Every so often Eads and *Submarine No. 4,* chugging to a new location, met a steamboat, freshly painted and good as new, which they had a few weeks earlier resurrected from the grave. The firm grew so prosperous that when the reactionary Pierce administration abandoned the valuable snag-clearing program begun by its predecessors in the Mississippi, Eads was able to buy the five government snag boats for $185,000 and convert them to *"Submarines."* He thought the abandonment of the snag-clearing a crime, and personally journeyed to Washington to lobby against it—even though the more snags, the more business for his company. He succeeded in getting a bill passed by the House to clear the Mississippi and its tributaries of logs, wrecked craft, and debris, but the bill was defeated in the Senate by the opposition of Jefferson Davis, Senator from Mississippi, who asserted that it would be a mistake to take up the proposal of a person "whose previous pursuits gave no assurance of ability to solve a problem in civil engineering." So much for Jeff Davis's perspicacity.

In this same year of 1856 a steamboat wreck occurred that had a tremendous bearing on Eads's future and on that of the Mississippi, though he was totally unaware of it at the time. The first bridge ever thrown across the mighty river was built at Rock Island, Illinois. The bridge was an unusual one, a timber truss in five spans mounted on stone piers, built to carry the Rock Island Railroad into Iowa. Two weeks after its completion the *Effie Afton,* steaming north against the current, careened into a pier. The shock overturned a pot-bellied stove, the flames leaped up, and the *Effie Afton* went down, though not before setting fire to the bridge, one span of which was lost.

The bridge was immediately repaired and the Rock Island's trains kept running. But the steamboat companies were up in arms. They brought suit to have the stone piers removed as an obstruction to navigation and a public nuisance. They had a strong case, and the railroad knew it. Its directors talked the problem over and decided that what they needed was a smart lawyer. They got Abraham Lincoln.

The case was heard in the "Saloon Building" at the southwest corner of Lake and Clark Streets in Chicago. As pilots, rivermen and bridge engineers testified, Lincoln rambled about the courtroom in his abstracted fashion and every now and then stirred laughter as he suddenly turned to correct a witness on the exact measurements of a truss span or pier. At one point he sat by the big courthouse stove, surrounded by cuspidors, whittling a stick of wood while a witness testified. Abruptly Lincoln straightened up and called for the original bridge measurements on the point under testimony. The witness was shown to be mistaken.

Summing up, Lincoln asserted that east-west "current of travel has its rights as well as that of the north and south," and cited figures on the volume of freight the railroad had hauled across the bridge since the disaster. In general, his two-day argument was that the railroad had as much right to cross the river as the steamboats had to navigate it. He concluded, "Gentlemen, I have not exhausted my stock of information, and there are more things I could suggest regarding this case, but as I have doubtless used up my time I presume I had better close."

The jury retired, but could not agree. The no-verdict was a victory for the railroad and the bridge and also, interestingly enough, for Chicago over St. Louis. St. Louis was the river metropolis; Chicago was the new rail town. The *Effie Afton* case sharpened the bitterest rivalry between two cities in American history.

The steamboat people appealed, and the case reached the Supreme Court six years later, by which time Lincoln was in the White House. The Supreme Court handed down an enlightened decision in favor of the defendants, finding that if the steamboat suit were granted, bridging the Mississippi could be prevented permanently.

By then Eads was fully occupied with an entirely different type of Mississippi obstruction. But to return to 1856, following the government's abandonment of the snag-boat program, he succeeded in organizing the steamboat insurance firms into a Western River Improvement Company. The company faced an immediate crisis when the winter of 1856–57 sent a tremendous ice floe crashing down on St. Louis, wrecking forty steamboats at the wharf, first in line among them the famous *Submarine No. 4*. But by spring Eads had no fewer than ten "submarines" in his flotilla. That spring his cousin James Buchanan was inaugurated as President. Eads, a moderate antislavery liberal, joined the opposition Republican party.

His wife had died of cholera in a heartbreaking tragedy aboard an Ohio steamboat, and he had remarried in 1854, his second wife the widow of a cousin. Both widow and widower had children. To accommodate the large household Eads bought a large house, on Compton Hill, which soon became a rendezvous for politicians as well as rivermen. In 1860, retired from the river by ill health, Captain Eads played host to Missouri Secessionists as well as Unionists while Lincoln was elected and South Carolina seceded. But his mind was already occupied with the looming armed conflict. He thought of the threatening outbreak in terms of the Mississippi. How could the river be kept open in the face of the secession of the downriver states? He conceived the answer: with gunboats, protected by iron plates against shore-battery fire.

More than two years before the *Merrimac* and *Monitor,* Eads began to design his ironclad river fleet. It had to be of shallow draft. The ships had to mount big guns and they had to be capable of firing rapidly and accurately. Through his friend Edward Bates, a St. Louis War Democrat appointed to Lincoln's cabinet, he won a hearing in Washington in the spring of 1861. Lincoln, familiar with Eads's reputation in the West, favored his idea. But Simon Cameron, the Secretary of War, found it ridiculous. Cameron was a Pennsylvania politician with no knowledge of military or naval affairs, but his view was strongly seconded by the regular Navy. These ocean sailors disliked and distrusted shallow-draft vessels and were especially antipathetic to iron. Instead they bought three wooden side-wheelers in Cincinnati, loaded coal bunkers around their boilers for protection, and made them so heavy that they ran aground. The War Department then asked for bids on seven ironclads. Although the whole idea of ironclads was Eads's, he was given no special invitation to bid. He entered a bid with a pledge to build the boats within sixty-five days.

The War Department, now headed by the able Westerner Edwin M. Stanton, accepted; Eads signed the contract in Washington on August 7. "In a veritable tornado of energy he . . . tied up telegraph lines for hours at a time," says his biographer, Florence Dorsey, "getting mills and shops in several states opened and manned, new ones hastily put up, machines for fashioning armor plate built. . . . In two weeks he had four thousand men working shifts seven days and nights a week, spurred on by tempting bonuses." William Nelson, Eads's boat-building partner of the *Submarine* days, was placed in charge of assembling the boats at St. Louis.

At Eads's and Nelson's Carondelet shipyard, The Union Iron Works, America's first ironclad warship was launched on October 12, 1861. Three other gunboats were under construction at St. Louis, three more across the river at Mound City, Illinois. But the target date of sixty-five days could not be met, partly because of the government's failure to make payments due. Eads used up all his own capital, borrowed from friends, and completed the seven gunboats, plus an eighth, far bigger and more powerful than her predecessors, carrying sixteen heavy guns. This redoubtable vessel, the *Benton,* was actually one of his old "submarines." Apprehending suspicion on the part of the War Department, he had her appraised at less than her worth, but the suspicion was stirred anyway. Eads pushed ahead in the face of an exquisitely exasperating situation; the War Department suspected him of cheating it and at the same time refused to meet its payments, threatening him with bankruptcy as thanks for a brilliant and patriotic contribution to victory.

By December all eight boats were finished. Captain, later Commodore, Foote was given charge of the flotilla. Foote was only moderately enthusiastic about his command, and when the 200-foot *Benton,* probably the largest warship afloat, grounded below St. Louis, Eads prudently withheld his advice for refloating her until the Navy had exhausted its temper and ingenuity. Foote then followed Eads's suggestion that a line be passed around a tree on shore to haul the mammoth free.

The wrangle over payment continued all winter, and in February, when Grant undertook his campaign against Fort Henry and Fort Donelson, the four ironclads that Commodore Foote led up the Tennessee River still belonged to James Eads. Perhaps Eads felt that his only prospect of getting his money back was to give his recalcitrant customer a sales demonstration. On February 6, the ironclads poured into Fort Henry a storm of shells under which the

Confederates cleared out without waiting for Grant's army. A week later, Confederate General Pillow was messaging from Fort Donelson on the Cumberland: "The Federal gunboats are destroying us." The gunboats took a pounding; Foote himself was twice wounded, but after a desperate sally from the fort was beaten back by Grant, the garrison surrendered—the first big Northern victory of the war.

The demonstration was a success. Eads's financial problems were solved, and those who had scoffed at his river monsters changed their tune to a cheer. On Washington's Birthday, St. Louis held a parade in his honor. The same day the gunboats hammered a third Confederate stronghold, Columbus, Kentucky, into submission.

In March, at Hampton Roads, Virginia, the *Monitor* and *Merrimac* fought their duel, an event that for various reasons drew history's spotlight. The *Monitor* and *Merrimac* were the first ironclad ships to fight each other; but Captain Eads's Mississippi gunboats were the first ironclads built on the American continent, the first to engage in battle in American waters or capture an enemy fort, and the first in the world to engage enemy warships—the Confederates' wooden Mississippi squadron.

The effect of the Western ironclads was far more decisive than that of the *Monitor,* whose hard-won victory merely made possible McClellan's unsuccessful Peninsular campaign.

Eads's gunboats, powerfully seconded by the ironclad rams of another notable bridge-builder, Colonel Charles Ellet, soon captured the important Confederate Mississippi fortress, Island No. 10, defeated the Confederates' own ironclad fleet in two battles, and joined hands with Farragut's ocean warships at Vicksburg in July 1862, cutting the Confederacy in two. Reinforced by new, more powerful products of Eads's St. Louis yards, the gunboats played a major role in the protracted siege of Vicksburg. "Only give me the ironclads built by Mr. Eads, and I will find out how far Providence is with us," Farragut messaged Washington, and in the memorable Battle of Mobile Bay two of Eads's ships, the *Chickasaw* and the *Winnebago,* led the onslaught that smashed the Confederacy's last naval force. Without the Union domination of the great river system, the decisive campaigns of Grant and Sherman hardly would have been possible.

With the return of peace, the country's enormously expanded industrial economy turned hungrily to peaceful enterprises. Foremost among these was the completion of the railroad to the Pacific Coast. This line, proposed by a weekly newspaper in Ann Arbor, Michigan, as early as 1832, just seven years after George Stephenson's

Rocket, had been delayed by rivalry between North and South over the route. As Secretary of War, Jefferson Davis had pushed hard for the Southern route, but with secession the South automatically abandoned its claim. The Union Pacific began building westward from Nebraska in 1865, and in 1869 its tracks met those of the Central Pacific, building east from California, in Utah.

East from Nebraska, the Union Pacific meantime built a connecting line to join the track coming west from Chicago, which crossed the Mississippi at Rock Island, of *Effie Afton* fame. Chicago, Western terminus of several great Eastern railroads, thus became the transportation capital of the nation.

The St. Louis business community watched this development with jealousy and alarm. Across the river the Illinois Railroad had long since reached East St. Louis, and the westward connection to the Union Pacific was easily feasible. But freight had to be clumsily ferried across the river at St. Louis, and during severe winters piled up on the shore.

Could the Mississippi be bridged at St. Louis? Talk of a bridge was as old as the town, but all schemes had proved chimerical. The commencement of the Union Pacific created a fresh sense of urgency and in 1866 the St. Louis and Illinois Bridge Company was formed and applied to the two state legislatures for rights. It was granted the rights, but the Illinois legislature laid down the requirement that the bridge must have either a main span of 500 feet or two spans of 350 feet in midchannel in order to minimize navigational obstruction.

By 1866, America had a corps of trained and experienced bridge engineers. Which of them would undertake the Mississippi? None of them. The project fell instead to a man who had never even thought of building a bridge before. But then, James Eads had never thought of building an ironclad gunboat before 1861. To his stupendous new undertaking he brought no formal technical training, but he brought experience no engineering school taught. He knew more about the Mississippi River than any other man alive. In addition he knew a good bit about iron and ironworks, a great deal about shipbuilding, and how to organize labor and materials in widely separated places into an effective pattern. He knew, from teaching himself, how to draw sketches and designs.

All the same, Eads's undertaking to build the St. Louis Bridge stands in the first rank among examples of heroic self-confidence. One is tempted to ask today, as very many of his contemporaries asked at the time, where did the man get his nerve?

16.

Captain Eads Builds a Triple Steel Arch

WHAT kind of bridge could meet the formidable demands of nature and man at St. Louis? Two hundred and twenty-five thousand cubic feet of water per second flowed past the city in the 1500-foot-wide stream. At high water, usually in June, this volume could be quadrupled. In the generation during which the level of the river had been measured, it had varied more than forty feet.

In high-water time the Mississippi races by St. Louis at twelve and a half feet per second. Huck Finn's raft covered a mile in seven minutes on this torrent. Down below, as James Eads knew, the riverbed swirled and flowed to a depth of a foot or more. What sort of piers and foundations could withstand the scour? The bed shifted unpredictably, making it virtually impossible to answer the question: how deep is the river? At the very point where Eads built his East Abutment, the bottom dropped away in seven years from twenty to a hundred feet. The bedrock, laid bare, showed smooth and waterworn.

In winter, huge irregular chunks of ice came barreling down from the north, freezing together in intense cold to form massive ice fields. In narrow passes, where islands occupied part of the stream, the ice jammed. More ice was wedged under the floe by the current, till little glaciers twenty feet deep were formed. The river sometimes was shut up tight from early December until late February.

These terrific problems notwithstanding, several hardy projects for a bridge had been advanced by 1867. Before his death at the head of his flotilla of rams in the war, the brilliant but rash Charles Ellet had offered to build a suspension bridge founded on piers in the river. A thoroughly unsound scheme, it was rejected because of its high cost. Several other proposals followed. Josiah Dent, a citizen of St. Louis, first proposed a railroad bridge in 1855, shortly after the Missouri Pacific reached the opposite shore. John Roebling, whose genius we shall encounter in the next chapter, offered two separate suspension plans, one a single tremendous span, something he was actually to achieve in Brooklyn, the second a triple span with varying lengths, requiring piers in the river. Probably Roebling considered the triple span safer for railroad loading. Between Roebling's two projects, a man named Homer put forward (1865) Robert Stephenson's iron tube, in three sections. Homer's superstructure was behind the times, but he had better ideas for his foundations. They should go to bedrock if it could be hit forty feet below low water; otherwise iron cylinders for piling should be driven by compressed air. Homer's estimated cost was three and a third million dollars, and he left a very important observation: the tall "chimneys" of Mississippi steamboats could be hinged for lowering under the bridge, greatly reducing the problem of clearance above high water. The truth was that all these schemes were unsound because none of them proposed sinking foundations for piers or towers to bedrock.

James Eads, studying the question in 1867, considered two distinct problems: the foundations and the superstructure. Of the two, the first was the more critical. Yet, for an enduring bridge, an enduring superstructure also was essential. Further, the two parts of the bridge were intimately related.

Iron, discovered in ancient times, could be remelted and cooled in molds as cast iron, hard and brittle. With most of the impurities removed in the liquid state, it became wrought iron, gaining considerably in tensile strength. But if this wrought iron was remelted and some of the carbon that had been taken out was put back again, a much stronger metal—steel—resulted. All this had been known for centuries. The trouble was that until 1856, reintroducing the carbon was very difficult, and steel was consequently rare and costly. In that year, Henry Bessemer stumbled accidentally upon his process for making cheap steel. Shortly after, Karl Siemens and Emile and Pierre Martin collaborated to create the even better "open-hearth" process, which became known in 1867, the very year James Eads conceived a great triple arch of steel as the means of bridging the Mississippi.

Steel was thus an absolutely new structural metal, never tried, never tested. Could it be produced in quantity with the crucially important uniformity?

Eads thought that it could—one of the great calculated risks of engineering history.

Before he could begin testing it, he had to overcome a problem of a non-engineering nature. A company had been formed, the already-mentioned St. Louis and Illinois Bridge Company, and had obtained a charter from the Missouri legislature. In the Illinois legislature, however, it ran head-on into the stone-wall opposition of the Wiggins Ferry Company, which operated the ferry that the bridge was designed to supplant. Gratz Brown, the leading St. Louis political figure of the day, also encountered resistance in introducing enabling legislation in Congress—not only from the steamboat interests, who feared a navigational hazard, but from the northern railroads, which objected to a bridge that would enable rivals to span the continent.

At this point Lucius Boomer entered the picture. This majestically named Chicagoan, a former partner of Amasa Stone, wished to build a bridge at St. Louis to serve the public good and make an honest profit. He stepped into a hornet's nest. Today only traces remain of the prescient animosity that St. Louis felt a hundred years ago toward its upstart rival on Lake Michigan. Boomer experienced its full brunt. Supported by the Chicago press, he succeeded in winning the exclusive Illinois bridge charter for his own Illinois and St. Louis Bridge Company. The St. Louis *Missouri-Democrat* promptly denounced "Chicago, that Babylon of houses that fall down, reaching after trade to support its fast horses, faster men, and fallen women."

At a meeting at the Planter's House, the St. Louis and Illinois Bridge Company appointed James Eads its chief engineer. The company decided to apply to the Keystone Bridge Company of Pittsburgh, leading bridge-building firm of the day, for the superstructure, and invited J. H. Linville, former bridge engineer of the Pennsylvania Railroad, now president of Keystone, to act as Eads's consulting engineer. Linville, who recently had built a wrought-iron truss over the Ohio at Steubenville with a 320-foot span, took one look at Eads's arch design and sent it straight back to St. Louis. "I cannot consent to imperil my reputation by appearing to encourage or approve [the design's] adoption," he announced. "I deem it entirely unsafe and impracticable." He thoughtfully enclosed a substitute plan of his own, a triple-span iron-truss with arched upper chord, to be floated on pontoons and raised to position. Probably the only reason, aside from Eads's own reputation, for the rejection of Linville's dire warning, was the fortunate ignorance of the company's directors of what at the time passed for engineering principles. An iron truss of 500-foot spans would have been a dubious substitute for Eads's soaring conception in steel. As we have seen, many an iron truss fell down in the next twenty years.

In mid-July 1867, Eads handed the directors a full outline of his plan. He had had his conclusions checked by two men, Colonel Henry Flad and Charles Pfeiffer, trained engineers who were to prove conscientious subordinates. One of Eads's valuable attributes was his capacity for inspiring confidence and loyalty. In August, the pile-drivers, workboats, derricks, engines, and barges began gathering at the foot of Washington Avenue, in the midst of the St. Louis waterfront.

Lucius Boomer promptly fired a propaganda salvo. Calling a convention of twenty-seven hand-picked engineers, he had resolutions passed declaring that piers could not be founded to bedrock in the Mississippi, that spans of five hundred feet were impossible, and that the right bridge to build would be a six-span truss. In defending the feasibility of Boomer's truss with its five piers in the river, his engineers very ignorantly declared that deep, costly foundations were not necessary because scour—destructive action of the riverbed against foundations—did not extend "to thirty feet below low water."

"Where Mr. Boomer expected to have things all his own way," Professor Woodward, author of the compendious *History of the St. Louis Bridge*, notes, "he found himself opposed by one who possessed to an uncommon degree the confidence of his fellow citizens, and who united to the skill of an engineer great executive power and unusual resources as a financier."

Eads coolly began construction of his cofferdam for the West Abutment on August 20, the day before Boomer's convention opened. The battle joined was real. Eads's company needed five million dollars, a good round sum that could be had only from the New York and London financial communities. Bonds had to be sold; investors had to be assured that the bridge actually would be built.

Eads chose the site for his West Abutment strictly on the basis of the bridge's future usefulness. Consequently it was located in the heart of the busy waterfront, at a point where all sorts of wreckage and debris lay in the riverbed. "The old sheet-iron enveloping their furnaces, worn-out grates, old firebricks, parts of smokestacks, stonecoal cinders and clinker, and every manner of things entering into the construction of a Mississippi steamer seemed to have found a resting place at this spot," records Professor Woodward. Two steamboats sunk in the 1849 fire reposed in the mud, one on top of the other, the bottom one only two or three feet above bedrock. The wharf had been built out since the fire, and rubble dumped to support it pinned the wrecks, making it impossible to refloat them. Eads devised a sort of monster axe, with a steel blade and oak handle, to cut through the mass. Into the cleft, the sheet piling of the cofferdam was thrust. As the cofferdam grew, more wreckage was encountered—four large barges. A delay; adverse publicity; cheers in the Boomer camp. Boomer began excavation on his own company's account at East St. Louis. His laborers were arrested for trespassing. More, his aggression rallied St. Louis around Eads.

Despite the under-river wreckage, the solid masonry of the West Abutment soon rose from the bedrock, 47 feet below the city *directrix.* (Because the Mississippi's level varied at least twenty feet a year, and annual high and low water fluctuated widely, some fixed mark was needed; the *directrix* stood at the high-water mark of the flood of 1828, highest water in the city's history.) Eads had scored his first victory; he had proved his intentions serious and his technique competent. It was enough to bring the Boomer camp, if not to capitulation, at least to negotiation. In Washington in the spring of 1868, Eads met David Garrison, president of Boomer's company. Garrison, a St. Louisan, keen for the bridge, agreed to submit the rival designs to an impartial board. The outcome was adoption of the Boomer company's name—The Illinois and St. Louis Bridge Company—and Eads's design. Originally the directors were drawn from both old companies, but Boomer and his friends soon dropped out.

The Illinois legislature gave in along with the Boomer crowd; what remained was to convince the Federal government and the financial community. With this end in mind, Eads already had been at work on a report designed to prove the practicability—and economy—of a steel-arch bridge. At $350 a ton, steel could not be wasted. Three "bowstring girder" spans—the design proposed by Keystone President Linville—would take double the amount of metal of the arch design. Such a truss theoretically would save money on the substructure (it was no coincidence that Linville's company dealt solely in superstructures) by requiring less substantial underpinning, but in a current like the Mississippi, solid, deep-founded piers and abutments had their own value. Eads cited not only the notorious scour, on which he was the foremost expert, but also the problems of flood and ice. Any strength less than absolute was a risk.

Eads's design called for a center arch of 515 feet, resting on two piers sunk to bedrock, connected with the shore abutments by spans of 497 feet (clear). The arch rise was one tenth the span length. Piers would be of limestone faced with granite. The arches would carry a two-deck roadway, a highway above and two-track rail line below. The width of 50 feet was later increased to 54 feet 2 inches.

Total estimated cost: something over three million dollars (exclusive of approaches), of which the substructure would represent a little more than half. Acquisition of land and the construction of approaches would bring the total to about five million dollars.

The report was a success. Congress passed the enabling act, and the financial community gave signs of support. Work on the West Abutment was pushed to conclusion. Part of the aim of Eads's report had been to explain the difficulties involved in this abutment because of the sunken wreckage: Boomer had assiduously promoted the skeptical question: if Eads's West Abutment was so troublesome, how could he ever expect to sink his other three foundations?

The reasoning behind this question lay in the peculiar profile of the river: bedrock was only forty feet down on the St. Louis side, but the rock shelved away so steeply that on the Illinois shore it was well over one hundred feet below mean high water—exactly how far below was not even known (*Figure 46*).

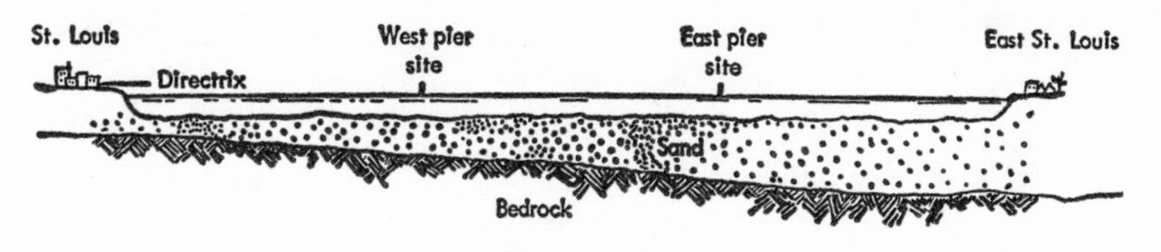

Figure 46

Eads himself was in doubt about the East Abutment. The other three supports would be carried to bedrock, but about this one, he hesitated. It would be carried to bedrock if possible; otherwise it would ultimately rest on piling driven into the sand. Eads, who had delivered a scathing reply to the ignorant assertion of Boomer's engineers that scour did not extend "to thirty feet below low water," cannot have been completely satisfied with his own plan at this point.

An accident set him on the road to the solution of the problem. In the fall of 1868 he contracted a severe bronchial ailment and finally quit the chilly damps of St. Louis to convalesce abroad. In December he returned to the United States, but stayed in New York, not risking the suspect climate of his home town. Early in the new year he crossed once more to France.

The leading French iron and steel firm, Pétin, Gaudet and Cie., had considered bidding for the superstructure contract. Eads took the opportunity to show M. Pétin, head of the firm, the plans. Pétin called in his chief engineer, M. Moreaux. Moreaux invited his American colleague to Vichy, where he was constructing a bridge over the Allier.

There Eads met another engineer, M. Audernt, who was sinking Moreaux's foundations inside a sheet-iron box filled with compressed air. This was Eads's first encounter with the pneumatic caisson, one of the greatest engineering developments of the nineteenth century.

The trick had been pioneered a generation earlier by French and British engineers constructing harbor works. Admiral Cochrane had invented the airlock to admit men into the sealed chamber of compressed air. Isambard Brunel, who had begun his career under the Thames, helping his father dig the world's first subaqueous tunnel, had made engineering history with his Royal Albert Bridge over the Tamar at Saltash. Needing a pier in the middle of the stream, Brunel had driven to bedrock more than seventy feet down by means of a caisson to withstand a pressure of thirty-five pounds per square inch above atmospheric.

Shortly afterward, a French engineer named Fleur St.-Denis, bridging the Rhine at Kehl, modified Brunel's caisson to a more efficient complex of four compartments, with two shafts equipped with airlocks, one for men, the other for material. St.-Denis also invented a wonderfully simple method of getting the excavated mud and rock out of the caisson without having to carry it up through the airlock. He constructed a third shaft leading down into the caisson, this one filled not with compressed air but with water. It terminated in a pool dug inside the caisson. An endless chain of buckets descended through this "water shaft" and brought up the excavated sand and gravel. St.-Denis's largest caisson at Kehl measured 77 by 23 feet, and was sunk to 65 feet below high water.

Audernt had built no fewer than forty piers by the pneumatic method, including one 75 feet deep at Piacenza, Italy. By 1868 compressed air even had been pioneered in the United States, though it is doubtful that Eads knew about it. William Sooy Smith used a small amount of compressed air in sinking pile foundations for railroad bridges over the Pee Dee and Santee rivers in the Carolinas in the 1850s, employing an airlock designed by Alexander Holstrom. Sooy Smith designed airlocks for deeper use of compressed air on a railroad bridge over the Savannah River in 1859, but the war intervened and he never built the bridge. Sooy Smith emerged from the war a general and soon returned to bridge-building. In 1869, the year Eads sank his caisson in the Mississippi, Sooy Smith sank one to a considerable depth in the Missouri for a railroad bridge at Omaha.

Whatever Eads knew of the labors of Audernt, St.-Denis, Brunel, or Sooy Smith, he had regarded their technique as too dangerous to try in the Mississippi. Studying Audernt's caisson in the Allier, he now changed his mind and resolved to use the pneumatic caisson to carry the East Abutment to bedrock—at a depth under water far beyond those reached by Brunel and Audernt. Very little was known at the time of the effects of compressed air on human beings.

Stopping off in New York long enough to explain his plan to a meeting of stockholders, Eads soon had Nelson and the Carondelet yard busy building a pair of the queerest structures the riverfront ever had seen. He postponed the deep East Abutment foundation, and instead prepared to carry out a simultaneous attack on the two piers, which would stand a third of the way from either shore, 520 feet apart. The experience gained in driving these shallower (though still deeper than any European) foundations, he correctly anticipated, would prove invaluable at the East Abutment. The two caissons he designed were rectangular boxes made of wood covered with iron. The West Caisson, which did not have to go quite so far down, was somewhat smaller than the 82-foot-long East. The air chamber at the bottom of each caisson was floorless, nine feet high, and topped with a heavy roof. On this roof the masonry foundation could be constructed in a hollow form, later to be filled with concrete. As the masonry pile rose, the caisson would sink deeper and deeper until it reached the river bottom.

Eads decided to begin with the deeper East Pier, believing that support for the bridge bonds, just going on sale, would be strengthened if this deeper of the two piers was sunk first. The intimate connection between engineering and financing, implicit in the records of many other bridges, is explicit in Professor Woodward's account of the St. Louis Bridge.

Materials came from far off. James Andrews of Pittsburgh contracted for the masonry, except for the granite facing, which was shipped from Portland, Maine, and dressed in Richmond. Two sailing vessels carrying granite were lost in a storm off Florida in the winter of 1869–70.

Iron plates were supplied by Gaylord, Son and Co., of Cincinnati, and were also obtained from another source: the old gunboat *Milwaukee,* bought from the government. The rivets came from the Norway Iron Manufacturing Company of Wheeling.

Before the caisson was floated to position, a careful probe of the bottom was made. A ten-inch tube was thrust fifteen feet into the riverbed. Within this tube a four-inch pipe was driven to bedrock, which proved to be 96 feet below the river surface—82 feet below the river bottom. The East Pier caisson, in other words, had to descend through a little water and a lot of mud.

In October 1869 the waterfront was treated to the curious sight of a huge armored rectangle, mounted on a false boat bottom, slid into the water at Carondelet and towed, rocking and swaying, to the bridge site, two thirds of the distance from St. Louis to the Illinois shore. A cluster of boats and barges, hoisting and pumping machinery sticking high above their low decks, waited. A crew of fifteen hundred manned this ungainly flotilla; lines, hoses, and cables were attached to the great gray box, compressed air was pumped into the chamber, the false boat bottom was freed and towed away, and the masonry begun. A week later, on a cold, raw day, with the sky further darkened by the smoke of the construction fleet, the cornerstone of the pier was laid.

The ceremony was brief; the hammers hardly paused. The barges loaded with limestone were tugged into position and unloaded. The big blocks were swung into their places in the growing column mounted on the air-chamber roof. As the caisson was lowered, the columnar pier was built up, kept well above the water in case of a sudden rise in the river. Within a few days the floorless bottom chamber hit the sand. Down the ladders inside the hollow masonry column went Eads's compressed-air workers, for whom the word "sandhog" had not yet been invented. At the bottom of the ladders, seven airlocks provided entrance to the working chamber. Entering an airlock, a group of workmen closed the door behind them, opened a valve, and let air into the lock. At this early stage the pressure needed to be raised only a few pounds above normal atmospheric (14.7 lbs. per square inch). When the pressure in the airlock equaled that in the working chamber below, they opened the working-chamber door.

The workmen, immigrant Germans and Irishmen, were a tough lot.

Eads always carried a sheath knife and revolver on the job—practically everybody on the Mississippi waterfront was so armed—but never had any trouble. Despite his slight build, he was a man of exceptional physical prowess, thanks to his years of cargo-mauling

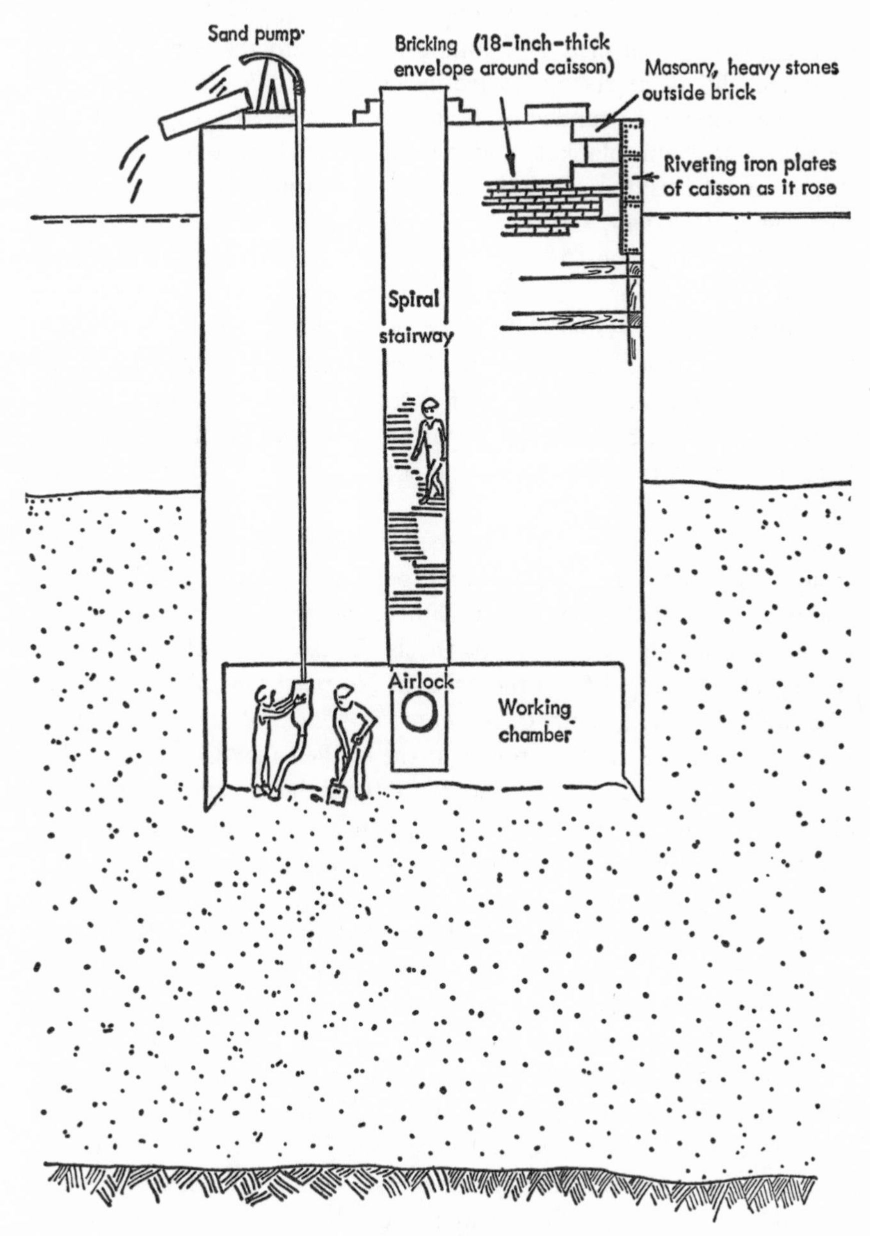

Figure 47

on the bottom of the river. He sometimes staged weight-lifting contests on the blacksmith boat (a good deal of horse and mule power was used to help run the machinery) and could outlift everyone except the chief blacksmith.

Four operations were going on at once (*Figure 47*).

The work was pushed all autumn and on into the winter; a bitter cold spell filled the river with ice cakes, and for a period of several days the men were stranded at the pier; one of the barges, the *Hewitt,* was provided with blankets and rations for such an emergency. The day before Christmas, Eads succeeded in getting his most powerful tug, the *Little Giant,* out to the "Hotel de Hewitt," where he found his sandhogs and construction gang in good spirits despite the cold. The ice subsided for a few days, then came back stronger than ever and threatened to smash the pier. Eads had built a breakwater against this danger; a mountain of ice piled against it. For a few days it was touch and go; then the weather warmed a little, the ice began to subside, and the threat passed. The men finally could travel back and forth between home and job again, and the work tempo picked up.

As the working chamber dug deeper and deeper, the air pressure inside slowly raised, to 20 pounds per square inch, to 25, to 30. Some of the men began to complain of stomach pains; one or two reported moments of fleeting paralysis. These occurred after work, when a shift emerged from the caisson. No particular alarm was felt. The men invented their own "cures"—bands of zinc and silver around wrists and ankles—for what they called the "Grecian bends," after a picturesque fashion of the day in feminine posture. At a depth of 76 feet, with air pressure at 32 pounds, one man suffered such severe abdominal pains that he had to be hospitalized.

Apparently up to this moment Eads had never heard of caisson disease, the terrible affliction of compressed-air workers. Yet as early as 1839 a French engineer named Triger had observed the effects of compressed air on men working under pressure in the quicksand of the Loire. Another French engineer, Cézanne, noted non-fatal discomforts among his men working on bridge foundations in Hungary and Lithuania. Isambard Brunel, too, had encountered caisson disease under the Tamar, and had overcome it by reducing his working shifts. Two French mining engineers, Pol and Watelle, had made the important discovery that incidence of illness was proportionate to speed of decompression, and that a return to compression gave relief.

An English doctor named Foley also had correctly prescribed slow decompression as a preventive. But scientific and medical news did not travel fast in the nineteenth century unless it had a direct connection with making money. The sorry story of compressed-air work—boldness, ignorance, tragedy—was acted out again and again on bridges and tunnels in Europe and America before the simple and effective solution was applied universally. Every engineer was on his own in that halcyon day of laissez-faire, and his men's lives depended solely on his judgment and heart.

Eads noted that many of the men who suffered from the mysterious malady were underfed or alcoholic. Very probably Triger, Brunel, and the others had made the same observation; "underfed" and "alcoholic" characterized a large proportion of the laborers of the day. Following oblivious in the footsteps of earlier engineers and acquiring experience of which later engineers would take no note, Eads issued his orders: only men in good physical condition should be employed in the compressed air; the day shift should be cut to three watches of two hours each. The night shift, on which most of the victims had worked, was abolished. These measures were partially effective; the caisson was driven to bedrock at 93½ feet without further serious cases. The event on February 28, 1870, was signaled up and down the riverfront with booming cannon and steamboat whistles.

The working chamber of the caisson, resting solidly on scraped rock, now was filled with masonry "till it was the size of an Irishman," at which point the last Irishman crawled out, the ladder was pulled up, and the space was filled. It seemed that the danger from caisson disease was over. But it was spring, and the Mississippi began to rise. The water went up faster than the upper part of the caisson could be filled in. Ten days after the freshet began, the air pressure was up to 44 pounds. A new man came out after a two-hour watch. He remarked that he felt fine. Ten minutes later he toppled over and died. This man, James Riley, was America's first caisson-disease fatality.

Horrified, Eads summoned his personal physician, Dr. Jaminet, to the pier. A floating hospital was fitted up, but in the next few days five more deaths took place. Eads cut the working day to two two-hour watches, with a long rest between, then to three one-hour watches. At Jaminet's suggestion he laid down strict rules on sleep and diet. The men complained bitterly about the strict rules. In April, while Eads was in New York, a new freshet came flooding down the valley, sending the water level to nineteen feet above the stone masonry of the East Pier; the sheet-iron and brickwork were rushed by round-the-clock effort. Down in the caisson the bends came back and the watches were cut to 45 minutes. On April 13 the flood burst through the brick-and-iron envelope and poured down into the caisson; in the frantic rush to escape the men did not stop to close the aircocks or the shaft doors. They escaped, but the accident delayed the work a month; two weeks after the damage was repaired, the pier was finished.

Meantime, Eads had simultaneously pushed the West Pier, which hit bedrock on April 1, 1870, in a submersion of 78 feet–86 feet below the *directrix*. The bridge now had three of its four great supports founded—the West Abutment, the West Pier, and the East Pier. The fourth, and deepest, the East Abutment, was now undertaken. On November 3, 1870, an enormous new iron-sheathed monster, requiring a boat-mounting with a ten-foot draft, was towed by three steamboats across the river to the Illinois shore.

With the bends in mind, Eads added several extra details to this shaft. He had an elevator built in to carry the men back and forth to the working chamber. In place of the oil lamps that had flickered eerily in the other chambers, he improved the illumination and the atmosphere with new calcium lights. A special rest barracks was provided, with free soup served for men off watch. There were various other palliatives, and of course the "health rules" were enforced as strictly as possible. It was all very well intentioned, but all these innovations had scarcely any more value in preventing caisson disease than the zinc-and-silver bracelets.

But one day during work on the West Pier, Dr. Jaminet had emerged from a visit to the caisson, returned to his office, and suffered an excruciating seizure. He was lucky enough to recover, and in analyzing his experience, hit on the real solution: slow decompression. British and French engineers and physicians had made this discovery years earlier. Yet in the years immediately following, neither Washington Roebling, sinking shafts for the Brooklyn Bridge, nor De Witt Haskins, attempting to drive the first tunnel under the Hudson, knew this important fact, any more than Eads knew it in 1870. For that matter, the rate of decompression Jaminet introduced for the East Abutment—six pounds per minute—was dangerously swift by modern practice, which calls for a rate of less than one pound per minute.

For the East and West Piers there had been ninety-one cases of the bends. Of these, thirteen died (all but one on the deeper East Pier) and two were crippled for life. Dr. Jaminet, who took charge of the medical aspect of work on the East Abutment when the caisson reached a depth of 56 feet (27 pounds pressure above atmosphere), reduced the watch to two hours at 32 pounds pressure and to one hour at 34½ pounds. Only a few cases were reported. When the caisson reached 100 feet, calling for a pressure of 44 pounds, several cases occurred; Jaminet cut the work to two watches a day of 45 minutes each. The pressure went up to 46 pounds, to 48; at 49 pounds a workman was stricken severely. Two weeks later the man died—the only fatality from caisson disease recorded on the East Abutment.

The bends were not the only natural hazard to afflict the shaft. Just after Christmas 1870, an ice gorge came piling down the river. Eads's foresight had provided a strong breakwater, which he now fortified with riprap as the pressure mounted through day after day of exceptional cold. Finally a break came and the gorge began subsiding. Then as the weather warmed, the spring flooding began, and the struggle turned to building up the abutment masonry rapidly enough to stay above water. This peril had no sooner been averted than a new one struck completely without warning—a tornado. Raging in from the southwest, it uprooted trees, flung trains from their embankments, leveled buildings, and crumpled the superstructure of the East Abutment in a matter of seconds. By a miracle, only one man was killed and eight injured. The damage was repaired and the work resumed, and a few weeks later the East Abutment at last stood on bedrock 127½ feet below the *directrix,* which at this high-water time was only a few feet above the actual river level.

Completed, this tremendous abutment contained five times as much masonry below high water as Isambard Brunel's celebrated central pier at Saltash.

After three and a half years of intensive effort, the four foundations stood unshakeable on the Mississippi bedrock, ready to receive the three great arches. Now, where were the arches?

Early in the work, iron and steel men all over Europe and America avidly sought the contract, but one look at Eads's specifications had discouraged most of them. Mass-produced steel, to the ironmasters, was a wonderful new product for which they foresaw an exciting demand. Eads, too, saw steel as a *potential* structural material of great value—its potential depending above all on the uniformity of hardness that could be imparted to it. The mere fact that hard steel could be produced meant nothing; when you built a bridge arch, a single weak rib, even a single weak tube, meant a threat of collapse.

The same truth applied to any steel structure. Possibly Eads was vaguely aware of what he was doing; more probably his single-minded concentration on his bridge kept him from noticing that he was supplying the revolutionary new metal with precisely what it needed to reach its limitless market: a pitiless demand for perfection.

Regardless of Eads's specifications, it was probably something of a foregone conclusion that the contract for the superstructure would go to the Keystone Bridge Company of Pittsburgh. This firm was unique on the American continent and perhaps in the world; it stood head and shoulders above all rivals in building the iron railroad bridges that spanned nearly every stream in the Eastern part of the country. As we have seen, the president of Keystone, J. H. Linville, had been offered the position of consulting engineer at the outset of the St. Louis project, and had turned it down on the grounds that to take part in so "entirely unsafe and impracticable" a scheme would imperil his reputation. Linville felt the same way in 1870, but his vice-president talked him into it. This was a thirty-five-year-old immigrant Scotsman and natural-born financial genius named Andrew Carnegie. A man of quick energy and quick wit, daring and imaginative, Carnegie was characterized above all by the respect for money traditionally associated with his nation. As a messenger boy in Pittsburgh he had once received a raise from $11.25 to $13.50 a month. Bursting with joy, he had run all the way across the Allegheny River bridge on his way home Saturday night, but had given his mother only the usual $11.25, reserving the other $2.25 till Sunday morning, when he produced it at breakfast. "The surprise was great and it took some moments for them to grasp the situation," he recalled fifty years later, "but it soon dawned upon them. Then father's glance of loving pride and mother's blazing eye soon wet with tears, told their feeling." With such parental guidance into the path of right, young Andrew swiftly rose to business success. Twenty-six years old when the Civil War broke out, he found numerous opportunities for making money while remaining at a safe distance from the front. (His American patriotism, as his autobiography makes abundantly clear, took second place to his Scottish.) In 1862 he organized the Keystone Bridge Company with Linville, who had been designing iron bridges for Commodore Vanderbilt's Pennsylvania Railroad, and with three other partners. Linville designed and Keystone built several notable iron-truss bridges during the war, including spans of more than three hundred feet over the Monongahela and Ohio rivers.

Carnegie first got involved with the St. Louis Bridge not as a steelmaker but as a bond salesman. Exactly how the St. Louis company happened to commission Carnegie to go to London to sell bridge bonds is not known, but he proved a persuasive and dynamic salesman. Going straight to Junius Morgan, father of J. Pierpont the elder, he offered a large block of bonds. Morgan made his acceptance contingent on certain changes in terms. The Atlantic Cable had just been laid by Isambard Brunel's huge iron steamship, the *Great Eastern*. Carnegie used it to telegraph Morgan's requests to St. Louis, and astonished Morgan by appearing in his office with the new terms two days later. Rewarded with a handsome block of shares, Carnegie at once formed a strong and distinctly Scottish attachment to the bridge. Talking Linville and his other partners into taking the superstructure contract, he arranged to subcontract the steel parts to the Butcher Steel Works of Philadelphia. The skewbacks, the enormous wrought-iron plates and sockets destined to receive the arch tips at the piers and abutments, Carnegie reserved for his own newly formed Carnegie and Kloman Company.

Very soon the Keystone Company, the Butcher Company, and Carnegie and Kloman received parallel jolts in the form of Eads's demands for quality, which struck all the contractors as highly inconsiderate. They were eager to sell Eads the steel and iron and to assemble his arches, but as for making sure the bridge actually would stand up—that was quite another matter. The Butcher superintendents were bewildered by Eads's specification of an "elastic limit." This phrase, used to describe the point to which a piece of metal could be compressed or stretched and still resume its original shape, went back to Hooke's Law of 1678. Yet Andrew Carnegie angrily complained, "Nothing that would and does please engineers is good enough for this work."

Eads's assistant engineers, Flad and Pfeiffer, had devised a testing machine that was installed in his St. Louis office. Eads caused a similar machine to be installed at the Butcher plant in Philadelphia. Through President Grant, whose friend he had been since Fort Henry, he borrowed a Navy engineer named Henry Fitch to inspect and advise at Butcher's. Despite his efforts, months went by without a single one of the steel tubes out of which his great arch ribs would be formed being found worthy even of testing. Finally, steel from another firm, the Chrome Steel Works of New York, had to be used; Linville and Carnegie at once announced abrogation of the contract because this steel was more expensive than Butcher's. The Bridge Company had to agree to a new contract, and the increased cost brought repercussions among the bondholders. At a meeting in New York, Carnegie demanded that "an experienced engineer," meaning Linville, be appointed to "alter, amend or curtail" the bridge plans to insure completion "at the least possible expense." Unruffled, Eads accepted the proposal, but got a well-known neutral engineer named James Laurie appointed consultant instead of Linville. Laurie journeyed to St. Louis, went over all Eads's drawings, specifications, bills, and contracts and turned in a report containing no serious recommendations for changes beyond a half-hearted suggestion for economizing on the approaches.

His report on costs showed $4,023,703.95 spent up to March 1, 1872, with another $2,815,082.94 estimated for completion. Thus the total cost of the bridge, including approaches, was believed to be running to nearly seven million dollars (actually, a slight exaggeration), compared with Eads's original estimate of three million dollars exclusive of approaches. Construction was costing approximately double Eads's estimate of 1867. This is so little unusual in the history of major nineteenth-century engineering projects that it might very nearly be called typical. The reason for it lies in what might be called economic psychology. Every engineer undertaking an important, and especially novel, enterprise was under the greatest pressure to keep the costs low enough for financing. Commonly, it was at the moment when estimated costs coincided with financing capacity that such an enterprise, after years of dreaming and discussion, became a practical reality. For this reason such estimates were not likely to err on the side of conservatism. Very little margin was allowed, and often no contingency fund was provided for the unexpected. Yet on just such enterprises—major and novel—the unexpected could be counted on to happen. In the St. Louis Bridge there were the wreckage under the West Abutment, the extra cost of sinking the East Abutment to bedrock, caisson disease, the tornado, and now the trouble with the steel.

Butcher's had as much difficulty in making good couplings as it had had in making good tubes. Eads finally went to Philadelphia himself. Through the summer of 1872 he worked in the Butcher plant to get production rolling. When he gave an incentive bonus, Carnegie jumped to protest the expense, which came out of the Keystone contract. Carnegie had to be quieted with an extra $25,000 for Keystone plus a $30,000 bonus for prompt delivery. In the end, Butcher again was unable to come through with sufficiently uniform couplings, and Eads had to fall back on wrought-iron couplings from Carnegie and Kloman.

At last the raising of the arches could begin. On every arch bridge ever built, the arch had been supported by centering—timber falsework in the river—during raising. Eads could not obstruct the Mississippi with centering. Of course he had figured out the solution long before: the arches would be carried out over the river by cantilevering, that is, by falsework above the abutment or pier built to balance the arch's thrust (*Figure 48*).

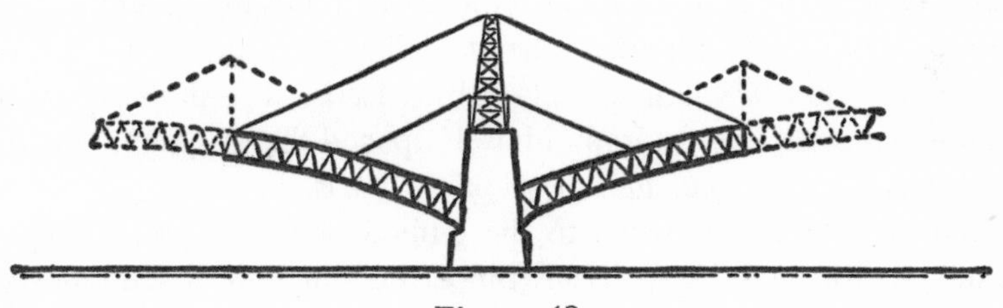

Figure 48

The cantilever cables were made of steel bars an inch thick and six or seven inches wide.

As the arches moved farther and farther out over the river in the spring and summer of 1873, a final problem came into prominence. How to join the arch halves? Eads had had each part multiplied by a factor of 1.000363, which would, he calculated, produce an overlap of 2.256 inches. The actual overlap produced proved to be slightly greater—3.252 inches. An absolutely exact meeting of the arch halves was impossible to bring about, and an overlap was essential to take the compression after removal of the cantilever cables.

Linville and Carnegie, who in the fall of 1873 succeeded in extracting an extra bonus of $35,000 from the bridge company, apparently were unable to figure out a way of joining the arches, and left the whole problem to Eads—who, of course, already had planned the solution. The final two steel tubes of each arch rib would be truncated five inches, and screw threads cut inside them. A short wrought-iron plug, fitted with two sets of threads, could then be screwed in, and at the arch closing, drawn out to fit across, holding the two together. A steel band would give the joint superior strength.

Colonel Henry Flad, Eads's chief assistant, also had thought up a solution to the arch closing. Flad's idea was to hump the arch slightly, a comparatively simple process with the cantilevering in place, and so bring the joining ribs together. The arch would assume its correct form when the cables were removed.

At the time of the closing, Eads himself was in London negotiating a new loan with Junius Morgan. The loan was contingent upon the closing of an arch as a sign to the investing public that the bridge was near completion. On September 14, five days before the deadline Eads had given Morgan, Colonel Flad set the men to jacking up the cables of the west arch ribs. Unluckily, an unseasonable warm spell hit St. Louis, and the ribs expanded instead of contracting slightly in the cool weather Flad had anticipated. Despite an ice-water trough built to cool them with thirty thousand pounds of ice, the arch could not be closed. In the end, Flad gave up and used Eads's screw connection. He immediately cabled Eads, care of Morgan, that the arch was complete. Morgan himself opened the dispatch, for Eads, with cheeky confidence, had gone off to Paris.

In October, Eads returned to the United States to find his bridge threatened from another quarter. Since the war had ended, the river steamboats, those romantic and dangerous queens of the water, had been competing more and more feverishly for speed. In the famous race of 1870, memorialized by Currier and Ives, the *Natchez* and the *Robert E. Lee* steamed upriver from New Orleans to St. Louis in four days. To get more speed, the shipbuilders sought more draft, and obtained it by lengthening their smokestacks. By 1873 some of these reached the dizzy height of one hundred feet above the water. When the river was at its highest, the arch centers stood only fifty-five feet above the water. The biggest steamboat company, the Keokuk Steamboat Line, got the ear of the Secretary of War, had a Board of Engineers convened at St. Louis, and obtained a report containing the preposterous recommendation that a canal should be dug behind the East Abutment at the expense of the St. Louis Bridge Company.

The Secretary of War, William W. Belknap, backed the steamboat demand. Without the War Department's approval, a bridge could not be built. Of course, the Army had approved Eads's design in the beginning of the project, but now Belknap threatened to take the approval back. Eads resolved to go over Belknap's head, to President Grant. It was a little embarrassing; in the last election Eads had supported the Democrats, his friend Gratz Brown having been on the ticket for vice-president. Not only that, but also Dr. William

Taussig, the vice-president and general manager of the bridge company, was the county judge who twenty years earlier had cast the vote that had barred the then penniless Captain Ulysses S. Grant from the post of county surveyor. But on this occasion as on others Grant proved himself a bigger man than his small physical stature indicated. Pointedly addressing Dr. Taussig as "Judge" to show that he had not forgotten the past, he listened to his callers' story, summoned Belknap, and asked him if the St. Louis Bridge conformed to the demands laid down in Congress and by the former Secretary of War. Belknap admitted that it did, but declared that he had the right to intervene and even to have the bridge razed. As Taussig described the scene later, Grant told Belknap: "You cannot remove this structure on your own judgment. And if Congress were to order its removal it would have to pay for it. It [Congress] would hardly do that to save high smokestacks from being lowered when passing under the bridge. If your Keokuk friends feel aggrieved, let them sue the Bridge for damages. I think, General, you had better drop the case."

Shortly after, Grant visited St. Louis and accompanied Eads and Colonel Flad to the bridge, walking the precarious plankway laid from arch to arch as coolly as he had reconnoitered the Confederate lines at Vicksburg. The President joined Eads in brandy and cigars at Eads's office.

Although the steamboat interests continued to make noise, and even had their engineers consider estimates for a canal, the issue was dead. If it needed a final burial, that came a year later with the very sudden resignation of Secretary Belknap to avoid impeachment for selling trading privileges in the Western Army posts.

Early in 1874, Eads returned to New York once more to reassure the bondholders and bankers that the job was nearly done. He had just gone to bed in his hotel when the bellboy knocked with a telegram. It was from Theodore Cooper, assistant inspector; the arch ribs had begun to break. Two tubes in the first span had ruptured.

Truly stunning news, and on the very eve of an important meeting with the financial backers. Refusing to panic, Eads sat down under the gaslight and thought. Finally he figured the thing out; the steel cantilever cables, still attached to the arches, were contracting in the cold and pulling the ribs up and back, a direction in which these compression members were not meant to take strain. He at once shot off a telegram to Cooper: loosen the cables. Next morning he addressed the investors with confidence.

Arriving home, he found the shores lined with people waiting for the bridge to break up as the cables were removed. But the cables were removed and the beautiful arches hung in the air in perfect security.

It was the last of Eads's problems, though not quite the last of his troubles. Carnegie's Keystone men lagged at their work on the bridge decks till inspired with fresh bonuses, and a true Keystone-cops comedy took place at one point when Carnegie barricaded the bridge entrance to make sure of collecting his money. The final cost of the bridge Professor Woodward puts at $6,536,729.99. The approaches accounted for well over one million of this. The superstructure represented over two million. The piers and abutments also ran to over two million; thus Eads had underestimated superstructure and substructure by about a half million dollars each. Considering all things, it was not a bad estimate. The remaining costs included tools and machinery, barges and boats, repairs, horses, hospitals, tornado damage, and various other items.

On May 24, 1874, the highway deck was opened for pedestrians to walk across; on June 3 it was formally opened for vehicles. A few days later the first locomotive crossed, carrying Eads, company officials, and their guest, General Sherman, the Army's Chief of Staff, who had come to St. Louis in order to get as far as possible from Secretary of War Belknap. Sherman drove the last spike on the Illinois side.

On July 1, Eads sent a trainload of gravel and iron ore across the bridge, and the next day held a public test: fourteen locomotives, their tenders filled with coal and water and crowded with passengers. First seven locomotives halted on each arch top; then all fourteen, seven on each track, crossed side by side; finally all fourteen crossed in single file. Eads had meant to line the entire bridge with heavy locomotives, but had been unable to borrow more. Two days later, St. Louis celebrated the Glorious Fourth. At 9 A.M., Simpson's Battery fired a hundred rounds and the parade started—floats and costumed marchers, the stove-makers, brewers, bakers, the manufacturers of buggies, harness, shoes and lightning rods, the temperance clubs and German singing societies, the United States Cavalry from Jefferson Barracks, and all the fire departments. The fifteen-mile-long procession wound under flags and bunting to a triumphal arch near the bridge portal, topped by a medallion portrait of Captain Eads, bearing the inscription, "The Mississippi discovered by Marquette, 1673; spanned by Captain Eads, 1874." President Grant applauded from the reviewing stand. Steamboats formed a rainbow and blew their whistles; in the evening, fireworks were shot off from the top of the bridge.

The *Scientific American* proposed Eads for President.

The St. Louis Bridge was the world's first steel bridge. It was the first important construction of any sort in steel. It was the biggest bridge of any type ever built anywhere up to that time. It involved not only the first significant use in America of compressed air and the deepest use of compressed air up to that time anywhere, but also a really astonishing record that reveals much about the innocent daring of the nineteenth century. The caisson that Eads sank for his East Abutment foundation remains to this day the deepest at which compressed-air workers ever have worked.

There were many other "firsts" and "news" and "biggests," including the size of Eads's caissons and the ingenious sand pump he devised for use inside the caisson. Possibly it should also be mentioned in this context that Andrew Carnegie's fortune was founded largely on the St. Louis Bridge.

But what strikes one most, looking back across nearly a century, is that this was the first of the long series of engineering feats with which, from the Civil War on, America astonished the world, feats that in hard, visible, tangible steel and concrete gave the world its image of modern America.

The bridge was not the last of Eads's achievements. A few years later, again in the teeth of skepticism and reactionary opposition, he built the South Pass jetties that transformed New Orleans into a year-round port for ocean shipping.

In 1920 when New York University inaugurated its American Hall of Fame, James Eads was the first engineer enshrined, which seems a rather modest glory.

Luckily, perhaps, a good bridge is itself an incomparable monument.

17.

John Roebling Spans the Niagara Gorge

THE suspension bridge did not enjoy an auspicious early history. In its ancient and primitive forms, it had blown about freely, often had dumped its travelers into the void, and in the best of situations never had been able to carry heavy burdens. Latter-day imitations in Britain and elsewhere in the eighteenth century were hardly an improvement over the creations of the Incas. Telford's bridge over the Menai Strait in the 1820s was a scintillating triumph, but not an unqualified one, barely surviving severe storm damage. Telford's friend Sir Samuel Brown built bridge after bridge, and all were blown down one after the other—at Berwick, at Brighton, at Montrose, and at Durham. On the other hand, British engineer William Tierney Clark built a suspension bridge over the Danube at Budapest which survived till the Second World War. A German engineer, Von Mitis, built a bridge over the Danube Canal at Vienna in which the suspension chains were made of open hearth steel, but by the time of steel's arrival the wire cable had superseded chain links and eyebars. A Swiss engineer, Henri Dufour, and a Frenchman, Marc Séguin, built several wire-cable suspension spans, and across the valley of Sarine, at Fribourg, Switzerland, in the 1830s, J. Chaley built the Grand Pont, a tremendous span over eight hundred feet long which lasted well into the twentieth century. This structure had a wooden roadway twenty-two feet wide, and was supported by four cables, each of 1056 wires of ⅛-inch diameter, with two more cables added in 1881. Isambard Brunel also made suspension spans hold up.

Under certain circumstances, a suspension bridge, even though it sagged a bit, could sustain fairly heavy loads—wagons, flocks of sheep, droves of cattle. It could hold out, even though whipped about a little, in gale winds. But no one quite knew how or why. The real secret of Tierney Clark's chain bridge at Budapest, for example, was its weight plus heavy railings, which gave it extra rigidity. Telford's Menai Bridge owed its survival to the railings it acquired in 1839. The function of such railings was very imperfectly understood, and no engineer dreamed that the best suspension bridge to build was the heaviest that could be supported. And while many were concerned with the very obvious problem of deflection under load—the tendency of the roadway to sink under the passing wagon—they were far from clear as to what ought to be done about it.

Apart from its reactions to storms and overloads, the suspension bridge had another, more mysterious characteristic. In 1831 a body of soldiers was marching over Samuel Brown's bridge at Broughton when it suddenly gave way. In 1850 an identical accident, on a larger scale, occurred at Angers, France. A regiment was marching over the bridge when it collapsed, killing two hundred men, actually the worst bridge disaster in history. In America, James Finley's bridges and others had been shaken to pieces by the passage of flocks or droves. Actually, all these bridges were either inherently weak or weakened by age—the wires of the Angers cables were corroded at the anchorage. The failures of these spans came from real "bugs"—not inscrutable mysteries. But they inspired the public with a healthy skepticism about suspension.

Yet the suspension bridge was tantalizing in its economy. Finley built his first bridge for six hundred dollars. To illustrate the superior economy of suspension, a nineteenth-century engineer calculated that a man could cross a hundred-foot chasm on a steel wire weighing only thirteen pounds, while a wrought-iron bar would have to be nine inches broad and twenty-seven inches deep to carry a man and its own weight the same distance. The bar would weigh forty-four tons. A French engineer, Louis Vicat, invented a method of spinning wire into cable on the suspension towers at the bridge site, which greatly facilitated construction. Marc Séguin and a Britisher, James Dredge, put forward a tentative solution to the problem of deflection under load—a truss on either side of the roadway. This was a real key, though not the final one, to the problem.

In mid-century, no European engineer would have thought of proposing a suspension bridge to carry anything heavier than horse-and-foot traffic. But in 1855, John Roebling undertook to build a suspension bridge to carry a railroad line, and furthermore, to carry it the incredible distance of eight hundred feet in one span. Where was such a span to be built? Of all places, over the gorge at Niagara Falls, a dizzy 240 feet above the rapids. This breathtaking American proposal drew from Robert Stephenson, inventor of the tubular railroad bridge, the comment (in a letter to Roebling): "If your bridge succeeds, then mine have been magnificent blunders."

The fascinating thing about the man who bridged Niagara is that he was no daredevil—far from it. Probably the greatest genius in bridge history, he was bold in his projects because he was sure of his facts.

Roebling was an American immigrant of a somewhat neglected breed—neither a religious fanatic like the Pilgrim Fathers, nor a hungry peasant like the endless shiploads welcomed by the Statue of Liberty. Roebling was the son of middle-class German parents, received an excellent education at the Royal Polytechnic Institute in Berlin, and landed at Philadelphia at the age of twenty-five with nearly four hundred dollars in his pocket, a sum few Philadelphians of 1831 could have matched. He came to America in search of neither God nor bread, but of success.

The world of 1831 was in some degree symbolized by three sights recorded by Roebling during his eleven-week ocean crossing in a small sailing vessel. In the English Channel, he saw his first steamship puffing hardily through the big waves. Later, in mid-ocean, a derelict hulk was sighted, the wreck of a sailing ship damaged by storm and abandoned by the crew. It was like a glimpse of the future and the past. Then one day a sinister-looking schooner overhauled Roebling's bark, drawing alongside close enough for inspection. On the stranger's deck swarthy men shouted to each other in an unknown language and a cannon mounted on a swivel made her nature clear: a pirate. Probably she was an Algerian from the Barbary Coast, where the centuries-old pirate trade was just being suppressed by the French. After a prolonged reconnaissance, the corsair departed without attacking, evidently concluding that Roebling and his fellow emigrants were numerous enough to put up serious resistance.

Once landed, Roebling and his companions headed for the frontier—western Pennsylvania. Most of them were farmers, and they soon settled down, founding the town of Saxonburg. Roebling kept up his engineering studies in the evening while doing farm work in the daytime and waiting for opportunity, which came in 1837.

Through a German student friend he got a job in his profession, with the Sandy and Beaver Canal. Two years later he was helping survey the route for the railroad from Harrisburg to Pittsburgh. In 1841 he narrowly missed his maiden bridge job when a friend almost got the contract for a new bridge in Philadelphia.

That same year he had his first great practical idea. A curious feature of the engineering landscape of that day was the canal portage incline. Canals, of course, were very numerous and heavily traveled. Where one was interrupted by a hill, rails were laid up the hillside. Each flatboat was mounted on wheels as it arrived, and towed to the top by pulley and winch. Heavy hemp cables were used as hawsers; not infrequently they broke. Roebling saw a hawser part one day and kill two men, and suddenly thought of using wire rope, an invention he had just read about in a German technical magazine. No one in America ever had seen a wire rope, much less made one, and the canal men did not think that it would work. Roebling had to create his own wire-rope-making machinery and train people to operate it; he turned his Saxonburg neighbors into an efficient labor force. The Kentucky-hemp interests did not take the threat of competition lying down; they fought with the bare-knuckle methods of the day, including cutting Roebling's new wire-rope cables when they were put into operation on a canal incline. But the wire rope was altogether too good to be denied; it outlasted hemp by an irresistible margin.

Roebling was established as one of the leading canal engineers of the middle border when the aqueduct carrying an important canal over the Allegheny River at Pittsburgh was wrecked by ice. One hundred dollars was offered for the best (that is, cheapest) plan for replacing it. Roebling proposed a suspension structure, with big wrought-iron cables to be spun on the site. He got the job and built the span at the low cost of $62,000, taking a very modest $3500 profit for himself. The two big cables, made of 1900 wires each, were protected against the weather by wrapping. The public was impressed. A Pittsburgh newspaper observed that the new aqueduct carried "six line boats, heavily laden" all at once one day shortly after its inauguration—not realizing that the aqueduct carried the same 2000 tons' weight continuously whether there were boats in the water or not.

While Roebling was still at work on the aqueduct, a fire broke out in Pittsburgh and swept through most of the town, destroying the bridge over the Monongahela. He offered to rebuild it as a suspension, and did so for $55,000—a remarkable piece of economy.

Converting the abutments of the old bridge into anchorages, he built foundations and towers in the stream. He stiffened his roadway with inclined stays and deep timber parapets in the form of lattice trusses. The bridge survived all the storms of the next forty years, after which it was replaced to accommodate increased traffic. Two other suspension aqueducts followed. By 1848, when the project of bridging the Niagara gorge was broached, Roebling was one of the two important suspension-bridge experts in America.

The other was Charles Ellet, a fellow Pennsylvanian. A native American, Ellet came from a plain farm family and received only an elementary-school education. A brilliant mind and a burning ambition carried him through several years' experience in canal work and study, climaxed by a year abroad, spent chiefly at the École Polytechnique in Paris. In one respect Ellet closely resembled Roebling—he saw the possibilities of the suspension bridge. But his concepts were more grandiose and less practical than Roebling's—a prodigious single-span over the Potomac at Washington, the even more dazzling bridge we have mentioned earlier over the Mississippi at St. Louis. In 1841, Ellet got the contract for the replacement of Lewis Wernwag's "Colossus" bridge over the Schuylkill, in which Roebling had been interested, and built a suspension span, supported by ten cables—the first wire-cable suspension bridge in America.

The Niagara bridge company received bids from four different engineers—Roebling, Ellet, Samuel Keefer, and Edward Serrell. Curiously, all four of them eventually built spans over the Niagara gorge.

Ellet was chosen by the company. His first problem was how to carry an initial wire across the gorge. He solved it with a bit of ingenuity and showmanship which has become a part of the legend of America. He offered five dollars to any boy who could fly a kite across the gorge. A lad named Homan Walsh succeeded in the feat; according to David Steinman, Roebling's biographer, Walsh still prized the memory eighty years later. After a succession of cords and ropes, an iron-wire cable was stretched over the chasm. Ellet, a born daredevil, had a basket carrier made and pulled himself across, with the rock-strewn waters swirling two hundred and forty feet below, the first man ever to cross the Niagara gorge.

A few weeks later he topped this exploit. Having erected a light suspension span, seven and a half feet wide, without railings, to use as a service bridge, Ellet mounted his horse and rode across. A breathless crowd witnessed the passage of the horseman in the sky, and women are said to have fainted. Twelve years later in the history of this most storied of our natural wonders, a French tightrope walker named Blondin eclipsed Charles Ellet's feat by walking a wire across the terrible abyss, then pushing a wheelbarrow across, and finally pushing a wheelbarrow across while carrying another man on his back.

Ellet's audacious ride was virtually his final contribution to bridging Niagara. His service bridge, given railings and opened to pedestrians, attracted so many tolls that Ellet and the bridge company quarreled over the money. Ellet, who probably already foresaw that his construction estimate of $190,000 was a bit low, quit.

Ellet was a remarkable man, imaginative and fearless, very nineteenth-century, very American. His career was climaxed by his death; in 1862 he was mortally wounded leading in victorious battle against the Confederate Mississippi fleet the squadron of rams he had himself designed.

Ellet's withdrawal from the Niagara project eventually led to Roebling's receiving the commission on considerably more favorable terms. In 1851, the year after the collapse of the bridge at Angers under a marching regiment, Roebling assembled his materials. He recently had transferred his flourishing wire-rope business to Trenton, New Jersey, and while he directed the work at Niagara, he undertook various other enterprises, notably a railroad suspension bridge over the Kentucky River at Danville. Steinman quotes a letter that Roebling wrote from Niagara Falls on January 6, 1854, to a Trenton plant official:

> Your letters of the 2nd and 3rd came to hand. You say in your last, that Mrs. Roebling and the child are pretty well. This takes me by surprise not having been informed at all of the delivery of Mrs. R. Or what do you mean? Please answer by return of mail.

The busy engineer was presumably at least aware of his wife's pregnancy.

A few months later, a dramatic piece of news reached Niagara Falls and the rest of America by telegraph and newspaper. The suspension bridge that Charles Ellet had constructed over the Ohio River at Wheeling, West Virginia (Roebling had bid unsuccessfully), in 1849 had collapsed in a storm.

Roebling took the alarm, messaging Trenton:

> A telegraphic dispatch from Wheeling states that the Wheeling Suspension bridge broke down on the 17th; the particulars I have not learned. This bridge was not safe against heavy storms. . . . I am anxious

to secure the new floor by Stays. I have no rope on hand to do it with. I can get along with 2000 ft.; but as soon as practicable, send on more.

And shortly after:

The destruction of the Wheeling Bridge is a fact. . . . I wrote you to send me 2000 ft. more of rope 7×7 No. 9, 3 lbs. pr. ft., for Stays. Do not neglect this. I must have this rope very soon to render the new floor safe. If possible send more as fast as you can make it. You can use any bridge wire for this rope, you have on hand; if it is a little larger, it does not matter.

Steinman points out that Roebling had recommended to the Wheeling people a shorter span than that which Ellet built and had wanted it stiffened by inclined stays, that is, by wire-rope cables running at an angle to the center of the roadway to check sway imparted by the wind. The fall of Ellet's thousand-foot span, the longest in the world at the time, was a tremendous lesson "lost to the profession," as Steinman says. He cites, in both his biography of Roebling and his *Bridges and Their Builders,* a remarkable newspaper account written for the Wheeling *Intelligencer* and afterward reprinted in the newly-founded New York *Times:*

With feelings of unutterable sorrow, we announce that the noble and world-renowned structure, the Wheeling Suspension Bridge, has been swept from its strongholds by a terrific storm. . . .

About 3 o'clock yesterday we walked toward the Suspension Bridge and went upon it, as we have frequently done, enjoying the cool breeze and the undulating motion of the bridge. . . . We had been off the flooring only two minutes, and were on Main Street when we saw persons running toward the river bank; we followed just in time to see the whole structure heaving and dashing with tremendous force.

For a few moments we watched it with breathless anxiety, lunging like a ship in a storm; at one time it rose to nearly the height of the tower, then fell, and twisted and writhed, and was dashed almost bottom upward. At last there seemed to be a determined twist along the entire span, about one half of the flooring being nearly reversed, and down went the immense structure from its dizzy height to the stream below, with an appalling crash and roar.

. . . The great body of the flooring and the suspenders, forming something like a basket swung between the towers, was swayed to and fro like the motion of a pendulum. Each vibration giving it increased momentum, the cables, which sustained the whole structure, were unable to resist a force operating on them in so many different directions, and were literally twisted and wrenched from their fastenings. . . . It is a source of gratulation that no lives were lost.

Ellet's span lacked *aerodynamic stability*. It was perfectly capable of holding up its own weight (dead-loading) plus any weight of horses, wagons, people, cattle, etc., that might crowd onto it at one time. Furthermore, it was strong enough to resist a considerable wind. What caused its fall was a pattern of vibrations set up by a prolonged wind. Steinman notes that in the newspaper account above, the key words are, *"Each vibration giving it increased momentum."* The description in the paragraph before of the final agony of the Wheeling bridge astonishingly foreshadows a suspension-bridge disaster far in the future, one that was, as we shall see, a pivotal event in the history of engineering.

For the time being, the true meaning of the Wheeling collapse was concealed except from the intuitive grasp of Roebling, who took immediate measures to strengthen his Niagara Bridge. Roebling's bridge, when completed, presented a curious appearance, the sixty-four stays supporting the two-level roadway forming, with the four suspension cables, a webbing unseen in later structures. Nevertheless, this was the first truly modern suspension bridge. In a report to the bridge company, whose directors had doubtless expressed alarm over the Wheeling catastrophe, Roebling gave an analysis that Steinman calls "proof of his genius":

A competent eyewitness [of the Wheeling collapse] stated that the waves of the floor, caused by the wind, rose to a height of over 20 feet. . . . No ordinary strength of cables can resist the momentum produced by such a weight falling even 15 feet. . . .

That bridge was destroyed by the momentum acquired by its own dead weight, when swayed up and down by the force of the wind. . . . A high wind, acting upon a suspended floor devoid of inherent stiffness, will produce a series of undulations. . . . These undulations will increase by their own effect until, by a steady wind, a momentum may be produced that may prove stronger than the cables. . . . Weight should be simply an attending element in a still more important condition, viz.: *stiffness.*

The destruction of the Wheeling bridge was clearly owing to a want of stability, and not to a want of strength. This want of stiffness could have been supplied by *over-floor stays, truss railings, under-floor stays, or cable stays.*

The italics in the passage are supplied by Steinman, whose pen very evidently is not adequate to his feelings in this emphasis on Roebling's remarkable grasp of a problem with which Steinman himself grappled even more dramatically eighty years later.

The "truss railings" to which Roebling alludes were, in the Niagara span, a heavy timber truss between the two decks, the first real stiffening truss ever used on any suspension bridge. The device was soon copied by Peter Barlow in England and by other engineers. Credit for this crucially important development—the addition that made the suspension bridge healthy—belongs to a number of men. John C. Trautwine, an engineer who designed a bridge to cross the Delaware at Market Street, Philadelphia, in 1851, planned to use wire cables and twenty-foot-deep trusses. His plan was exhibited at the Franklin Institute and the Merchants' Exchange, and may very possibly have been the source of Roebling's idea.

Roebling's rational gift was unequal to another problem that came up during the Niagara project, though his rational faith may have helped him survive it. Cholera, a recurrent scourge of Europe and America in that period, invaded Niagara Falls. Workers by the score fell ill, many of them dying. Roebling resisted the disease by "hydropathy—internal and external application of water—" one of the nostrums of the day. Nearly all the unfortunates on whom he tried it died. Experiencing the symptoms himself, he walked his room all night, pitting his will power against the malady. "Keep off fear—this is the great secret," he wrote rather pathetically as the epidemic waned.

On March 6, 1855, in defiance of cholera, storm, and the inscrutable treachery of suspension bridges, the Niagara Bridge carried the first train in history to cross a span sustained by wire cables. The inaugural load was a formidable three hundred and sixty-eight tons—a locomotive plus a string of double-loaded cars. Steinman gives the total cost of the bridge as "less than $400,000." The sum was more than double that originally planned, which Ellet had found inadequate, yet this was a remarkably economical bridge in comparison with its contemporaries of equal length and equal loading.

In his final report to the bridge company, Roebling set forth a blunt truth in trenchant language.

Professional and public opinion, he noted, had been adverse to suspension bridges for railroads. The Niagara Bridge sustained railroad loading with the aid of "Weight, Girders, Trusses and Stays. With these any degree of stiffness can be insured, to resist either the action of trains, or the violence of storms, or even hurricanes. And I will here observe, that no Suspension Bridge is safe without some of these appliances. The catalogue of disastrous failures is now large enough to warn against light fabrics, suspended to be blown down. . . . A number of such fairy creations are still hovering about the country, only waiting for a rough blow to be demolished."

And he went on to this prescient forecast: "Bridges of half a mile span, for common or Railway travel, may be built, using iron for the cables, with entire safety. But by substituting the best quality of *steel* wire, we may nearly double the span, and afford the same degree of security."

Robert Stephenson had written, "If your bridge succeeds, then mine have been magnificent blunders." Roebling now wrote a paper that constituted a courteous but absolutely affirmative reply. Published in London in 1856, Roebling's paper pronounced the Menai Strait tubular bridge a mistake based on the belief that a suspension span could not be made rigid enough for railroad loadings.

And Peter Barlow in England pointed out that the Niagara Bridge used only about one fourth as much iron as the Menai tubular, though it was able to carry even heavier loading. The Menai, it will be remembered, consisted of two spans of 460 feet each; the Niagara's single span was 821 feet.

John Roebling's Niagara Bridge is a unique landmark. The future did not actually lie with railroad suspension bridges at all; very few were built. But it was the strong and healthy forebear of the whole endless series of modern long-span suspension bridges. Its wooden roadway was replaced by iron, and its masonry towers by steel, but it remained in continuous service until 1897. By then the bridge was carrying three times the loadings for which it had been designed, and it was retired to make way for a double-track bridge.

Before this, two other suspension spans had been carried across the Niagara gorge. In 1851, even before Roebling's bridge was completed, Edward Serrell's crossing for carriages and pedestrians was opened at Lewiston, a few miles below the Falls. Shaken by a storm in 1855, it was saved by bracing guys added by Roebling. These were loosened by an ice jam in 1864, and somebody forgot to tighten them again; an April storm tore the bridge down.

Samuel Keefer, the fourth of the quartet of engineers who had believed in the Niagara project, built his bridge in 1867–69. A record-breaking 1268 feet, with a roadway only ten feet wide, this picturesque span soon became known as the Honeymoon Bridge, and enjoyed a very profitable career until the night of January 9, 1889, when a hurricane swept it away. No time was lost in replacing this money-making bridge; on March 22, a duplicate, made from the same blueprints, was started; it was opened May 7. In 1897 this bridge was replaced for increasing traffic (electric trolleys) by a steel arch, destroyed in turn by the great ice jam of 1938. Today the Rainbow Bridge, built in 1940–41, stands on the site (*Figure 49*).

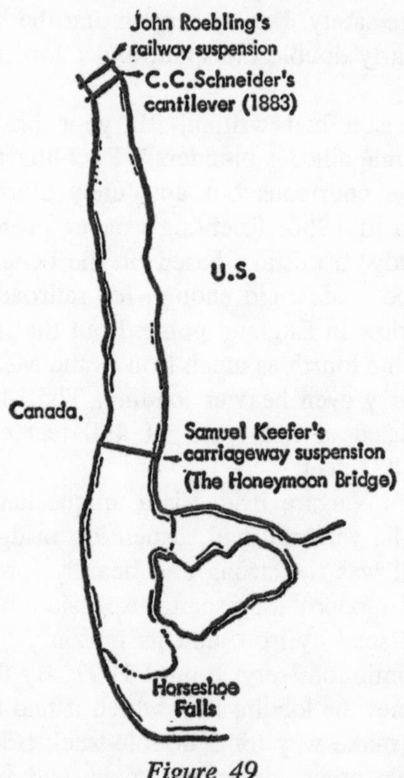

Figure 49

Roebling's bridge, incidentally, failed to win the unqualified approval of that indefatigable traveler, Mark Twain, who noted:

> You drive over to Suspension Bridge and divide your misery between the chances of smashing down two hundred feet into the river below, and the chances of having a railway-train overhead smashing down onto you. Either possibility is discomforting taken by itself, but, mixed together, they amount in the aggregate to positive unhappiness.

Mark Twain to the contrary notwithstanding, Niagara made the fortune of both the suspension bridge and John Roebling. Two major commissions soon followed, at Pittsburgh and Cincinnati. The Pittsburgh bridge was to replace the one Andrew Carnegie ran across in his messenger-boy days. In the new construction, Roebling had the assistance of a brand new engineer, one of the first graduates of Rennselaer Polytechnic Institute, a pioneer among America's engineering colleges. This young man, who had written his senior thesis on "Design for a Suspension Aqueduct," was Washington Roebling, as engagingly American as his father was severely German. Father and son were alike, one might say, only in their work; Washington, like John Roebling, was heart and soul a believer in the suspension principle, and like his father he possessed a combination of determination and thoroughness that fortified his natural intellectual power.

The Allegheny Bridge, designed by John Roebling, was constructed largely under the supervision of Washington. Suspension cables were strung by a traveling wheel hung from an endlessly moving rope that journeyed back and forth from shore to shore over the towers 4200 times in stringing the two main cables, and 1400 times from anchorage to anchorage in stringing the two outside cables. The entire construction was completed in slightly more than a year, was financially successful as a toll operation from the start, and stood for thirty-two years before being replaced by a heavy steel truss to meet the enormously increased loadings, including electric streetcars, of 1891. So sound was it deemed that the company did not even carry insurance. Its only mishap came in 1881, when the flooring was damaged by a fire of mysterious origin. After considerable detective work, the incendiaries were discovered by John Harper, president of the bridge company; they were "those feathered English pests," the sparrows, whose innumerable nests had filled the underside of the spans with hay, straw, etc., which had been ignited by sparks from the smokestacks of steamboats passing at high water.

The Cincinnati Bridge took considerably longer to build—in fact even to get started. Steamboat interests opposed it for years, and in 1854, when it finally seemed that these could be overcome, the Licking Bridge disaster struck the project a nearly fatal blow. The Licking, a small suspension structure connecting Newport and Covington, Kentucky, collapsed in 1854 two weeks after opening, under a drove of trotting cattle. Coming four years after the famous collapse of Angers, France, under a marching regiment, and followed shortly by the fall of Ellet's Wheeling bridge, the Licking failure scared off Cincinnati bridge investors. Roebling himself was no little alarmed: "He feared the effects of trotting cattle on a suspension span more than he did any strains or vibrations that might be produced by heavy locomotives or speeding trains," Steinman says.

Eventually an energetic businessman named Amos Shinkle took charge, raised money, and put the Roebling father-and-son team to work. An engineering difficulty succeeded the financial one; on the Cincinnati shore the clay bank had washed away and had been replaced by dirt from cellar excavations as the town grew. This "made ground" was very soft and pervious; as the bridge foundation was sunk, water from under the city flowed into the huge excavation; while the Roeblings struggled vainly to pump out their cofferdam, the city's residents complained that their wells were running dry. John Roebling finally designed his own big pumps, powered by Amos Shinkle's tugboat, *Champion No. 1,* and carried his foundation to gravel, abandoning his original intention of planting it on bedrock. The problem was almost solved when the Panic of 1857 swept the country. Suddenly it was not possible to collect payment for stock already subscribed, let alone to sell bridge bonds. The bridge came to a complete standstill. By the time financial conditions improved enough to permit resumption, another outside event intervened—the Civil War.

The war was an outside event from the point of view of the bridge, but not from that of Washington Roebling. Enlisting as a private the day after Lincoln's call for volunteers, he was soon commissioned lieutenant and transferred to General McDowell's staff as an engineering officer. In the spring of 1862 he designed and built his own first suspension bridge, at Front Royal across the Shenandoah, teaching soldiers how to build piers and rig cables with wire rope ordered from the family plant at Trenton. After the summer's campaign, during which he was present at the battles of Antietam and South Mountain, he built a bridge over the Rappahannock at Fredericksburg and another at Harpers Ferry. In the spring of 1863, after the battle of Chancellorsville, Lieutenant Roebling became one of history's first airborne soldiers, ascending every morning in a balloon to reconnoiter the enemy army across the Rappahannock. He was the first to discover Lee's movement westward toward the mountains, whence the Confederate general carried out his invasion of Pennsylvania.

A month later, Lieutenant Roebling, attached to the staff of the Army's Chief of Engineers, Major-General Warren, was standing on Little Round Top, a wooded hill on the extreme left of the Union line at Gettysburg, watching the puffs of smoke that marked the fire fight raging in the Peach Orchard below. Warren suddenly perceived that Hood's Texans, on the extreme Confederate right, were swinging well wide of the Union line, and heading straight for the hill on which he and Roebling stood. Racing down the other side of the hill, Warren and Roebling caught some Union regiments just arriving on the field and led them back up barely ahead of the advancing Confederates. Lieutenant Roebling helped drag the first guns up. Most historians have called the repulse of the Confederates from Little Round Top the turning point of the battle. Two days later, Lee's shattered army began its retreat to Virginia and on the same Fourth of July, Vicksburg surrendered to Grant, whose campaign had been powerfully abetted by the ironclads of James Eads. Thus the future builders of America's two greatest bridges contributed to the double climax of the Union victory. No mere coincidence either, in a war fought between the engineering-industrial society of the future and the hand-labor agrarian society of the past.

Serving with Warren through the bloody campaign of 1864, young Roebling was promoted to captain, then major and aide-de-camp. During the siege of Richmond he distinguished himself in the raid that destroyed the Weldon Railroad line. Shortly after this exploit, on January 1, 1865, his commission expired. Having received word that his father needed him badly in Cincinnati, he left the army, receiving a brevet as full colonel and a citation for "gallant and meritorious service." Not only that, he got a wife, too—Emily Warren, sister of the general, who was to prove herself a woman of exceptional fortitude and intelligence in the terrific adventure that lay a few years ahead.

Colonel Roebling arrived in Cincinnati to find the suspension towers under way. Paradoxically, Confederate General Morgan's cavalry raids into Ohio had stimulated Cincinnati's desire for a bridge to Kentucky, to facilitate movement of troops. Two 230-foot towers were completed under Washington Roebling's supervision by September 1865; the bridge span between them was a record 1057 feet. The cable-stringing was done by means of a flatboat; the 2½-inch wire rope from the Trenton factory was passed over the tower saddle and coiled in the bottom of the boat. As the boat crossed the river, the wire it trailed was allowed to sink to the bottom so that it would not interfere with the passing river steamers; then it was hoisted over the opposite tower and drawn up. The first step was a 27-inch-wide wooden service bridge; an old gentleman seeing it remarked sourly, "After all the talk about a fine bridge, it is a very flimsy affair."

For the real bridge, John Roebling as usual took solid precautions to insure rigidity and horizontal stability. "Every [diagonal] stay constitutes the hypotenuse of a rectangular [right] triangle, whose short sides are formed by the tower and by the floor," he pointed out (*Figure 50*).

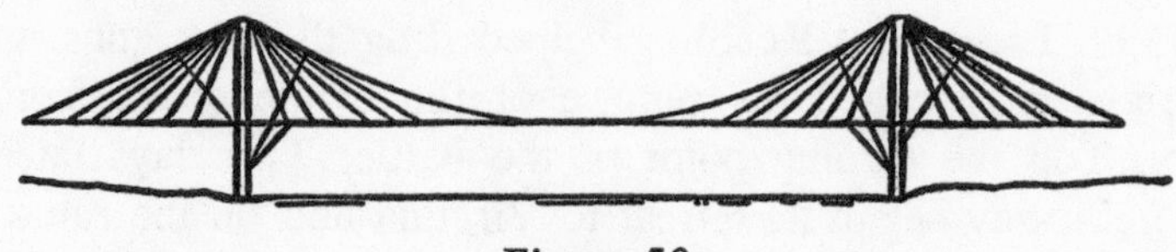

Figure 50

"To further guard against injurious oscillations which might be produced by the blow of a hurricane, eight heavy counter or check stays are anchored to the towers below the level of the lower cornice [just below the level of the roadway] and run up to the cables. Their sole office is to counteract any undulations which may be imparted to the cables by a severe gale."

The opening of the "biggest bridge in the world" on December 1, 1866, drew huge crowds; tickets were sold, and forty-six thousand people crossed by sunset, one hundred and twenty thousand the next day.

The Cincinnati Suspension was as well built as Roebling claimed. Seventy years later, in the great flood of 1937, it was the only span kept open over the Ohio between Steubenville and the Mississippi. Fire engines from Michigan and Ohio crossed it to go to the aid of flood victims in Kentucky.

It was a good bridge, the best as well as the biggest bridge of its day, but it was neither revolutionary in design nor formidably difficult in execution. Engineering is the art of the efficient, and the success of an engineering project often may be measured by the absence of any dramatic history. But certain engineering achievements soar above the level of technical excellence, not only dazzling their contemporaries, but also, even after the passage of decades or centuries, retaining a quality of grandeur. There is a strain of classic tragedy in this grandeur of the Pyramids, the Pont du Gard, the Simplon Tunnel, the Brooklyn Bridge. Somehow they suggest suffering and death as well as creation and life. In Yeats's words, "a terrible beauty is born."

18.

The Brooklyn Bridge: Grandeur and Tragedy

On the ferry-boats the hundreds and hundreds that cross,
returning home, are more curious to me than you suppose,
And you that shall cross from shore to shore years hence
are more to me, and more in my meditations, than you
might suppose.

Others will see the shipping of Manhattan north and west,
and the heights of Brooklyn to the south and east,
Others will see the islands large and small;
Fifty years hence, others will see them as they cross,
the sun half an hour high,
A hundred years hence, or even so many hundred years hence,
others will see them,
Will enjoy the sunset, the pouring-in of the flood-tide,
the falling-back to the sea of the ebb-tide.

—*Walt Whitman:* "Crossing Brooklyn Ferry."

AT THE time Whitman wrote, Brooklyn businessmen already were talking about replacing the famous ferry with a bridge. The East River, the strait dividing Long Island from Manhattan, is sixteen hundred feet wide at downtown New York, about the same width as the Mississippi at St. Louis. Essentially the same problems would have to be met. The cost must be kept within the limits of reasonable financing, navigation must not be obstructed, the bridge must carry railroad (in the form of rapid transit) as well as highway traffic.

Looking back to that point a hundred years ago, one is struck by a fact that seems far more extraordinary now than it apparently did then—James Eads and John Roebling solved twin bridge problems virtually simultaneously by totally different means, and each with epoch-making success.

Roebling first declared a suspension span at Brooklyn feasible in a letter to Abram S. Hewitt in June 1857. Hewitt was the partner of Peter Cooper in the latter's iron business in Trenton, where of course Roebling's own wire-rope factory was located. A leader in New York financial circles, Hewitt had Roebling's letter printed in the *Journal of Commerce*. Some years passed in discussion, largely on the financial question; in 1865, Roebling produced a design with an estimated cost of four million dollars. On December 21, 1866, a momentous meeting took place in what is now Owl's Head Park, Brooklyn, where a tablet commemorates the occasion. Present were William C. Kingsley, a Brooklyn businessman who long had been the principal proponent of a bridge, Alexander McCue, whom Kingsley had recently converted to the idea and who had arranged this meeting, and a powerful politician, State Senator Henry C. Murphy, who opposed the project. In a long question-and-answer session, Kingsley met all Murphy's objections with reasoned arguments derived from Roebling. A few weeks later, Murphy introduced the enabling act in the legislature. Its passage was facilitated by the weather—an exceptionally severe winter shut off ferry service for weeks at a time.

In the spring of 1867, John Roebling was appointed chief engineer for the Brooklyn Bridge, at a salary of eight thousand dollars a year.

His first task was to write a report to The New York Bridge Company. The company's name is interesting; the promoters of the bridge were Brooklynites, not New Yorkers; it was they who needed the bridge, and so they thought of it not as a bridge to Brooklyn, but as a bridge to New York. The aim of the report, of course, was to convince the financial community of the soundness of the enterprise. It was a remarkable document, revealing a grasp of the future given to few men in any field. Here are its highlights:

On the bridge site: "For the next fifty years to come, the City Hall Park will remain the great focus of travel, from which speedy communications will ramify in all directions." Despite slightly greater cost than other possible crossings, it was "the true route which will most favor the interest of the community, as well as of the Bridge

Company." Roebling foresaw future Williamsburg and Queensborough bridges farther north.

Span length: "Any span inside of 3000 feet is practicable. A span of 1600 feet or more can be made just as safe, and as strong in proportion, as a span of 100 feet. The larger span is not a question of practicability, but simply a question of cost." Roebling's prediction, of 3000-foot spans, which sounded fantastic in 1867, was surpassed sixty years later in the George Washington Bridge.

Approaches: Roebling worked out this very important problem for a metropolitan bridge in great detail, specifying fireproof flooring to serve as a roof for warehouses beneath.

Steel cables: To employ steel instead of iron wire for the cables was a "revolutionary proposal," Steinman says, much like Eads's dramatic introduction of the steel arch in St. Louis. As we have seen, the Board of Trade in Great Britain prohibited use of steel in any structures.

Storms: The Wheeling collapse was only eighteen years in the past, and many suspension bridges had blown down since. "To guard against vertical and horizontal oscillations," Roebling wrote, "and to insure that degree of stiffness essential to meet the effect of violent gales in such exposed situations, I have provided six iron trusses, which run the whole length of the suspended floor from anchor wall to anchor wall. . . . My system of design differs radically from that formerly practiced, and I have planned the East River Bridge with a special view to fully meet these destructive [wind] forces."

Stays and towers: The structural details of the Brooklyn Bridge long have gratified artists and architects. Roebling was by no means unmindful of the esthetic question. "In a work of such magnitude, and located as it is between two great cities, good architectural proportions should be observed. . . . The impression of the whole will be that of massiveness and strength." The stays, which radiate downward from the towers to the floor, have been one of the bridge's most admired artistic features. They also contribute signally to the span's enduring strength: Roebling pointed out that the stays alone would hold the bridge floor up, without the cables.

Foundations: Roebling conceded that it might be impossible to plant these on solid rock, in which case "other means" must be provided. Borings, he explained, were currently in progress to determine the level of the bedrock at the two tower foundations.

The Promenade: This very distinctive feature of Brooklyn Bridge, the broad walkway above the upper roadway, would, the builder predicted, "allow old and young to stroll over the bridge on fine days. . . . In a crowded commercial city such a promenade will be of incalculable value." It still is, though too few visitors to New York are aware of the incomparable view of the harbor from the Brooklyn Bridge promenade.

Cost: Roebling's estimate was realistic—seven million dollars, exclusive of acquisition of land for the approaches. Putting the rhetorical question of the bridge's value, he affirmed, "If the proposed bridge shall possess capacity of 40,000,000 annually, these 40,000,000 will be there as sure as the bridge is built." To speak of forty million people crossing the East River in a year sounded like science fiction in 1867, but today, with four other bridges and twelve tunnels in operation, the Brooklyn Bridge still carries twenty-five million passengers a year. Roebling convincingly explained how the bridge would pay for itself in the proposed railway passenger fares alone, quite aside from tolls for the vehicular roadways and promenade. And he accurately predicted that the increase in property values in Brooklyn would surpass the cost of the work in three years.

The report ended on a note of perhaps pardonable egotism: "The contemplated work, when constructed in accordance with my designs, will not only be the greatest bridge in existence, but it will be the great engineering work of this Continent and of the age." At practically the same moment James Eads was handing in his design for the St. Louis Bridge. In 1868 the world's first subway was driven by means of the Beach tunneling shield, and soon began operating experimentally hardly half a mile from the Brooklyn Bridge site. In the spring of 1869 the first transcontinental railway was joined. It was quite a time for engineering feats on this continent. Roebling's want of diffidence is probably a reflection less of vanity than of the need to reassure and inspire his backers. The daring bridge design stirred as much protest from engineers and skepticism among the public as that of Eads in St. Louis. It took most of the next two years for Roebling to win final approval by a Board of Consulting Engineers. A commission of Army engineers also gave its indispensable imprimatur, specifying an elevation of 135 feet. A Federal enabling act was passed by Congress, and in the early summer of 1869 the final detailed survey began.

It was at this point that tragedy—and irony—struck. The Brooklyn Bridge plans were complete in every detail; they traced, as David Steinman asserted, the masterwork of a master builder, the crowning achievement of John Roebling's life. One morning in July, Roebling was standing on a cluster of piles at the Fulton Ferry slip on the Brooklyn shore, taking signals from an assistant on the New York side, with the object of locating the Brooklyn tower precisely. A ferryboat entering the slip crashed into the fender, forcing the fender rack against the piles. Roebling's foot was caught and crushed.

In that pre-drug medical age, recovery from such an injury, like recovery from a war wound, was a matter of pure luck. Roebling was not lucky; tetanus set in, and in two weeks he was dead. A robust sixty-three, he doubtless would have lived to a ripe age and completed many bridges besides the Brooklyn.

It was a case of the king is dead, long live the king. Colonel Washington Roebling, thirty-two years old, his father's chief assistant on the Cincinnati Bridge, already was engaged for the same role at Brooklyn. Perhaps less brilliantly original than his father, Washington Roebling nonetheless possessed engineering genius as well as skill and training; the Brooklyn Bridge gave him his opportunity to show it. Men who knew Washington Roebling in the war remembered him for his easy-going, unmilitary good humor and his sangfroid. When the irascible General Meade suddenly had pointed a finger and demanded, "What's that redoubt doing there?" Major Roebling's retort had been, "Don't know, sir, didn't put it there." Looking back late in life on the events of his childhood, he commented with dry humor, "I was baptized by the postmaster, Mr. Shilly, there being no preacher as yet—have perceived no ill effects therefrom."

On his father's death, Washington Roebling resigned his post as president of the wire-rope company in Trenton, leaving the firm in the hands of his two brothers, and from that day forward threw himself into the great bridge as passionately as ever his father would have done.

His first decision was to use pneumatic caissons to sink the tower foundations. James Eads, it will be recalled, had brought back the pneumatic-caisson idea from France and had launched his first caisson in the fall of 1869. Early in 1870, Colonel Roebling made a trip to St. Louis, and Captain Eads showed him the inside of one of his caissons at work. Acrimony developed later over what Eads thought a rather liberal borrowing of his ideas. However, the Brooklyn caisson actually was launched on March 19, 1870, and it seems fairly evident that Colonel Roebling had determined independently the main features of this so-novel engineering tool.

Sinking the caisson to its initial position at the ferry slip where John Roebling had met his fatal accident proved an unexpectedly difficult job. The material on the East River bottom at this point was not rock, but "hard pan"—a very dense, rocklike clay that actually had to be blasted with powder charges. It was not until the first of May that the caisson could be put in position. A few more weeks were spent building up the heavy timber roof, and completing the interior structure. Colonel Roebling's caisson differed somewhat from that of Captain Eads (*Figure 51*).

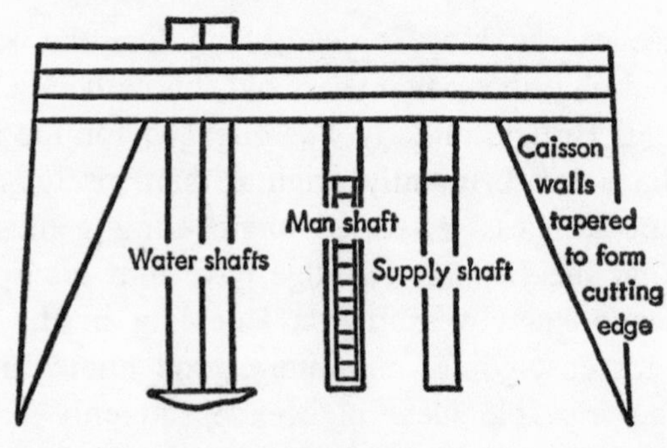

Figure 51

The man shaft and supply shaft had their airlocks close to the working chamber, as in Eads's caisson. The water shafts were those of Fleur St.-Denis. Material was shoveled into the pool and drawn up through the column of water by an endless chain of "grab buckets." But here the arrangement did not always work smoothly. Hardpan boulders got stuck under the edges of the shafts; a workman would then strip, dive into the water, and wrestle the boulder into position to be taken by the grab bucket. This difficult and hazardous feat was rendered somewhat easier by the compressed air; a man could stay under water as long as four minutes with his lungs full of compressed air.

Unlike the St. Louis bridge crew, the Brooklyn gangs did not work on Sundays. One Sunday the watchman on duty on top of the caisson did not notice that a leak had occurred in the little dam surrounding the pool in which the water shaft terminated. The water level of the pool inched down . . . and suddenly, with a roar that deafened persons outside, all the compressed air in the caisson escaped in one blast. A column of water and mud was flung five hundred feet in the air, raining splashes of mud on houses for blocks around. People poured from their houses and fled up Fulton Street, presently colliding with a crowd from farther away running toward the waterfront to find out what had happened.

Only three men had been on the caisson (none inside it), and they all escaped serious injury, though frightened out of their wits. Amazingly, the caisson was not damaged. Air pressure had been only fifteen pounds above atmospheric; as this vanished, the airlock doors fell open, but no water entered the caisson, which had settled ten inches. The water shaft soon was refilled and air pressure restored.

The editor of *The American Artisan,* who visited the caisson at about this time, gave this picture:

> We passed into the shaft. The attendant shut down its circular cover, and told us not to be alarmed if we felt strangely. We told him we wouldn't, and he turned the brass handle of a valve. The compressed air from below came in with a sound like the rush of waters, and our ear drums felt as if to split. . . . This lasted but a very little while. A plate was removed from the center of the floor on which we stood, and under us was revealed the deep round shaft, having within it an iron ladder, upon which we descended to the space below, where the work of excavating underneath the caisson was being carried on.
>
> This work of excavation is very simple, albeit very hard for the laborers. . . . The bed of the excavation is slush and mud, slowly carried by shoveling to the apparatus by which it is removed. Numerous large boulders are met with, and are drilled and broken to fragments before being taken out. Small calcium lights throw steaming luminous jets into the corners where the workmen are busy, and sperm candles stuck in sockets fixed on iron rods serve as torches for visitors threading the planks laid down for paths in the submarine cavern. The mud and silt under foot, the dank wooden walls at the sides, the chambers dim in the scattered lights, and the laborers moving like good-natured gnomes in the shadows, complete the picture. . . . After ten minutes we come up the ladder to the air lock, the opening in the floor closed, another brass valve handle is turned, and not without some of the uncomfortable feelings incident to entering, the air is reduced to normal pressure and the cover of the shaft is thrown open.

The caisson did not rest simply on its sides; its enormous weight was borne largely by partitions inside it which were held up by blocks as the floor was dug away; then the workmen knocked out alternate blocks and the mass slowly settled on the remaining ones. The worst problem was the boulders—traprock, gneiss, sometimes even quartz. One of Roebling's assistants, E. F. Farrington, gave this vivid picture:

> Inside the caisson everything wore an unreal, weird appearance. . . . The pulse was at first accelerated, and then sometimes fell below the normal rate. . . . It became a great effort to speak. What with the flaming lights, the deep shadows, the confusing noise of hammers, drills and chains, the half-naked forms flitting about, with here and there a Sisyphus rolling his stone, one might, if of a poetic temperament, get a realizing sense of Dante's inferno. One thing was noticeable to me—time passed quickly in the caisson.

The caisson was sinking at a rate of only six inches a week under the handicap of the hard river bottom. Colonel Roebling determined to try the effects of blasting inside the caisson—a potentially very dangerous expedient never before attempted. He first fired his revolver several times, then tried small blasts of gunpowder, and finally worked up to heavy charges. The experiments were successful, and blasting was introduced forthwith. Fire burns fiercely in compressed air, and several times small fires started despite vigilance. Careful prior preparations sufficed to deal with them.

The blasting filled the chamber with a dense cloud of smoke which was hard to disperse and added to the already thick gloom. This was ameliorated by using the new "smokeless powder" just invented by Alfred Nobel.

Three hundred and sixty men were employed in three shifts of eight hours each—eight solid hours, with mid-shift meal on the job. Pay was two dollars a day—two and a quarter after the caisson reached twenty-eight feet.

Despite all precautions, fires continued to break out. They were not really serious; if worst came to worst, the caisson could always be flooded, as it was early in the work. As the caisson sank into the hardpan of the river bottom, flooding became more difficult, so large hose connections were prepared. But the severe fire that finally struck the work in December 1870 upset all prevision. The oakum calking of the timber roof was ignited from inside the caisson, doubtless by one of the candles, and burned for several hours before being detected. This very heavy timbering (fifteen courses deep) was by now supporting an enormous weight of masonry (*Figure 52*). Immediately on the discovery of the insidious, charring, penetrating fire in this great mass of wood, Colonel Roebling was summoned. The

THE FORTH CANTILEVER

25. A bridge form dating back to ancient China and India, pioneered in Germany and America in the 1860s, 1870s, and 1880s, achieved its most powerful expression across Scotland's Firth of Forth in the wake of the Tay disaster. The huge cantilevers of the Forth contrast significantly with the slender viaduct over the Tay.

26, 27. *(Above)* To carry the world's first steel arch ribs across the Mississippi without obstructing the river with timber falsework, James Eads executed the world's first arch-cantilevering operation. The huge timber webs support the growing arches from above. Joining the arches was another critical problem to which Eads found an ingenious solution. *(Below)* The St. Louis Bridge stands in durable majesty after a century, chief monument to Captain James Buchanan Eads, an authentic American hero in peace and war.

THE BROOKLYN BRIDGE

28. Perhaps the most photographed of all bridges, the mighty masterpiece of John and Washington Roebling is caught here in a picture by G. A. Douglas which seems to echo the haunting poetry of Hart Crane:

> Through the bound cable strands, the arching path
> Upward, veering with light, the flight of strings,
> Taut miles of shuttling moonlight syncopate
> The whispered rush, telepathy of wires . . .

THE STEEL ARCH

29, 30. *(Above)* Naked in an industrial setting, O. H. Ammann's Bayonne Bridge, longest steel arch in the world, spans the Kill Van Kull between Staten Island, New York, and Bayonne, New Jersey. *(Below)* Ornate and sophisticated, the steel-arch Pont Alexandre III, built in 1895, is one of Paris' handsomest crossings.

THE CONCRETE ARCH

31, 32. The arrival of the bridge as an art form was signaled by designs in reinforced concrete, a structural material developed in France in the 1860s but not really exploited till the twentieth century. *(Above)* One of the three arches of the Brest-Plougastel Bridge, designed by Eugene Freyssinet, under construction in 1929. *(Below)* One of Robert Maillart's inspired Swiss creations, over the Arve at Geneva.

GALLOPING GERTIE'S
DANCE OF DEATH

33. *(Above)* The Tacoma Narrows Bridge, built in 1940, was long and narrow, and was stiffened by a shallow plate girder. For four months its flexible length undulated noticeably but harmlessly. Then on the morning of November 7 the motion suddenly became torsional and violent, though the wind was only forty-two miles per hour. One side of the roadway and then the other rose and fell at increasingly sharp angles.

THE COLLAPSE OF
GALLOPING GERTIE

34. *(Right)* At 10:30 AM, one floor panel dropped out. The writhing contortions increased, the sides of the deck rising alternately nearly thirty feet. At eleven, with a crowd of spectators watching and amateur photographers and cameramen shooting, the climax arrived: a 600-foot section of roadway and girders tore loose and plunged down into Puget Sound. Note the single car marooned on the remaining portion of the deck, which fell ten minutes later.

A CANTILEVER CRASHES AT QUEBEC

35. This famous bridge disaster was recorded by camera twenty-four years before that of Galloping Gertie. On September 11, 1916, the suspended span was being raised to position by hydraulic jacks when something snapped, and the 5000-ton mass of steel dropped into the St. Lawrence, carrying eleven men to death. An amateur photographer caught the moment of impact.

36. The Tower Bridge, erected in London in 1894, is one of the first modern drawbridges. The drawspan is a double-leaf bascule; the side spans are eyebar suspensions.

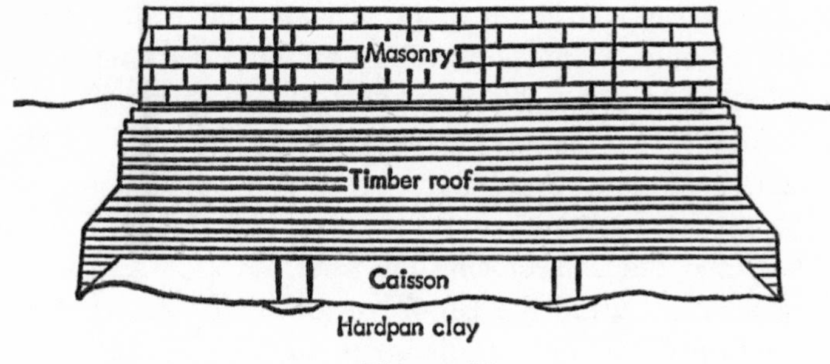

Figure 52

question he faced was how to keep the tower from crashing down through the weakened caisson roof. Washington Roebling spent the whole night fighting the strange, smoking, elusive fire; at five in the morning it seemed conquered, and he collapsed.

As a final precaution, he ordered several holes drilled upward into the roof timbering—two feet, three feet, finally four feet. At four feet, the bore suddenly opened up a mass of living coals. The unhappy decision to flood the caisson—a dangerous expedient at this depth, because the whole great mass might be wrecked—was taken by Colonel Roebling. Executing it was not simple, now that the huge rectangular cube nestled in the impermeable hardpan and clay. Harbor fireboats and Navy tugs had to be called in; by midday the caisson was flooded. It was left that way for two days and a half.

When the air pressure was restored and the water pushed out, it seemed at first that all was well. But the persistent odor of smoke over several weeks brought on further borings and though the fire was found to be thoroughly extinguished, its effects proved to have been far more destructive than had been imagined. Cement grout (liquid cement under pressure) was first squirted into the timber through drill holes. Then it was found necessary to cut away huge sections of the deep roofing to track down all the honeycomb vagaries of the fire.

Five big vertical cuttings were made upward from the caisson; workmen then crawled in among the courses of burned timber, scraped off the charred planks, and filled the crevices with cement.

It was a sobering experience, but Washington Roebling was finally able to report—though probably some people did not believe it —that "the burnt region has now been made fully as strong, if not stronger, than the rest of the caisson."

Two weeks later, one of the supply shafts blew out—a load of broken stone and gravel jammed the airlock, and with the air pressure escaping freely, Colonel Roebling and the working crew were trapped below as all the lights went out: "I . . . groped my way to the supply shaft where the air was blowing out. Here I was joined by several men in scraping away the heaps of gravel and large stones . . . which prevented the door from being closed." In a couple of minutes they succeeded in closing the door.

Other accidents marred the Brooklyn tower's history, but by May 1872 the masonry had been built up to seventy-five feet above the river and the foundation below was secure.

Altogether, the Brooklyn tower was difficult, novel and at times alarming—but it was the New York tower that became a landmark in bridge history.

The Brooklyn caisson rested on bedrock at only 44½ feet. The New York caisson would have to go to 78 feet. This was by no means as deep as Eads's pier and abutment foundations, but it was enough to require an air pressure of 35 pounds per square inch, and the bends made their frightful appearance.

By the time the disease struck, several very difficult problems had been met and mastered. The New York caisson was enormously greater than its Brooklyn counterpart—with its masonry tower complete, the whole thing weighed 53,000 tons. Keeping such a tremendous mass on perfectly even keel as it descended was tricky enough. But in addition, the New York side of the East River bottom was found to have some very special features. First of all, the surface layer was the former dumping ground for the city's garbage, and created an overpowering stench when exposed to the air inside the caisson. Many men actually were overcome and had to be carried out. It was necessary to keep the caisson a foot deep in water to make it bearable.

Once the garbage was dug through, the work progressed well. Colonel Roebling had conceived the ingenious idea of expelling sand from the bottom by means of compressed air. The caisson air had to be changed constantly in any case, and instead of allowing it to leak out under the sides, it was made to escape via a number of iron pipes terminating a foot from the bottom of the caisson. Sand was piled around a pipe's end, a valve was opened, and the compressed air in the caisson rushed up, carrying the sand with it. As the caisson sank farther, the increased pressure heightened the force of the escaping air; the sand, tearing up the iron pipe, did terrific abrasion damage before spouting hundreds of feet into the East River air. To minimize this, an elbow was put in the pipe, but the sand blast cut through a cast-iron elbow in an hour or less. A removable chilled-iron buffer finally solved the problem.

Accidents were surprisingly few. One boatman in the river had a finger shot off by a pebble blasting out of the pipe end.

Next came quicksand. The grab buckets in the water shafts could not handle this material, which was either so fine as to leak out of the buckets or appeared in combination with stones so hard as to defy grabbing. The sand had to be shot up through the sand pipes, and these now frequently were clogged by the stones. At seventy feet the very slow progress was complicated by the contour of the bedrock just below, composed of irregular projections and depressions, with a difference in elevation of 16 feet.

While these final problems were being solved, men were dying. The first fatality occurred on April 22, 1872; two more followed. Over a hundred men were seized with bends serious enough to require medical treatment—such as it was. Colonel Roebling engaged a young doctor named Andrew H. Smith, who prescribed a set of strict health rules which had nothing to do with the disease—eat well, get enough sleep, don't drink, wear warm clothing, etc. Did Dr. Smith not know anything of what Dr. Jaminet in St. Louis had discovered? Apparently not. As we have seen, Dr. Jaminet's inspiration about slow decompression had reduced miraculously the toll of caisson disease on the deep East Abutment at St. Louis. The efficacy of Dr. Smith's rules—formulated a year later—may be compared with that of Dr. Jaminet's thus:

	New York tower of Brooklyn Bridge	*East Abutment of St. Louis Bridge*
Depth	78 feet	136 feet
Air pressure	35 pounds	50 pounds
Cases of bends	110	28
Fatal cases	3	1

There is room for grim speculation in the report that Colonel Washington Roebling had an acrimonious falling-out with Captain James Eads during the nearly parallel construction of the two great bridges. Very possibly if the Colonel had remained on better terms with the Captain, Dr. Smith would have profited from Dr. Jaminet's discovery. Perhaps some of the appalling toll the bends took of sandhogs on New York's under-river tunnels—one death a month on the

Hudson Tubes—would have been cut down. And perhaps Washington Roebling would not have been carried helpless out of his New York caisson on a summer day in 1872, paralyzed for life.

The underwater work was practically finished when the thirty-five-year-old colonel was stricken. The big New York caisson was already firmly in position on the irregular rockbed and nearly filled with concrete. The last workers ascended by means of the emptied water shafts. Both foundations stood rooted in the riverbed.

But ahead lay an enormous amount of work demanding the most exacting knowledge and foresight. John Roebling was dead; Washington Roebling lay in his apartment on Columbia Heights, racked with pain and scarcely able to talk.

It would be romantic to imply that no engineer in America could have finished the Brooklyn Bridge if Washington Roebling had perished. What is indisputable is that none could have done it so well, and considering the precarious financial situation—the cost was running over John Roebling's seven million dollar estimate by a good two million—it is very possible that completion might have been postponed indefinitely.

But Washington Roebling's determination to finish the Brooklyn Bridge himself reflects something deeper in man's psychology than response to social-economic pressure. A man gets involved in a creation to a point at which he simply cannot let go whether it is keeping him alive or killing him. The man whose lighthearted courage had distinguished him during the war now fought with a courage that was far from lighthearted; nearly every motion was torture. Sometimes the sound of a strange voice was unbearable.

The nineteenth century, which bore the Horatio Alger myth, also created the image of the wife who stands behind every successful man. Emily Warren Roebling, sister of a famous soldier, in the hour of crisis played the heroine. She nursed her husband as any wife would, and while she was nursing him she learned mathematics and engineering. In a few weeks she was able to take his memoranda down, to transmit his orders to his assistant engineers, to visit and inspect the work, to carry his instructions to the staff. She became his eyes, hand, and voice.

From the apartment on Columbia Heights the crippled engineer scanned the rising towers through field glasses, while through his intelligent and devoted wife, he made the intricate and ponderous work follow his commands. David Steinman, the brilliant engineer who wrote a knowledgeable and impressively conscientious biography of the Roeblings, hit on a felicitous metaphor: Washington Roebling was like a wounded general, who from his hilltop command post still directed the battle through a skilled and unflinching chief of staff.

In the summer of 1873, Washington and Emily Roebling went to Germany in search of the therapeutic waters that doctors of that day confidently recommended. The journey apparently did no good, but the crippled engineer and his tireless wife immediately resumed supervision of the tower construction.

Each of the stupendous piles of masonry took five years to build; the Brooklyn tower was finished in June 1875, the New York tower in July 1876. Behind each tower, on the land, a huge anchorage block was erected in the heel of which were imbedded the four giant anchor plates that would hold the four cables. The Roeblings, Steinman points out, somehow correctly figured that the wires themselves should not be imbedded in the masonry, but should be connected with wrought-iron-bar chains. Later bridges built with the cables themselves imbedded in masonry anchorages suffered disastrously from corrosion.

In the summer of 1876 the preparatory work for the cable spinning was executed; the temporary cables, traveler ropes, cradle ropes, footbridge cables, etc., were strung, all under the minute supervision of the colonel in his command post on Columbia Heights. The wire ropes for these temporary cables were made at the plant of John A. Roebling's Sons in Trenton—after competitive bidding.

Because shipping in the busy waterway could not be interrupted, carrying the first wire ropes across the river was a trick. The giant reel carrying the first traveler rope rested on a scow in front of the Brooklyn tower while the free end of the rope was drawn up over the tower and back to the anchorage nine hundred feet away. Trestles had been erected along the route, and men were stationed on the roofs of buildings to pass the rope along. The end having been secured at the anchorage, the next step was taken; the scow was towed across the river while the strand behind it was permitted to sink to the bottom. At the New York side, the end of the rope was passed over the New York tower and fastened to the hoisting engine at the tower base. Lifting the cable off the riverbed originally had been scheduled for a Sunday morning when the river traffic was light, but the engineers decided that they could bring it up in a few minutes' interval during a week day, and this they did on August 14. Crowds were gathered on shore and in boats; Colonel Roebling's glasses were trained on the scene from Columbia Heights. The engineer on the scene waited for enough open water to give the signal; a cannon shot was fired to warn shipping, and in a few seconds the rope broke the surface on both sides, a cascade of sparkling drops marking its swift rise. The space of water between the two visible parts of the rope narrowed until, amid cheers of spectators and workmen, it vanished and the cable broke free, rising higher and higher till it hung above all the masts below. Later in the day the second traveler rope was raised.

On August 25, E. F. Farrington, the master carpenter of the bridge, rode across by Bos'n's chair while thousands of spectators squinted and gasped. Ferryboats stopped in the middle of the river; whistles sounded up and down the waterfront; men and boys shouted, ladies shrieked and waved their handkerchiefs. Farrington waved his red bandanna in response. Nearing the New York side, his ride became almost perpendicular, and he stood up in his chair, as the cheering reached a crescendo. Farrington was the hero of the hour, and had to dodge hysterical crowds seeking to carry him on their shoulders. The pioneer crossing was a sort of 1875 version of the more grandiose flights of Lindbergh and the astronauts. Farrington was indeed something of a record-setter; he had also been first man across John Roebling's Niagara and Cincinnati cableways.

A temporary catwalk soon was constructed, not a straight suspended walkway such as had been built at previous suspension-bridge sites, but a free-curving structure that followed the cables. This was an idea of Washington Roebling's to save the need of dangerous rope ladders. The catwalk was strengthened against lifting wind force by "inverted" cables underneath it, curving in an arch form. It worked; while the footbridge over the Ohio had been blown down three times in a few months, that over the East River withstood gales for its two years of existence.

In his 1867 report, John Roebling had made the revolutionary proposal of steel cables. Nine years later Washington Roebling stuck to his father's decision; steel, though never before used for suspension cables, was "the metal of the future." He specified a tested strength of 160,000 pounds per square inch, nearly double the strength of the iron wire his father had used at Niagara and Cincinnati. The wire was galvanized—coated with zinc—to protect it against rusting in the briny atmosphere of the East River, a precaution some later engineers neglected, to their bridges' cost.

As soon as the long, curved catwalk was finished, it attracted visitors by the thousands. Some found it exhilarating, others were terrified and had to be helped back, and a few at least took an intelligent interest in the novel engineering process that was being carried on. From the spinneret atop the Brooklyn anchorage, the strands of each cable emerged, carried by a "traveling wheel" that crossed and recrossed the traveling rope, climbing up over the Brooklyn tower, descending in a gentle curve to the middle of the river, rising again toward the distant New York tower, then descending over the rooftops to the New York anchorage (*Figure 53*).

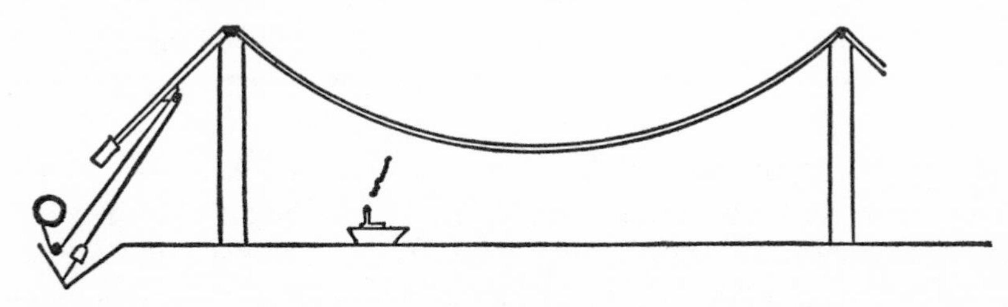

Figure 53

The traveling wheel carried a loop of wire which drew out longer and longer as the wheel progressed away from the Brooklyn anchorage; at the New York anchorage, this loop was cast over a strand shoe and the wheel sent back empty while a second wheel brought another double wire over from Brooklyn. Each wire was continuous for the whole cable strand. Each cable strand of nearly three hundred wires was bound together parallel, without twisting. Nineteen strands bound together formed each cable. The number nineteen was not chosen at random. John Roebling had made his cables of seven strands arranged in a hexagon with one strand in the middle, and compacted together. Washington Roebling took his father's pattern and added twelve strands around it, keeping the hexagonal form.

In the summer of 1878 the bridge made headlines with two sensational incidents. First, the wire contractor, J. Lloyd Haigh of New York, who had narrowly underbid Roebling's Sons of Trenton, was caught in a barefaced fraud. When wire was rejected after testing, it was sent to a certain part of the Haigh warehouse in New York; when wire was approved, it was loaded on a wagon and taken straight to the bridge—or so everyone assumed. Actually the approved wire was taken around to the rear of the building and dumped. The wagon was then reloaded with rejected wire—and the good wire sent through the warehouse again and presented to the inspector to earn another certificate of inspection. This brazen swindle had been going on for some six months; many of the erected strands were full of the condemned wire. Colonel Roebling, who had sold his interest in his own family's company in order to permit it to bid on the cables, must have had a few remarks to make about the Haigh company's low bid. He finally decided against tearing up the already erected strands, and merely ruled that the contractor had to place additional good wires at his own expense in sufficient number to make up for the calculated loss of strength.

The second sensational incident came while the Haigh fraud was under investigation. A cable strand about to be fixed in the New York anchorage suddenly broke loose and, carrying its big cast-iron shoe and attachments, swept from the anchorage, knocking off several men and flying in a tremendous nine-hundred-foot leap all the way to the yard under the New York tower, grazing houses and buildings en route. For an instant it lay in the yard amid the startled workmen, then up it jumped again as the weight of the sagging strand in midstream yanked it, snaking in a flash up the tower and over the top and plunging in a tremendous dive down into the river, where it narrowly missed a crowded ferryboat.

This accident, in which two men were killed and three injured, was only the most spectacular of a long succession of mishaps. Tools fell from the towers, killing or maiming; wrought-iron hooks straightened and dumped blocks of granite; hands were caught in cable-spinning machinery; men were blown off the towers in high winds.

With all the great problems solved and the bridge nearly completed, a storm broke over the head of the paralyzed engineer in Columbia Heights. The bridge cost already had exceeded estimates, and with the acquisition of the land approaches, the whole bill was running above thirteen million dollars. The original private bridge company had been liquidated and the whole financing taken over by the two municipalities, a foreshadowing of modern public "bridge authority" financing.

In 1881, simmering public dissatisfaction with the bridge's cost came to a head over the disclosure that an additional thousand tons of steel had been put into the trusses to make the floor (which, incidentally, was all-steel) rigid enough to carry heavy locomotives and cars. Exactly why this decision, very wise and farseeing, was taken is not clear; Washington Roebling and some of the trustees (directors of the municipal authority) made it, and so guaranteed the bridge's great twentieth-century future. At the moment, however, it was a strategic error. Robert B. Roosevelt led a violent attack in the Board of Trustees; the New York *Times* denounced the engineers' "stupidity" and foolishly asserted that the added weight would weaken the bridge.

The *Engineering News* answered the attacks in sensible and restrained language:

> The cost of a few additional tons of steel . . . is in reality but a healthy outgrowth of expanded ideas of the importance of this structure. In the fourteen years since the bridge was designed, enormous strides have taken place, in the volume, weight and character of railroad intercommunication. . . . The bridge, when designed, was in advance of the highway bridges of the day. . . . City travel, as then conducted, required cars of but two or three tons weight. . . . We believe that it is entirely owing to what the *Times* is pleased to consider as the stupidity of the present engineers that the structure will be capable of withstanding all the strain which by any possibility it can be subjected to. . . .

Nevertheless, the idea that the added weight would prove too much for the cables spread insidiously, until the trustees adopted a motion of Robert Roosevelt's to request a statement on the strength of the cables from the Chief Engineer. Washington Roebling submitted a report in which he gave the margin of safety of the cables as four—that is, the cables would support four times the total anticipated dead and live loading. By way of emphasis, he mentioned that if the bridge were overloaded, the cables would be strong enough to uproot the anchorages.

The attacks persisted. In 1882 the trustees called on Colonel Roebling to appear in person and answer criticism. The Colonel replied that "everyone knows I am sick, and they must be as tired as I am of hearing my health discussed in the newspapers." He asserted that despite his handicap he was doing his job and that any delays in construction were owing solely to the often retarded delivery of steel. His reply did not save him from a resolution naming his first assistant, C. C. Martin, Chief Engineer, and himself, as consolation, Consulting Engineer.

The American Society of Civil Engineers was meeting in New York. Washington Roebling wrote out his defense of himself and his bridge, and Emily Warren Roebling, profiting from an unheard-of concession from the august and very masculine body, read it. The engineers and the whole public were won over.

The bridge was finished. Alfred Ely Beach's *Scientific American* called it "the grandest piece of engineering the world has yet seen," and a parade with the Seventh Regiment in dress uniform, the United States Marines, Governor Grover Cleveland, and President Chester A. Arthur (Garfield had just been assassinated) marched down Broadway to City Hall Plaza, wheeled left, reached the bridge portal, and moved across the bridge as cannon, from Governor's Island to the Brooklyn Navy Yard, fired a salute. On the Brooklyn side there were speeches.

And up on Columbia Heights Colonel Roebling sat at his window with Emily, watching through field glasses.

The crippled hero lived to see his bridge finished, and, astonishingly enough, for long afterward, too. He and Emily retired to a house near Troy, New York, where he made a partial recovery from his affliction. Presently they moved to Trenton, to be near the family business and the family. Emily Roebling died in 1903; Washington lived alone with the house and the servants for five years, and then, rather surprisingly, married a second time, a Charleston, South Carlina belle named Mrs. Cornelia Witsell Farrow, who proved quite as devoted as Emily Warren.

Meantime the other two Roebling brothers, themselves exceptionally able men, built their father's firm to a forty million dollars a year volume by the end of the First World War, diversifying production even to the point of manufacturing automobiles for several years—their Mercer Raceabout is a collector's item today. The deaths of the two elderly heads of the firm within a few months of each other created a crisis. Who took over? Colonel Washington Roebling, eighty-four years old. He went to the office every morning by streetcar, having recovered some of the use of his body while at the same time acquiring a distrust for automobiles. He changed the plant from steam to electric power, accepted and completed the contract for the Bear Mountain Bridge cables, and directed the company's affairs until his nephews were able to take over. He lived on to the age of eighty-nine.

By that time Brooklyn was a city of two million people, and some hundred million passengers a year were crossing by bridge to New York in subway trains, streetcars, and automobiles.

And by that time a differently gifted and differently tortured young man named Hart Crane occupied the apartment on Columbia Heights whence Washington Roebling had scanned the tower-building and cable-spinning in the river below. Looking down on the marvelous bridge, he created another kind of masterpiece . . .

Again the traffic lights that skim thy swift
Unfractioned idiom, immaculate sigh of stars,
Beading thy path—condense eternity:
And we have seen night lifted in thine arms.

Under thy shadow by the piers I waited;
Only in darkness is thy shadow clear.
The City's fiery parcels all undone,
Already snow submerged an iron year . . .

O Sleepless as the river under thee,
Vaulting the sea, the prairies' dreaming sod,
Unto us lowliest sometime sweep, descend,
And of the curveship lend a myth to God.

19.

The Monster in the Firth of Forth

IN THE nine years from 1874 to 1883, the two terrific feats of St. Louis and Brooklyn, one might say, pulled bridge engineering all the way from the eighteenth to the twentieth century. During the same nine years, Ashtabula, the Tay, and dozens of lesser failures had thrown the engineering profession into a state of confusion, not to mention their effect on the public. In the United States, the older generation of "engineers," few of whom held degrees from engineering schools, carefully guarded their trusted "formulas" while promoters and salesmen continued to paint rosy pictures of solid, beautiful structures in iron, or even wood and iron.

In Britain the words of Samuel Smiles on the Britannia Bridge about "the perfection of our tools, the ability of our mechanics . . . the improvements in iron manufacture . . . the genius of the railway engineer . . . the collective mechanical genius of the English nation" now were reversed. British engineering, British workmanship, and British iron manufacture were all under a cloud.

One of the first results of the catastrophe, as we have seen, was the cancellation of Sir Thomas Bouch's design for the Firth of Forth bridge. A second was the hasty new regulation from the Board of Trade on wind pressure.

It might be thought that the shock of the tragedy, plus the new requirement from the Board of Trade, would have postponed the Tay Bridge reconstruction. On the contrary, it was rebuilt at once and the Forth Bridge undertaken very shortly. The explanation of this paradox is simple; the one thing the Tay Bridge had demonstrated clearly in its brief career was that it paid.

"The doubts and questions which had been raised prior to the erection of the first Tay viaduct were now far from being brought forward as objections to the preparation of plans for reconstructing it," a contemporary observed. The first plan for reconstruction even included use of Sir Thomas Bouch's old pier foundations, strengthened by arch connections with parallel new foundations. The new railroad was to be double-tracked, decisively improving the bridge's stability and reflecting the economic success of the line.

Doubt about the piers led the railroad to ask an eminent engineer for a report. The man they chose was William Henry Barlow, one of the three members of the Board of Inquiry. Barlow carried out experiments on the old piers, and though he found them fully up to their designed strength (a sad little minor vindication of Thomas Bouch), he recommended a completely fresh start. In 1881 Parliament passed a bill approving a bridge sixty feet west (upstream) of the old one. In Barlow's design, the new piers were placed directly opposite the old in order to leave the navigation openings the same. But Barlow proposed to lower the bridge from one hundred feet above high water to seventy-seven, which brought immediate, violent outcries from Perth shippers. The North British, however, was more than ready to accommodate, and soon achieved a treaty agreement with the Perth Town Council, written out and signed, in which among other things the railroad promised to tow large vessels under the bridge.

William Henry Barlow, presently Sir William, used a great deal more metal in his bridge than Thomas Bouch had. But he used the same material, iron, and in fact to a large extent, identically the same material, the very iron of Thomas Bouch's girders, taken down and re-erected. Instead of box girders, Barlow used bowstrings from 20 to 30 feet deep. There were two significant differences. Each of Barlow's High Girders (superstition notwithstanding, there were again thirteen of these, exactly opposite the fallen spans) weighed 500 tons, compared with 190 for their predecessors. Altogether, there was a weight of metal of 25,000 tons, more than twice that of the old bridge. Of this, 16,000 tons was new wrought iron, very much more resistant to buckling than cast iron. These heavy trusses carried a guarantee of wind resistance of 56 pounds per square foot, the Board of Trade's new standard, in place of Sir George Airey's airy 10 pounds. (Today, wind resistance requirements in all countries are considerably lower, which may or may not be altogether a good thing.) Part of this strong wind resistance at the New Tay was achieved by a feature perhaps more visible and dramatic than technically effective—a five-foot parapet helped protect the train of cars on the bridge from wind uplift.

The New Tay Viaduct was completed in Queen Victoria's Jubilee Year of 1887, reaffirming in some wise Britain's engineering and industrial power. But under way thirty miles to the south was a bridge project of truly imperial dimensions, one designed far to outlast such ephemerae as Queen Victoria's new title of Empress of India. It was "the biggest bridge in the world"—and in several senses it still is.

The Firth of Forth is a very different stream from the Firth of Tay. The Tay is only about eighty feet deep; founding piers with compressed-air caissons presented no serious difficulties. The Forth, on the other hand, is more than twice that deep, reaching a maximum of 218 feet in its north channel. Founding piers at such a depth was out of the question in that day; air pressure in the caissons would have had to be something like eighty pounds per square inch, far beyond working toleration.

But in the middle of the Firth lies the low, rocky isle of Inchgarvie. Sir Thomas Bouch had chosen this as a pier foundation, as Stephenson had used Britannia in the Menai Strait. By placing his central pier just north of the isle, on the submerged rock, an engineer could achieve two equal spans. But even placing his outer piers in the water as far offshore as he could get them, he was left with spans of 1600 feet. Thomas Bouch had proposed to build these as suspensions (*Figure 54*).

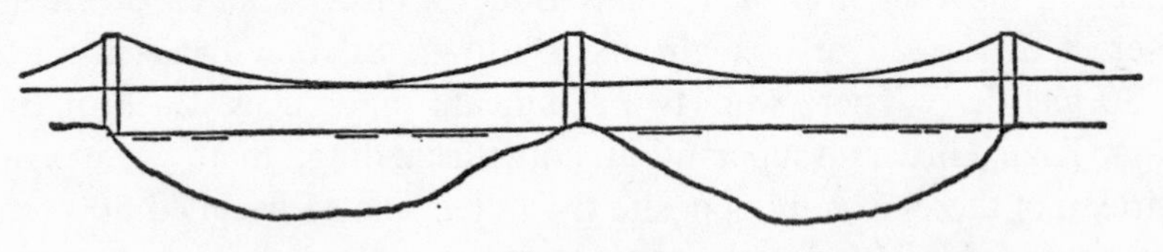

Figure 54

It was a daring design, but in view of the success of the Brooklyn Bridge's 1595-foot span there is no reason to conclude that it could not have been built. One may legitimately suspect Thomas Bouch's capacity to build it. He lacked the background in both practice and theory to design a suspension bridge strong enough for railroad loadings—his proposed cables were of course of iron—and he lacked Washington Roebling's character to drive such a project through with an inflexible insistence on high, rigid standards.

In any case, Thomas Bouch's preference was sufficient to condemn the suspension principle for the Forth. What everyone wanted was a design that Sir Thomas had had nothing to do with, and it happened that a young (fortyish) engineer in London named Benjamin Baker had one. Baker was an assistant to Sir John Fowler, consulting engineer of the North British Railroad. Baker had conceived his idea some years earlier, and though he had built no bridges, had expressed it in writing. For that matter, it was hardly new, being the ancient Chinese cantilever. But this Oriental form recently had made a very successful Occidental debut in Germany, where an engineer named Heinrich Gerber had built a highway bridge over the Main at Hassfurt in 1867. Gerber derived his idea largely from a combined arch and chain suspension design that another German engineer had proposed, but never built, to span the Bosporus, with piers in the stream.

Gerber's bridge was copied widely, especially in the United States, where the form was long known not as the cantilever but as the Gerber. Two notable examples of it were built by Charles Shaler Smith and C. C. Schneider over the Kentucky and Niagara rivers respectively. Shaler Smith's bridge was completed in 1877, Schneider's in 1883. A number of mixed types, including some combination suspension-and-cantilever, were built at the same time. The true cantilever, as pioneered by Gerber, Shaler Smith, and Schneider, had two salient advantages: first it avoided obstructing the river with falsework during construction (and in this respect, James Eads was the great pioneer); second, it provided a way around a very tricky problem of engineering mathematics. This is the problem of static determination, of calculating the exact stresses that will be placed on a bridge by loading. In a simple truss the loading is carried by the truss and its two end supports. A series of such trusses, each of which is fully determinate, may be built. But if one single "continuous" truss is given intermediate supports, the problem of calculating the stress at any given point suddenly becomes very intricate. George Shattuck Morison, who built a major truss bridge in two spans over the mouth of the Ohio and a great cantilever at Memphis, used continuous trusses for his approach spans at Memphis, but this was the only use of such trusses in the United States in the nineteenth century. Shaler Smith built a continuous truss over the St. Lawrence in 1888, the only continuous truss in North America until 1917 (*Figure 55*).

In Europe, engineering theory was somewhat ahead of its American counterpart, but even in Europe the continuous truss had a disad-

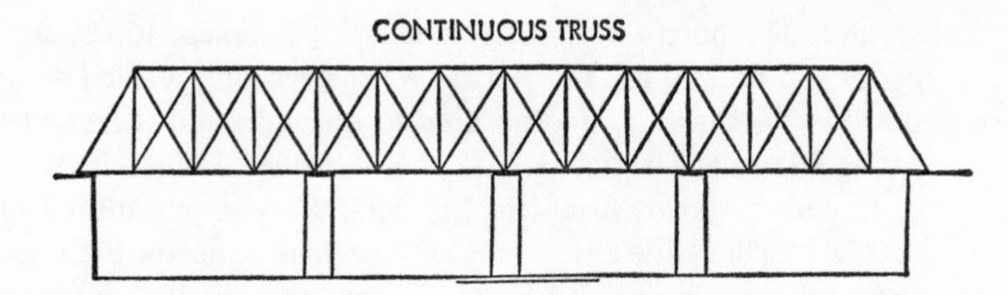

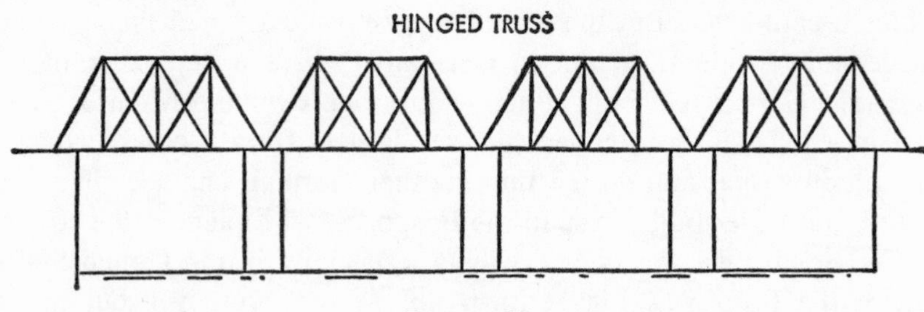

Figure 55

vantage. Resting on a number of supports, it demanded exceptionally careful foundation work, as the settling of any one foundation would affect the whole bridge.

Benjamin Baker pointed out that the cantilever provided a means of giving maximum strength to a truss bridge while keeping it statically determinate (*Figure 56*).

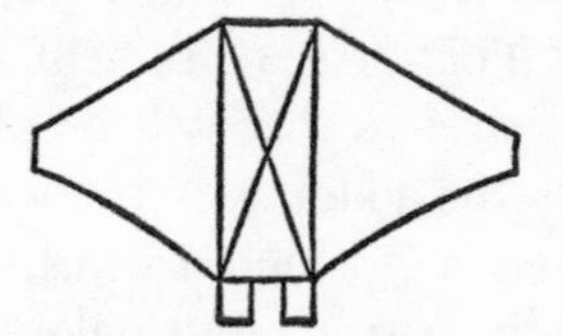

Figure 56

Two cantilevers, one on either shore, could support a short suspended span in the middle of the stream. With two cantilevers and a suspended span, Gerber supported a 425-foot truss over the Main, and Schneider's span over the Niagara was 495 feet. Now Benjamin Baker proposed a triple, rather than double, cantilever, of unheard-of size, with two suspended spans (*Figure 57*).

Each suspended span, resting in air 150 feet above high water in the Firth, was 350 feet long. Each of the three huge cantilevers, standing solidly on a pair of tremendous masonry pedestals, meas-

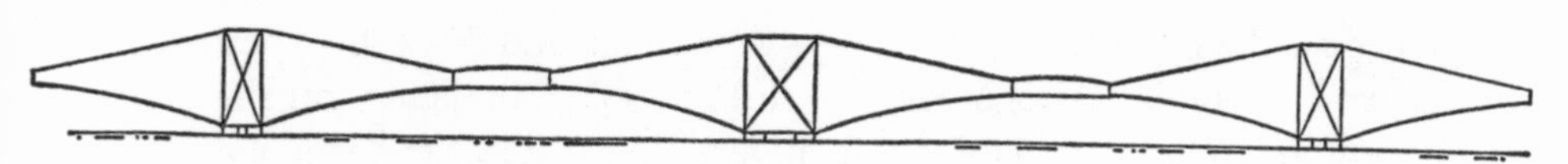

Figure 57

ured 1350 feet from end to end, making the two clear spans 1700 feet each. At their middles, over the piers, they stretched 350 feet deep; thus the cantilevers were as deep as the suspended spans were long. The giant spiderweb, whose biggest threads were tubes of 12-foot diameter, tapered down to the depth of the truss of the suspended span, itself a sturdy 50 feet deep.

Sir Benjamin Baker (he was knighted with no unhappy afterthoughts) never, in his numerous lectures on the Forth Bridge, referred to it as a cantilever (much less as a Gerber bridge), and where the name cantilever ("cant" plus "lever"?) came from is something of a mystery. But the Forth Bridge made the cantilever the great British long-span type. Even after the problem of static determination of a continuous truss had been solved by mathematicians, the cantilever kept its other advantage: non-obstruction of the stream. In the matter of strength versus economy, the Forth Bridge launched a debate that went on for several decades.

Whatever else it was, the Forth was not a cheap bridge. The amount of steel called for in Benjamin Baker's design was 42,000 tons, compared with only 11,000 tons of iron and steel in James Eads's St. Louis Bridge, and the steel ultimately used at the Forth amounted to the staggering total of 58,000 tons. The cost including the approach spans came to $16 million, making it even more expensive than the Brooklyn Bridge, the $13 million total of which had included expensive real estate acquisition, and more than twice the $6.5 million of the St. Louis. Thomas Bouch's suspension design for the Forth was estimated at $10 million.

The Forth Bridge is certainly a monster, and in more ways than sheer size, but its construction presented only moderate difficulties. Each of the great cantilever foundations was quadruple, and some of these had to be sunk fairly deep (maximum 88 feet) to hit bedrock in the appropriate position. This caisson work was subcontracted to an experienced French firm, Coiseau and Cie., which embarrassed, though only slightly, the Union Jack tone of Benjamin Baker's speeches. One caisson got stuck in the mud and caused some delay. But no such harrowing experiences as those of St. Louis and Brooklyn disturbed the work, on which American and French experience proved valuable. Altogether, the foundations, though requiring an enormous amount of labor and materials, exacted no particular enterprise or ingenuity.

Surprisingly, perhaps, neither did the stupendous superstructure. The big cantilever arms were built outward from the piers, the suspended trusses were developed from both sides, bit by bit. There were fifty-seven fatal accidents, but given the size of the labor force —4500 men at the height of the work—the death toll was perhaps not disproportionate. British engineering historian Shirley Smith comments that most of the fifty-seven fatal accidents "appear to have been due to carelessness or indifference," a callousness perhaps explained partly by the fact that the men were nearly all Italians and Belgians. The toll—far higher than for St. Louis or Brooklyn (or, incidentally, the Tay)—is another of the queerly huge statistics of the Forth Bridge. Like the others, it somehow leaves no deep impression. The man staggering erratically under the blow of a hammer dropped three hundred feet is as dead as the man carried vainly back into the airlock. But these "normal" construction accidents—very normal in the nineteenth century—miss the quality of mystery and horror of the deaths under the pressure of the Mississippi and the East River. The Forth, even in its tragedy, seems merely very large.

The bridge, which opened to traffic in 1890 in the heyday of pre-Raphaelite England, did not attract very warm critical notices from the esthetic side. William Morris, a poet of now-waning distinction, declared that "every improvement in machinery [was] uglier and uglier until they reached the supremest specimen of all ugliness, the Forth bridge." The criticism is reminiscent of that voiced at almost the same moment in Paris over the Eiffel Tower, whose creator, Gustave Eiffel, was a bridge-builder of note. Structural steel was not an instant artistic hit, yet as we shall see later in the George Washington Bridge, it eventually won surprising accolades.

Twentieth-century critics have thought the Forth a rather handsome monster, and more than one has been reminded of a dinosaur or sea serpent. Somehow, other cantilever bridges do not resemble it. This is partly because later ones were built more economically and present a less intricate crisscross of metal to the eye. Moviegoers may remember Robert Donat escaping from the train and climbing down the Forth truss in Alfred Hitchcock's thriller, *The Thirty-Nine Steps*. In its unique setting in the broad river mouth, it was a well-known landmark to British and American flyers in the Second World War, while German flyers dropped bombs that had hardly more effect than so many tennis balls.

A song popular with the personnel of Britain's Royal Air Force was possibly inspired by the cheerful sight of the triple-backed saurian skeleton:

We never flew no higher than five hundred ------- feet,
We always flew through snow and ice or even ------- sleet.
The compass always pointed south instead of ------- north,
And we made our ------- landfall on the Firth of ------- Forth.

The first steel bridge was of course the Eads bridge at St. Louis. The first to be built exclusively of the new metal was also an American achievement. In 1878, General William Sooy Smith, the first American engineer to use compressed air, bridged the Missouri at Glasgow, South Dakota, with a wholly steel structure that made a vitally important point—that an all-steel railroad bridge could be constructed economically. The suspicious and hostile railroads refused to pay the necessarily high tolls to use the Eads bridge for several years after its completion, and to their dishonor forced the St. Louis and Illinois Bridge Company into bankruptcy. But General Smith proved in 1878 that an all-steel truss made a first-rate railroad bridge, and the next year the Ashtabula disaster proved that the railroads could not afford to ignore the lesson.

Within a few years, steel bridges were going up not only all over America, but all over the world. The form, for virtually all short and medium spans, was the truss—the same triangles that sprang from the minds and hands of the New England carpenters who created the old covered bridge. Take a train anywhere in the world and you will cross a few of these steel versions of the designs of Timothy Palmer and his Yankee rivals. German engineers early adopted the Town lattice for the Dirschaubrücke over the Vistula on the Berlin-Königsberg line, six spans of 430 feet. These European metal copies of the covered bridge were riveted together. In America, where distances were longer and many bridges were built in sparsely populated districts, skilled labor often was in short supply. Pin connections were preferred because maximum fabrication could be done in the factory and the parts simply assembled in the field. Consequently, in America the favorite railroad bridge truss was the simplest, the Warren—named for a British engineer, but actually antedating the covered bridge itself, and going back to American and European barns and mills of the eighteenth century.

The Warren truss still is used widely today, but it has probably been surpassed in number of examples by a purely American type, the Pratt. Invented by Caleb and Thomas Pratt, another of the numberless father-and-son engineering teams, this was originally a wood-and-iron combination similar to the Howe, only in reverse, with the iron used for the diagonals, which in the Pratt design were in tension. This arrangement was a little less economical than the Howe, because the diagonals were longer than the vertical members, and iron was of course more expensive than wood. But, made all of iron, the Pratt truss was as satisfactory as any iron bridge, and in steel its simplicity made it a favorite.

The "continuous truss" is also a descendant of Robert Stephenson's iron tube over the Menai Strait. Given steel as a structural material, of course, no one would dream of building a solid tube, but today bridges still are built with solid, shallow side supports instead of deep trusses. These are known as "plate-girders," and are commonly used for short crossings, viaducts, high level expressways, etc. Most people erroneously assume that the stalwart parapets are there to keep automobiles from falling off. For a while the plate girder threatened to supersede the truss as a suspension-bridge stiffener, a development with very unexpected consequences.

The distinction between "cantilever" and "continuous truss" is frequently subtle (*Figure 58*).

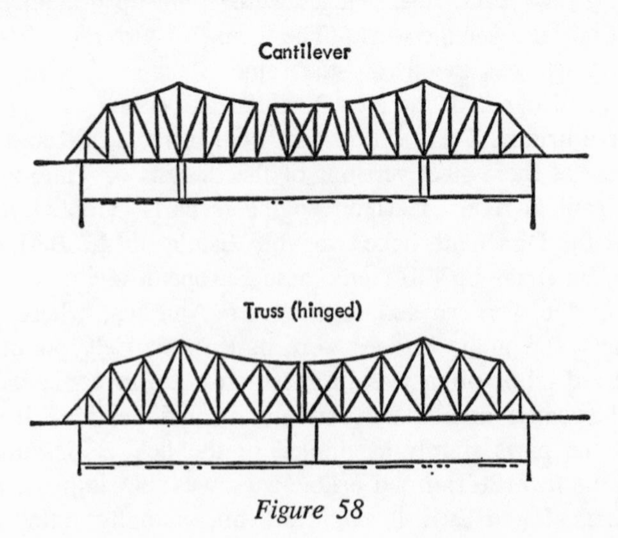

Figure 58

In any case, the railroad problem was solved. For bridge engineers, the nineteenth century was over, and the twentieth—the century of the automobile—was coming up. Bridge engineering was entering a new phase and heading for a new climax.

20.

Quebec: A Cantilever Crashes

As THE new century dawned, the question was no longer how to build a bridge, but which bridge to build. The revolution in structural materials had brought a proliferation of forms. As long as stone had been the solitary material considered for permanent bridges, the arch had ruled unchallenged. The Yankee truss gave wood an unexpected new life, though it is open to question whether a wooden bridge ever can be considered "permanent." The real significance of the truss, as we have seen, came in iron, and ultimately in steel. The arrival of steel—and incidentally, the development of numerous kinds of steel alloys with varying characteristics—created a real battleground of forms. The Firth of Forth proved the cantilever a sound answer to long-span construction. But was a cantilever better than a suspension bridge? Was it stronger for railroad loading? Was it safer in a storm? Last, but hardly least, was it cheaper?

Of course the arch and truss forms were also in the competition. Both had undergone further sophistication. The steel arch was usually hinged—that is, the ends of the arch rested on great "rolling pins." The function of these pins was to take the tendency of the arch to bend under loading and transform this stress into simple thrust on the abutment. The two arch halves sometimes were also hinged at their point of juncture. Thus a single-span arch might be one-hinged (top only), two-hinged (at bases only) or three-hinged.

In America, the truss was also usually hinged to make it statically determinate. For this reason, the truss was not used for very long spans during the early years of the century. The battle was between the solid, imposing, ponderous heavyweight cantilever and the graceful, slightly mysterious, suspiciously lightweight suspension. It was fought out in cities, and especially in river-bound New York. In 1893, the New York and New Jersey Bridge Company proposed a cantilever over the Hudson at Seventieth Street, Manhattan. In 1899 the North River Bridge Company launched, also vainly, a plan for a suspension bridge designed by Gustav Lindenthal. This was "a remarkably bold and well-conceived plan," in the words of New York's dean of engineers, Othmar H. Ammann. The heavy cables were to be braced in pairs to form rigid trusses suspended from two pairs of steel towers. The plan originally envisioned six railroad tracks, and was later modified to permit addition of even more. In its final form Lindenthal's design is possibly the most ambitious suspension bridge ever proposed. It called for two decks each of the fantastic width of 235 feet. The lower deck was to carry twelve rapid-transit tracks, two trolley tracks, two bus lanes, and two 15-foot sidewalks. The upper deck was to carry sixteen passenger-car lanes. Eventually the proposed functions of Lindenthal's grandiose bridge were taken up by a whole complex of subaqueous tunnels—the Hudson tubes (not yet finished in 1899), the Holland and Lincoln tunnels, and the Lincoln Third Tube. The last-named alone cost ninety million dollars so it is very possible that Lindenthal's idea, however extravagant it seemed sixty years ago, was a very sensible and farsighted one.

Nevertheless, the subaqueous tunnel was a far better solution to the problem of bringing railroads into a city than a bridge could be, and even proved to have considerable advantages for vehicular traffic, especially because it eased the approach problem. But on the other side of Manhattan, where crossings were demanded more urgently, a second bridge over the East River was undertaken just after the turn of the century. The Williamsburg was a suspension, like the Brooklyn—but with a notable difference. The stiffening truss was no less than 40 feet deep, compared with only 17 feet for its predecessor. This tremendous truss gave the bridge an unquestioned rigidity, but made it very ugly. A suspension that rigid might just as well be a cantilever.

On the other hand the Queensborough, at what is now midtown Manhattan, was a cantilever that might as well have been a suspension. Blackwell's Island (now Welfare Island) made intermediate piers possible, and because the bridge was intended to carry four tracks of the new subway line, the supposedly stronger form was decided on. The engineer was the same Gustav Lindenthal who had designed the giant suspension span over the Hudson. Perhaps it was because Lindenthal favored suspension bridges that the new bridge as it finally emerged looked very much like a suspension bridge—so much so that most New Yorkers today think it is one. The spans were of unequal length (*Figure 59*).

Figure 59

As a cantilever the Queens had one very distinctive feature: no suspended span. The cantilever arms over each of the two channels simply meet. The result is a continuous truss of peculiarly baffling characteristics, apparently entirely unforeseen: a load at any point on the bridge sets up stresses throughout the whole length, making it very difficult if not impossible to determine the strains under various conditions of loading. Despite foundations on solid rock and the use of extra-hard nickel steel to the enormous quantity of 50,000 tons—nearly as much as in the far longer Forth Bridge—the Queens proved inadequate for its intended loading. Two of the four subway tracks were diverted to a tunnel under the river.

How was it discovered that the new bridge was insufficient for its intended loading? Thereby hangs another drama, another tragedy.

This one was played in an exceptionally beautiful setting, the St. Lawrence River valley at Quebec. The bridge, of British-inspired design, was a tremendous cantilever, with a total single span of 1800 feet—100 feet longer than each span of the Forth. The Quebec engineers employed a different technique from Benjamin Baker's. Baker had developed his cantilever arms simultanously in both directions, then had raised and hung the suspended spans panel by panel. Thus the center cantilever was always in balance and the two shoreside cantilevers were anchored securely (*Figure 60*).

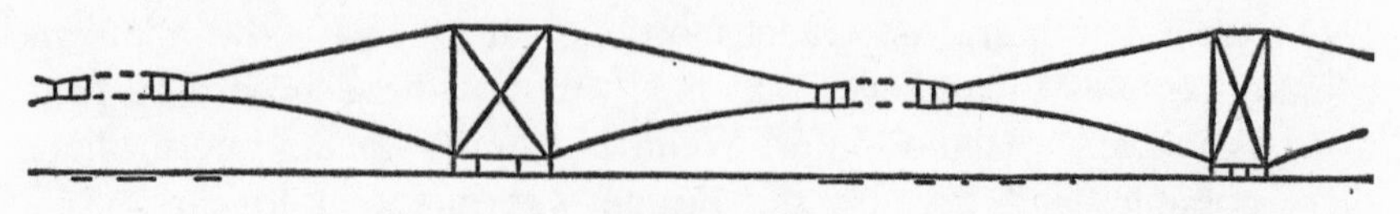

Figure 60

The Quebec engineers, dealing with only two, shore-based cantilevers, built the anchor (shoreside) arms of the cantilevers first, resting them on falsework. Then they built the cantilever arms outward over the river (*Figure 61*).

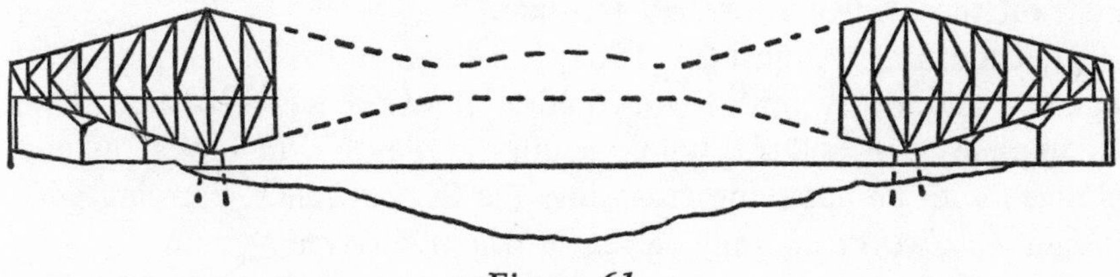

Figure 61

The cantilever arms complete, the two halves of the suspended span were erected outward from the two cantilevers (*Figure 62*).

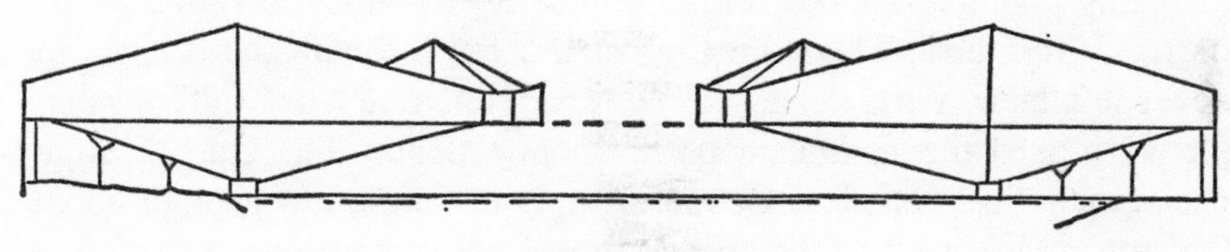

Figure 62

The consulting engineer was Theodore Cooper, who had gotten his engineering start as James Eads's superintendent on the St. Louis Bridge. During that memorable adventure, Cooper once fell one hundred feet into the Mississippi, and not only survived, but went back to work the same day. By the turn of the century, Cooper was America's most famous bridge engineer, a figure of national prominence. In 1907, however, his health did not permit him to visit Quebec during the construction. One day in August he received word that the suspended span building out from the south cantilever was deflecting downward by a fraction of an inch.

Thirty-three years earlier Cooper had sent the telegram that had informed James Eads at midnight in New York that one of the arch ribs was rupturing. Now Cooper found himself in the position Eads had occupied, but with a fatal difference. Cooper had been forced to accept a reduction in the quantity of steel he had recommended, and now felt a growing apprehension. He sent off a message recommending an immediate investigation of the deflection, apparently assuming that work would be halted in the meantime. The engineers on the spot, however, blind to the danger Cooper feared, sent the men to work on the suspended span as usual while commencing their investigation of the deflection. They never completed it. Even though the deflection increased visibly, the crane was moved out to the next panel of the suspended span. When Cooper in New York learned that work was proceeding, he dispatched a telegram ordering every man off the bridge. It arrived too late.

That morning, August 29, 1907, a sudden sound of tearing metal signaled the worst bridge-construction disaster ever recorded. The incomplete span and the whole south cantilever arm broke off and plunged with an appalling crash into the St. Lawrence, carrying with it eighty-six workmen, only eleven of whom survived.

Never before, never since, has anything equaling the Quebec catastrophe happened. Willa Cather got her writing start with a novel, *Alexander's Bridge,* in which her hero, modeled after Theodore Cooper, perished in the collapse. Miss Cather attributed the failure to penny-pinching by the bridge authority, in which she was partly correct. Of course, Theodore Cooper did not fall with the bridge: he never left New York during its construction. But Miss Cather completely missed the significant point about Quebec. The Quebec engineers, including Theodore Cooper, simply did not know enough about the stresses involved in their work to avert a catastrophe. Insufficient bridge theory, construction theory, engineering mathematics—these were the real deficiencies that killed seventy-five workmen in the tangle of steel that plunged into the St. Lawrence.

An investigation was undertaken. Investigations of disasters have varying results, but this one was extraordinarily fruitful. C. C. Schneider, builder of the cantilever over Niagara, was commissioned to make it, and he took to Quebec with him a twenty-seven-year-old assistant named Othmar H. Ammann. Young Ammann was a Swiss with a German technical education who, like John Roebling, had come to America to seek his fortune, and his future career did not fall much short of Roebling's. In 1962, eighty-three years old, dean of American, and in fact of the world's bridge engineers, still active head of his own engineering firm, Mr. Ammann recalled for the writer of this book his experience at Quebec.

The main factor in the failure, Mr. Ammann said, was "a lack of knowledge on the part of engineers of that day of the proper proportioning of compression members."

The compression members in the Quebec cantilever were perfectly adequate for compression—that is, as vertical columns receiving direct downward pressure. But during construction some of those members were subjected to a pressure that tended to bend them outward, and under this stress one deflected and ultimately gave way. The breaking point was at the lattice joints. These were insufficiently riveted to withstand the buckling type of pressure—only two rivets were used at points where eight were required. It will be remembered that rivets were still a very new feature of American bridges, which had held to the cheaper pin connections long after European engineers had adopted rivets. It will also be recalled that buckling—that is, lateral bending—of a compression member, was the initial failure in both the Ashtabula and Tay disasters. Rivets were a relatively minor item of cost; while the penny-pinching to which Willa Cather alluded may have played a role in limiting the number used, so glaring a deficiency clearly revealed a serious want of theoretical knowledge. The connecting plates between compression members had only thirty percent of the strength of the members themselves, rather than the one hundred percent required today. The splicing between compression and tension members also was inadequate.

The strain placed on a construction member in a different direction from that in which it is designed to receive its principal pressure is called a "secondary stress." These "secondary stresses" had been less closely investigated in America than in Europe, where bridge theory was further advanced, and where cantilever and continuous truss bridges were more numerous.

The calculations of these stresses on the Quebec Bridge led to major changes in American methods. The "rule of thumb" by which thousands of bridges had been built in the United States and by which the big cantilever web had been pushed out over the St. Lawrence was discarded. Scientific analysis, grounded in a rapidly growing body of mathematical theory, began to take over the dominant role in engineering for the new century.

21.

The Automobile Age: Beauty and Trouble

THE twentieth century is the century of the automobile bridge. Railroad lines in Europe and America approached saturation at the same time that the automobile was creating a new dimension in travel and transport. For a few years a flurry of rapid-transit bridging took place in some large cities, but the advantages of the subaqueous tunnel soon ended that phase. More and more, the bridge became the automobile's, usually exclusively, occasionally in partnership with the railroad.

Where the bridge was shared by auto and railroad, the structure built actually was a railroad bridge with an extra deck for autos. Railroad loadings being far heavier than automotive, the auto played hardly more of a role in such bridges than the addition of pedestrian promenades. It was where the auto occupied the bridge alone that new and surprising bridge history was written in the new century. A distinguished American engineer, Charles J. Merdinger, reviewing the history of civil enginering a few years ago, wrote that the introduction of the automobile "was to the twentieth century what the railroad had been to the nineteenth and the canal to the eighteenth."

The story of the automobile bridge divides into two parts—short-span and long-span. These are not different lengths of the same kind of bridge, but two totally different kinds of bridges. The first derives, curiously enough, from horticulture rather than from engineering. Back in the 1860s a Paris plant-grower named Joseph Monier was using a new building material, concrete, for tubs for his large plants. Finding that the concrete by itself had to be used in inconvenient bulk to achieve adequate strength, he hit on the idea of embedding a web of iron wire in the material during its preparation. Monier was not the first to think of combining concrete with iron or steel: the idea had been patented earlier in both France and America. But Monier's wire-netting was the first such arrangement to work. Within a few years it was being used for a dozen structural purposes. In his second series of patents, taken out in 1877, Monier included bridges, the first of which, a 50-by-13-foot span, he had built in 1875.

Engineers and builders in both hemispheres soon added refinements, and attempts were made to analyze the stresses in reinforced concrete to provide a firm theoretical basis for the new structural material. Long concrete arches began appearing. Joseph Melan, an Austrian, built a number in both Europe and America, culminating in the triple-arch Capellen Bridge in Minneapolis, one span of which was 400 feet long. A French engineer, François Hennebique, contributed the "slab beam" of T-shaped cross-section, and he and his disciple, Robert Maillart of Switzerland, created a series of remarkable designs. As employed by Hennebique and Maillart, the new material was a revelation in grace and simplicity. Even flatter than the Perronet stone arch, the reinforced concrete arch had a quality that has been described as "monolithic"—"single stone," a unified creation. Suddenly bridges began to be discussed by art critics.

Unfortunately, the development of theory did not keep up with practice in reinforced concrete any more than it had with iron and steel. A series of building collapses—notably that of the Hotel zum Goldenen Baren in Basle, Switzerland in 1901—alarmed the authorities, and measures were taken that actually went much too far in the direction of caution. The result was that for some years reinforced concrete could be used only in thicknesses practically indistinguishable from those of ordinary concrete. Years later, Robert Maillart noted, "It is usual to believe that massive structures are necessarily strong. Mighty pillars and thick arches arouse confidence in the mind of the observer, while light-membered structures cause more anxiety than delight. . . . A massive building is also considered more durable, and not only by the layman!"

The First World War, with its wholesale destruction of bridges, gave reinforced concrete a new prestige by revealing its strength to French and German military engineers, who found bridges built of it difficult to demolish. What eventually won authorities—and the general public—to the designs of Maillart was their economy. It may seem ironic that the breathtaking structures with which Maillart succeeded, incredibly, in embellishing the Swiss Alps, and which have been compared with the creations of the twentieth century's great abstract sculptors, are there not because of their beauty but because of their low cost.

Very early in the history of reinforced concrete, in 1888, an American named P. H. Jackson of San Francisco had an even better idea. If steel wire were used in the reinforcing, and the wire stretched tight to begin with, the result would be a much stronger kind of reinforced concrete which could be used in much smaller quantities. Jackson's experiments never were successful, probably because the steel wire of his day could not take enough tension. It was not until about 1930, when Eugène Freyssinet in France began using high-strength steel wire, that the new "prestressed concrete" suddenly made its dramatic entrance. "Prestressed concrete" has been compared with a row of books held between two hands; you can pick up the row and carry it as long as you maintain the pressure at both ends. Prestressed concrete is widely used today in Europe and the United States. With it, spans can be safely built much longer than with plain reinforced concrete. Its esthetic effects are dazzling.

The layman's confidence in mass, to which Maillart alluded, probably also played a role in delaying the triumph of the suspension bridge over the cantilever. Slowly but surely, however, the once suspect form forged ahead for long-span construction, mostly because it was cheaper.

Before we take up the story, the main thread of our narrative for the twentieth century, we must mention another important bridge development at the end of the nineteenth. This was the drawbridge, that fascinating feature of many a family auto trip. The drawbridge has an ancient and romantic pedigree, deriving from those feudal lords of the Middle Ages whose indifference or even hostility to other kinds of bridges we observed earlier. The medieval draw was of course a defensive rather than a navigational mechanism, yet its principle was precisely the same as that of the modern bascule, whose French name indicates its Norman-keep origin (in modern French, *bascule* is the name for a children's seesaw). The secret of the bascule is the counterweight, which was not absolutely essential in the little draw spans of medieval castle gates, but which added to efficiency. For one thing, it permitted a great increase in the weight of the draw, which became part of the castle wall when raised (*Figure 63*).

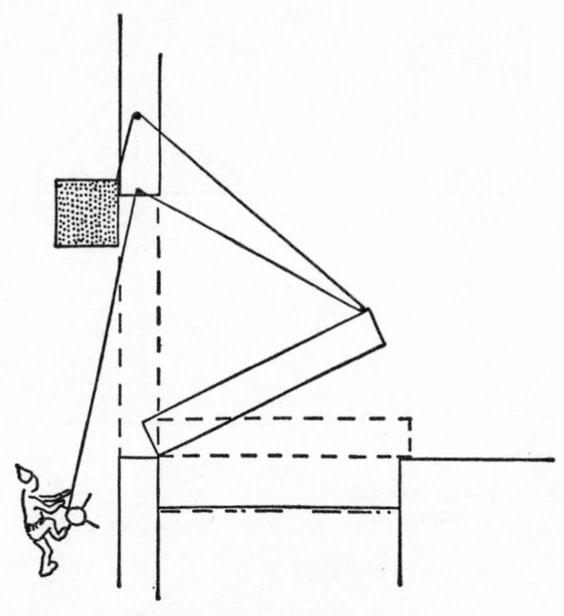

Figure 63

The bascule is what most people picture when they think of a drawbridge, but there are two other important types. One is the swing bridge, also known at least in late medieval times. Leonardo da Vinci invented one, turning on a pivot—also a purely military design. The third type, the vertical lift, did not make its appearance until the nineteenth century. Squire Whipple, the redoubtable York State Yankee, built several of these over canals in upper New York. In this type, the whole span rises (*Figure 63a*).

Where was a drawbridge first used for navigational rather than defense purposes? A candidate for the honor is Old London Bridge, whose tiny drawspan, designed to keep rebel peasants out of London, occasionally was raised as early as the fifteenth century to let certain boats pass, those with masts too tall to go under the center arch, yet narrow enough of hull to squeeze through the draw.

The first drawbridge built specifically to accommodate navigation goes back at least to the sixteenth century. America's first, a bascule built by Job Lane and Theodore Atkinson of Massachusetts, dates from 1662. By the eighteenth century, a number of drawbridges were creaking up and down in Europe, especially in such canal-rich regions as the Netherlands. In the nineteenth century, drawbridges increased in numbers and variety. Lewis Wernwag, creator of the

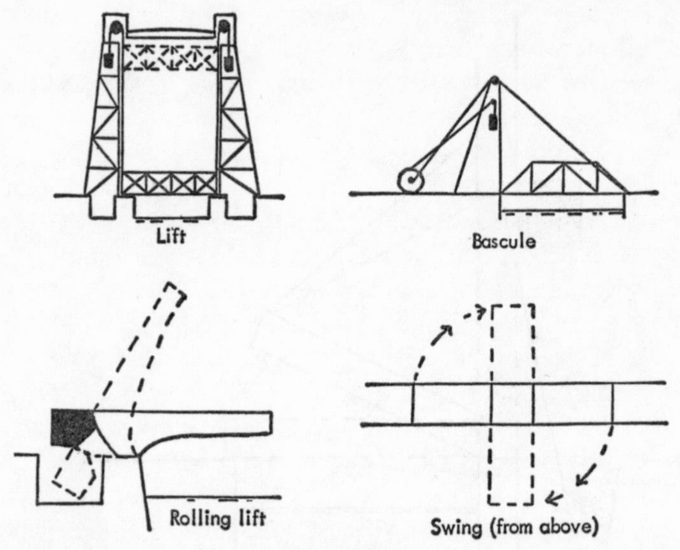

Figure 63a

"Colossus" at Philadelphia, built two famous bascules over Neshaming Creek and Frankford Creek, to carry the old Post Road from New York to Philadelphia. Squire Whipple designed his vertical lifts for New York canals. The railroads soon made new demands for drawbridges as for other types, and America's, if not the world's, first railroad drawbridge accident occurred in 1855 when a trainload of New England doctors returning from a convention in New York ran through an open draw at Norwalk, Connecticut, plunging into the Norwalk River.

But the modern drawbridge actually dates only from the 1890s. It was the confrontation of the modern big city and the modern heavy railroad which created the giant, smooth-operating power bascules and lifts of today. The first three were built almost simultaneously, two in Chicago, one in London. One was a vertical lift, eventually to prove more economical for long spans than the bascule. J. A. L. Waddell originally designed one for the Duluth ship canal, but it was foolishly vetoed by the War Department. In 1893 the same design was built at South Halsted Street over the Chicago River, its broad span 130 feet long. Two counterweights helped lift it 155 feet above the river.

At almost the same time two big bascules were built—the Van Buren Street Bridge in Chicago and the Tower Bridge in London. The success of these, especially the Van Buren Street, led to widespread repetition and rapid development; within a few years Chicago alone had more than twenty movable bridges.

The modern bascule, of course, still relies on the counterweight, which balances the draw span so nicely that only a modest amount of power is needed to raise it. But several of the special problems involved in the massive modern draw never were thought of by the varlet who manipulated the windlass in the Norman keep. For one thing, the roadway and bracing system receive entirely different stresses when tilted vertically, and so must be given special strength. The position of the operator's house, at first glance a minor detail, creates a problem in design because it must be placed where the operator can see both river and roadway. The orthodox solution is to erect four buildings or towers, one at each corner, or two massive towers through which the roadway runs.

Waddell's vertical lift at South Halsted Street remained the only one of such size for some fifteen years. Then suddenly they were built over and over, bigger and bigger. By the 1930s, vertical lifts of upward of five hundred feet were being erected. Spans bigger than the famous iron tubes Robert Stephenson built over the Menai Strait rose smoothly and majestically above the Cape Cod Canal and other United States waterways, thanks to a combination of modern design, modern steel, modern power, and old-fashioned counterweights.

The swing bridge, which turns on a table, has been built less frequently than the other two forms because despite its advantages for some locations, it blocks the channel more during opening and closing. Nevertheless, for some time its economy made it a long-span favorite. Incidentally, the principal delay involved when you are waiting in your car to cross a drawbridge is not the time it takes to raise and lower the bridge, which is done quite expeditiously, but the time taken by a ship to pass through. The draw operator must open the span as soon as the ship signals and, of course, not close it until the ship is clear. Family cars can wait.

Many historians consider that the twentieth century began in 1914. This is at least an appropriate point at which to make the transition from the adventure-laden nineteenth century, with its daring, often rash exploits, its strokes of genius and its disastrous mistakes, its talented carpenters and rule-of-thumb engineers, to the twentieth, with its intellectual approach, its vast theoretical knowledge, and the astounding failure it perpetrated.

On the eve of the First World War, the bridge situation stood thus:

1. The bascule and other movables had solved the important problem of short crossings inside cities and at other points where highways or railroads could not be carried economically over navigable waters at high levels.

2. Reinforced concrete was not yet being used effectively, because of the conservatism of the authorities, but its future was assured.

3. The steel truss had long since put an end to the great railroad age of disaster; few new-site railroad bridges were being built, but the long process of replacing old iron and wooden crossings was under way.

4. The big remaining question mark was the long-span bridge, especially the long-span highway bridge. In a score of places in the United States alone, long spans were badly needed to save time and relieve growing congestion. New York, Detroit, San Francisco, New Orleans, cities on the Ohio and Mississippi, and many other places needed them. How would they be built?

For ten years the competition among the long-span forms remained very even. In New York, 1914 saw the commencement of the third East River suspension, the Manhattan. This bridge was designed by a brilliant young emigrant from Russia, Leon Moisseiff. By comparison with the heavy Williamsburg or even the Brooklyn, the new bridge was more slender and graceful, owing chiefly to the use of a shallower truss.

The next long span, also in New York, reverted to the steel arch. But this bridge was designed to carry four railroad tracks across the East River at the opening of Long Island Sound, at a point known as Hell Gate (*Figure 64*).

Gustav Lindenthal, the engineer in charge, designed an arch in a single thousand-foot span, the resulting bridge becoming the heaviest in the world—it still holds the record for heaviest loading. The enormous superstructure had to be cantilevered out from both sides till the arches joined, the method Eads had used over the Mississippi. More trouble was encountered with the foundations. Ward's Island, where one of them stood, proved to have a bad rock fault that actually had to be bridged over with concrete cantilevers and arches sunk to position with compressed-air caissons—a sort of gigantic dentistry job.

In 1916, Quebec tried the cantilever once more—and again with

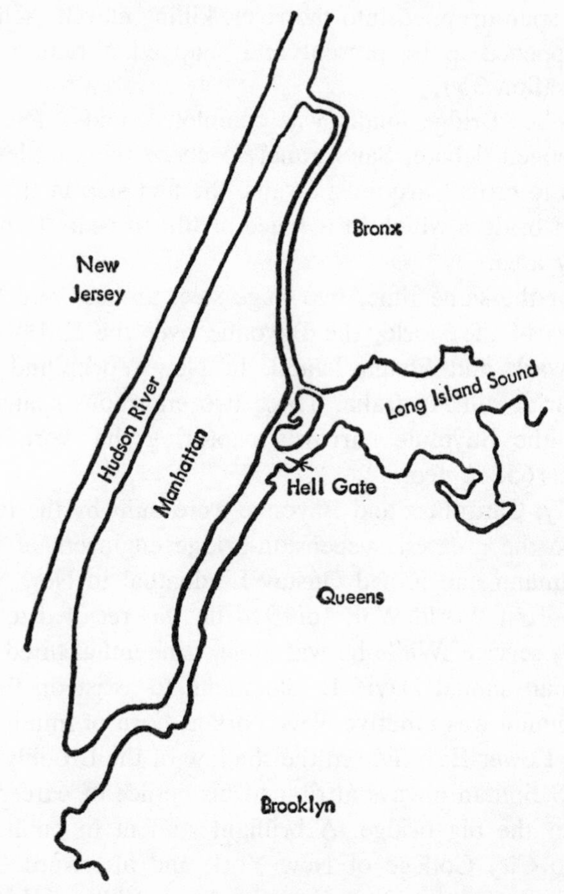

Figure 64

disastrous results, though on a less tragic scale. The cantilevers were erected successfully, and the plan was to raise the suspended span to position from the river instead of trying to build it out from the two arms (*Figure 65*).

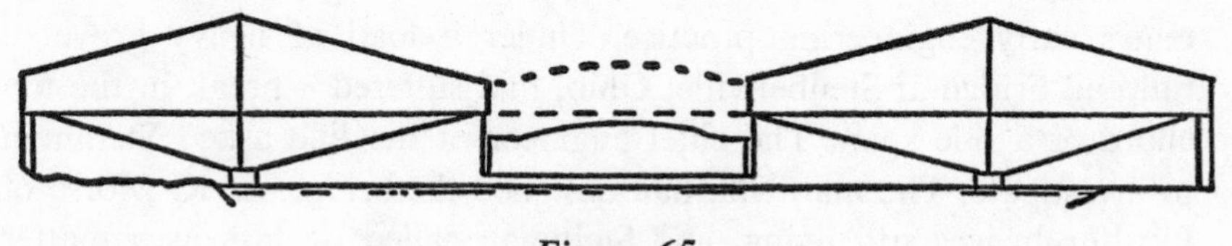

Figure 65

Unluckily, another blunder had been made, apparently in the manufacture of a casting, which failed during the lifting operation. The suspended span dropped into the river, killing eleven men. A photographer happened to be present and snapped a remarkable picture (see illustration 35).

The Quebec Bridge finally was completed, and a few years later, after prolonged debate, San Francisco chose the cantilever over the suspension to cross Carquinez Straits, the first step in the tremendous complex of bridges which in a space of fifteen years transformed the whole Bay area.

At about the same time, two huge steel arches were built on opposite sides of the world, the Bayonne over the Kill Van Kull, between Newark and Staten Island, in New York, and the Sydney Harbour Bridge in Australia. These two enormous spans were 1650 feet each, the Bayonne narrowly capturing the world's record by measuring 1652½ feet.

Ironically, Carquinez and Bayonne were built by the two men destined to be the greatest suspension-bridge engineers of the century. O. H. Ammann had joined Gustav Lindenthal in New York shortly before the First World War. In 1914 he was recalled to Switzerland for military service. While he was gone, Lindenthal hired in his place a young man named David B. Steinman, to assist on the Hell Gate Arch. Steinman was a native New Yorker, born of immigrant parents on the old Lower East Side in the shadow of the Brooklyn Bridge. In later life, Steinman always attributed his choice of career to his boyhood under the big bridge. A brilliant student in public school, he went on to City College of New York and afterward to Columbia University, where he studied under Professor William H. Burr, one of the great bridge engineers of the day. Steinman's doctoral thesis on suspension bridges won the unusual distinction of regular publication. He assisted Lindenthal on several notable bridges after Hell Gate Arch, including the Sciotoville, Ohio, continuous truss, which tardily introduced this European form in the United States in 1917. His biographer, William Ratigan, tells a revealing incident of Steinman's early engineering practice. Under a load of heavy gravel a railroad bridge at Steubenville, Ohio, had suffered a break in the top chord of a side span. The chief engineer of the line asked Steinman to investigate. The man who had designed the bridge, E. K. Morse of Pittsburgh, was still living, and Steinman called on him as a matter of diplomacy. He found an octogenarian occupied chiefly in tying trout flies, who, however, readily co-operated. The old gentleman unlocked a secret drawer in his desk and took out a little red notebook.

In it was his "formula"—he had inherited it from an older engineer and guarded it carefully. Steinman recognized it at a glance, and noted that it was inappropriate to the Steubenville Bridge. A look at the blueprints revealed that Morse had used the same chord section throughout the bridge, main and side spans alike, regardless of the variation in stresses, and even on the approach spans, though these were of different lengths and structurally unrelated.

Steinman, a little appalled, proceeded to examine the bridge itself. He found it full of dangerous defects, which he spelled out in his report, a copy of which he sent to Morse, who told the railroad officials to disregard it. Some minor repairs were made, and the bridge broke down again. Steinman was then summoned to carry out real strengthening, which he did, and was later cordially blackballed by Morse for membership in the American Institute of Consulting Engineers.

In the 1920s, in partnership with Holton D. Robinson, Steinman built the Florianopolis bridge in Brazil, a unique steel-eyebar truss-suspension connecting the mainland with Santa Catarina Island, and the Carquinez Strait cantilever, his own preference for a suspension being overruled.

Meantime, Gustav Lindenthal's other former assistant, Othmar Ammann, back in the United States after his army service, was also moving from success to success. The arch over the Kill Van Kull was followed by renewed discussion of the biggest of all New York's bridge projects, a span over the Hudson River. By the mid-1920s the potential site had moved north, as real estate for the approaches became prohibitive in the midtown area. Ammann suggested a location at Fort Washington to Governor Sulzer of New Jersey, and eventually the New York Port Authority, with participation by both states, undertook a toll bridge at that point, with Ammann in charge. The bridge eventually drew its name from its location. The George Washington Bridge, begun with test borings in 1925 and completed in 1931, is the greatest single landmark in suspension construction, or indeed in bridge engineering, after the Brooklyn Bridge.

The George Washington did not merely set a new record in span length. At one stroke it *doubled* the previous record for bridges of any form. The terrific advance that Ammann's creation represented can be appreciated best through a comparison chart (*Figure 66*). John Roebling's Cincinnati span represented an increase over Chaley's Fribourg Grand Pont of about one sixth. At Brooklyn,

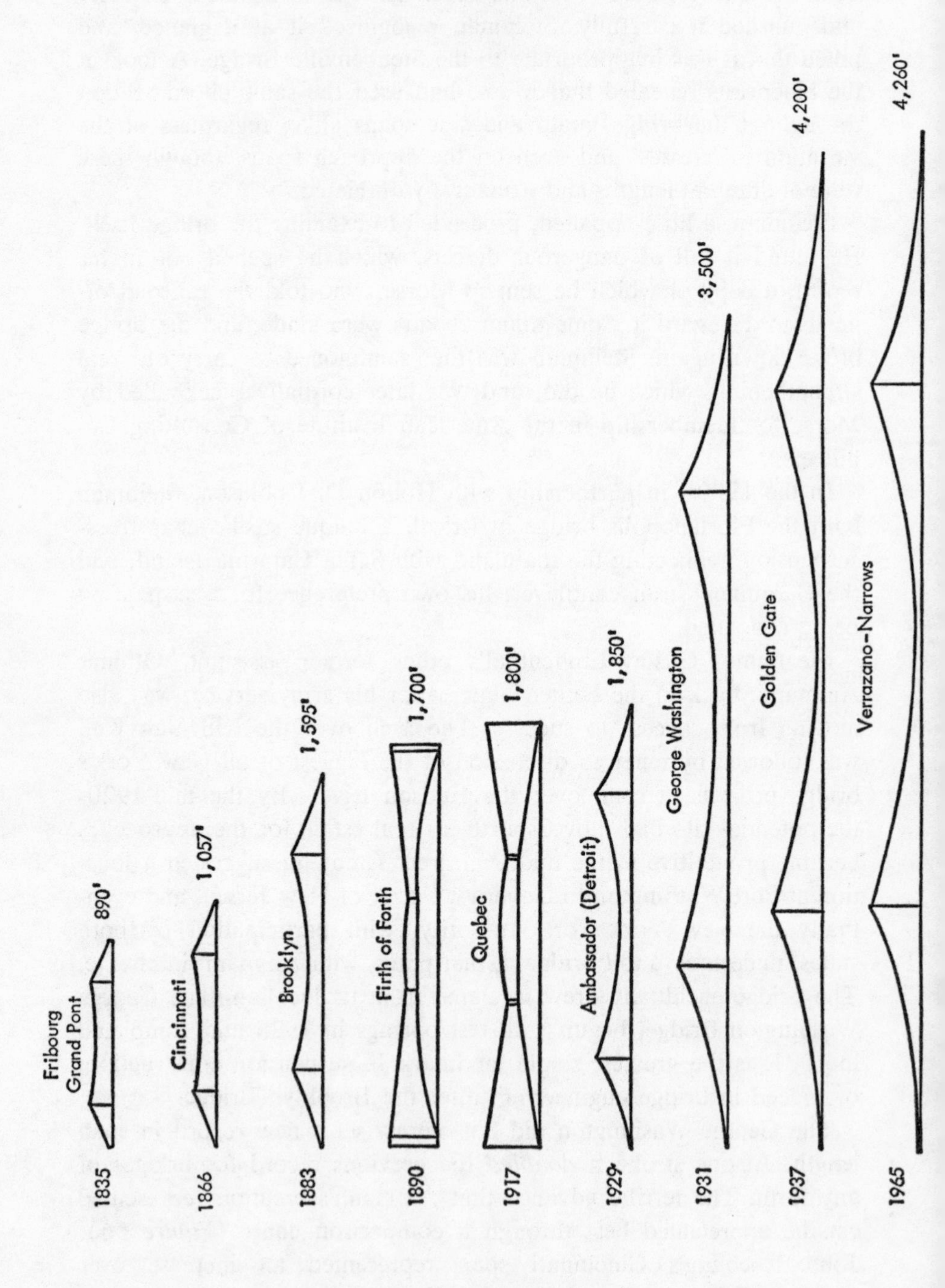

1835
Fribourg Grand Pont
890'
1866
Cincinnati
1,057'
1883
Brooklyn
1,595'
1890
Firth of Forth
1,700'
1917
Quebec
1,800'
1929
Ambassador (Detroit)
1,850'
1931
George Washington
3,500'
1937
Golden Gate
4,200'
1965
Verrazano-Narrows
4,260'

Figure 66

Roebling surpassed his Cincinnati span by better than fifty percent. From this point on, the successive span increases achieved at the Firth of Forth, Quebec, and Detroit over a period of nearly fifty years represented a total increase of only one seventh. Then came the George Washington, a jump of 89 percent. Backers and engineers who had been discussing the bridge across San Francisco's Golden Gate received a powerful impetus of confidence from Ammann's success; their bridge, instead of representing an increase over the previous largest suspension of 127 percent, suddenly was reduced to the rather modest increase of 20 percent. Even Ammann's new Verrazano-Narrows Bridge over New York Harbor will beat the George Washington by only 22 percent.

The George Washington represents a jump in bridge size not limited to length of span; it involves a significant increase in weight for a suspended structure, made possible by improved steel wire. It also represents striking and radical departures in design. The steel towers, of course, established a new record in height, six hundred feet. Yet this increase was smaller proportionately than the increase in span length, which means that the catenary (cable curve) is exceptionally flat. The side spans were unusually short. But most extraordinary of all, the bridge was built with no stiffening truss. This incredible feature resulted in part from an accident. Originally the bridge was given a double-deck mission—autos on top, rapid-transit tracks below. But during its construction the rapid-transit line to New Jersey was abandoned and the lower deck omitted from the finished bridge. Ammann decided to skip the 29-foot truss that would have linked the two decks. This at-first-glance reckless decision was based on careful calculations derived from the bridge's very special characteristics of breadth and weight. The eight-lane roadway of the 119-foot-wide single deck brought the total dead weight to 56,000 tons—dwarfing the weight of all previous suspensions. The trusses, as Ammann already had pointed out, actually were flexible—that is, they exerted little restraint on distortions of the cables.

The trusses were added in 1962, when the second deck was finally erected to meet the increased demands of automobile traffic. At this second dedication of his bridge, O. H. Ammann was the guest of honor, and the recipient of a unique accolade: his bust was installed on the bridge.

One more detail of the George Washington construction is worthy of mention. The architectural consultant designed towers encased in masonry. But in 1931, the heyday of "functionalism" in art, a number of art critics and art lovers protested that the towers were better left in their original steel. Ammann and the Port of New York Authority decided to leave them, and no one has regretted the decision since. The naked towers give the great bridge a distinctive and characteristic appearance. Seen close up, the vast geometry wears a truly awesome aspect.

The George Washington practically clinched the long-span championship for the suspension form. The cantilever continued to be used for certain locations and problems, as in the Huey Long Bridge at New Orleans, whose channel span of 790 feet rises 135 feet over the Mississippi, carrying two railroad lines and a highway deck. The steel arch also survived, as in the beautiful Henry Hudson Bridge over the Harlem River in New York, which David Steinman first used as a subject for his civil-engineering thesis at Columbia and later built exactly as he had described it in his college days. Reinforced concrete was making new strides at this time, with Freyssinet and others building arches in Europe of more than five hundred feet (eventually the Sandoe, in Stockholm, reached 800 feet). The continuous truss, whose long-span career Steinman had helped inaugurate at Sciotoville, was reaching farther and farther. Yet, for such enormous distances as that across the Hudson River, the suspension was king.

The next chapters in bridge history, which saw the scene move across the United States from New York's rivers to the inviting indentations of the Pacific Coast, emphasized this. San Francisco followed up the Carquinez Strait Bridge with the great Oakland-Bay complex, two end-to-end suspension spans of 2310 feet with side spans of 1160 feet running from the city to Yerba Buena Island; then through the rock by the world's biggest-bore tunnel, a half mile long, then across the East Bay by a cantilever with a main span of 1400 feet. Immediately after came the Golden Gate, a stupendous suspension span of 4200 feet—four fifths of a mile, seven hundred feet longer than even the mighty George Washington. The Golden Gate continued the trend toward the longer and the shallower—its stiffening truss was only twenty-five feet deep.

While the suspension form achieved its leadership on the basis of economy, it was winning more and more approval on esthetic grounds. Awards were instituted for beautiful bridges, art experts and pseudo art experts wrote articles, the public admired. Bridge engineers naturally reacted, and consciously strove to produce more beautiful bridges. David Steinman painted his Mount Hope Bridge over

Naragansett Bay an attractive light green, the first steel bridge to be painted a decorative color, and strung lights along the cables, producing for the first time the beautiful and now familiar necklace effect of a suspension span at night. After saving $850,000 by ingeniously driving his south anchorage halfway into the clay bottom of the bay, then using riprap rock to provide solid grip, he turned around and persuaded the bankers to put $70,000 into landscaping the approaches with evergreens and banks of roses.

But these embellishments were trivial in comparison with the great basic of suspension-bridge esthetics—the long, flat inverted arch itself. And just as in the regular arch, the longer and flatter, the more appealing to the eye. In the case of the suspension bridge, another esthetic rule was evident: the shallower the truss, the more appealing.

By the beginning of the Second World War in Europe, the American long-span suspension bridge, beautiful and self-assured, was moving into a limitless future, slimmer, more graceful, more irresistibly economical.

On July 1, 1940, an exceptionally beautiful suspension bridge was opened over the Narrows of Puget Sound, connecting the Olympic Peninsula with the mainland of Washington. From its first days there was something a little extraordinary about the behavior of the Tacoma Narrows Highway Bridge. Motorists crossing the 2800-foot, two-lane ribbon over the sparkling waters of the Sound frequently saw the car in front of them appear to sink into the roadway. At times, indeed, it vanished completely. No one was alarmed. Engineers and automobile drivers explained to each other the advantages of the flexible suspension design. Some stays were added to give a bit more rigidity. Meantime motorists enjoyed the roller-coaster sensation, and gave the bridge a jocular nickname, "Galloping Gertie." Tolls ran higher than anticipated.

Then, four months after the bridge was opened, on the morning of November 7, with a fairly high wind, about 42 to 44 mph, far below hurricane force, blowing, "Galloping Gertie" suddenly went into an alarming series of convolutions. One side of the roadway lifted, the other fell, at the same time that waves rippled along the length of the span. The bridge was closed to traffic; the last venturesome motorist, a newspaperman, stopped his car a third of the way across, and climbed out amid terrifying deck motions. His dog, frightened, refused to leave the car, and the reporter succeeded in making his way back alone. A few minutes later the violent rhythmic dance of the roadway tore loose some suspenders, and a 600-foot length fell into the Sound. The remaining center deck continued to whip about in a frenzy. Then, ripping free from all its restraining steel and wire, it too plunged down to the water. With it went not a single human life, but a whole generation of engineering thinking.

22.

Who Wrecked Galloping Gertie?

"Drove across the bridge at about 8:30 as usual to observe the behavior as the wind during the latter part of the night had been quite severe and was still blowing moderately. The bridge appeared to be behaving in the customary manner, the east side span being practically quiet, the main span oscillating in a four-noded manner and the west span oscillating considerably from the temporary holddown to the tower. All of these motions, however, were considerably less than had occurred many times before so I came to the office at about nine o'clock. . . .

"Yesterday in a conference it had been determined that we would proceed immediately to streamline the southerly side of the main span. I was to prepare detailed sketches . . . as quickly as possible. . . . Upon my return to the office at nine o'clock, I immediately undertook the preparation of these sketches. At about ten o'clock Mr. Walter Miles called from his office to come and look at the bridge, that it was about to go. This was the first indication I had that anything of an unusual or serious nature was occurring.

"I immediately drove with Mr. Miles to the dock, from which we could see the bridge. The center span was swaying wildly, it being possible first to see the entire bottom side as it swung into a semi-vertical position and then the entire roadway.

"It was at once apparent that instead of the cables in the main span rising and falling together, they were moving in opposite directions, thereby tilting the deck from side to side. I could observe one car, stationary, some distance east from the center. It appeared that the center of the span was remaining about horizontal and the two halves were revolving about a longitudinal axis of the bridge.

"I then returned to the office, took my own car and went to the bridge, where all traffic had been stopped and several people were coming off the bridge from the easterly side span. I walked to Tower No. 5 and out onto the main span to about the quarter point. The east side span was practically quiet, there being but a few inches of vertical motion. . . . Then I observed on the main span that the concrete sidewalk around the stiffeners of the girders was failing badly. The curbs at the construction joints were also failing. Adjacent to the girders, it appeared that the concrete was entirely free and the girders and the concrete were working back and forth continuously three or four inches. The concrete roadway showed no signs of cracking. The main span was rolling wildly. . . . The wind had not moved it a noticeable amount sidewise. The deck, however, was tipping from the horizontal to an angle approaching forty-five degrees.

"Beyond the center of the span at the lamp posts the deck was tilting in an opposite direction. The entire main span appeared to be twisting about a neutral point at the center of the span in somewhat the manner of a corkscrew.

"At Tower No. 5 I met Professor Farquharson, who had his camera set up and was taking pictures. We remained there a few minutes and then decided to return to the east anchorage warning people who were approaching to get off the span. From the east anchorage I advised . . . the Coast Guard and the U. S. Engineers. . . .

"The main span was still rolling badly and the east side span was still quiet. . . . At that time it appeared that should the wind die down, the span would perhaps come to rest and I resolved that we would immediately proceed to install a system of cables from the piers to the roadway level. . . . I returned to the administration building. . . . I called Mr. Frincke of the Bethlehem Steel Company and requested him to send us a superintendent and a pusher immediately. . . . I then called the Weather Bureau . . . and was informed that the barometer was rising and in all probability the wind would quiet later in the day. . . .

"I was then informed that a panel of laterals in the center of the span had dropped out and a section of concrete slab had fallen. I immediately went to the south side of the plaza. . . . The bridge was still rolling badly about the center as it had been doing previously. I returned to the toll plaza and from there observed the first section of steel fall out of the center. From then on successive sections towards each tower rapidly fell out. . . . I requested that all persons be cleared from the administration buildings. . . . Shortly thereafter . . . coinciding with the dropping of the sections of the center span, I observed the side span settle rapidly and was momentarily expecting the towers to come down. I did not observe the exact time that the center section fell out although I was later informed that it was 11:10."

—Clark H. Eldridge, Bridge Engineer, Washington Toll Bridge Authority

GALLOPING GERTIE'S tumble into Puget Sound was the most spectacular of all bridge collapses. It was also the most completely observed and minutely recorded. Several engineers were present at the dance of death, and one, Professor F. B. Farquharson, wind expert from the University of Washington, made a movie which became a newsreel classic. If firsthand testimony alone were needed, there would have been no difficulty in uncovering the cause of Gertie's demise.

Certainly, no time was lost in fixing the blame. All the engineers connected with the erection immediately stepped aside and allowed the full spotlight to focus on the designing engineer, Leon S. Moisseiff of New York. In one sense this was fair. Moisseiff's design for the Tacoma Narrows had been accepted by the state and federal authorities, including two boards of consulting engineers, very largely on the basis of his reputation. How had Moisseiff acquired his reputation? By designing or helping to design practically every major long-span bridge of the century. From 1897 to 1914, he had been engineer of design in the Department of Bridges, New York City, for both the important Manhattan Suspension and the Hell Gate Arch. He was designing engineer for the Delaware River (suspension) Bridge at Philadelphia. As Consulting Engineer for the New York Port Authority, he participated in the design of the George Washington and the Triborough bridges. He was Consulting Engineer on the Ambassador at Detroit, the Golden Gate, the San Francisco Bay Bridge, and, most recently, the Bronx-Whitestone in New York. At sixty-eight he was indisputably the most eminent design engineer for suspension bridges in the world.

It was hardly any wonder that nobody questioned Moisseiff's design for the Tacoma Narrows. True, it represented a considerable departure from previous long-span suspensions. But Moisseiff was the recognized authority, and the departure involved in the Tacoma bridge was of a kind that does not readily stir doubts. It was not a move in a new direction, but simply a further advance in the direction in which suspension bridges had been moving steadily ever since the Williamsburg. Ammann, Steinman, Modjeski (chief engineer of the Philadelphia-Camden), Woodruff (design engineer of the Golden

Gate), and all the rest had steadily lengthened and narrowed their bridges. They had a logical theoretical basis for their trend. The clumsy, heavily trussed Williamsburg had been built in accord with the primitive and erroneous "elastic" theory of the nineteenth century, now supplanted by the "deflection theory" propounded by Melan, the Austrian engineer who also had contributed significantly to the development of the reinforced-concrete arch. Simultaneously the railroad was replaced by the automobile as live loading—requiring far less stiffening against deflection.

The scope of this development, which represents virtually the whole history of the modern suspension bridge, can be shown most graphically in a comparison chart:

	Length in feet	*ratio of truss or girder to span length*	*ratio of width to length*
Williamsburg	1600	1/40	1/14
Manhattan	1500	1/60	1/13
George Washington	3500	0	1/33
Golden Gate	4200	1/164	1/47
Bronx-Whitestone	2300	1/209	1/31
Tacoma Narrows	2800	1/350	1/72

The trusses got steadily smaller, which, of course, represented an economy, and also contributed to the gracefulness of the bridge's appearance. In the early thirties a still further economy, heightening still further the bridge's slender charm, was introduced, first on several small suspension bridges, then on larger ones. This was the plate girder—a solid but very shallow metal strip that took the place of the truss. Plate girders were used by Moisseiff on both the Bronx-Whitestone and the Tacoma Narrows. At first glance, this tendency may seem so obviously dangerous an economy that common sense might have avoided it, but this is by no means the case. In the first place, the purpose of the stiffening truss was not to protect the bridge against the wind, but to keep the roadway from deflecting vertically under live loading—to keep cars from sinking into a trough as they drove over it. The wind itself was not regarded as a hazard. If this in turn sounds rash in view of some of the disasters previously recorded—such as the Tay Bridge—it should be clearly realized that wind-tunnel tests, carried out by the same Professor Farquharson who took the famous film of the collapse, proved that winds even of gale force could not blow down the Tacoma Narrows Bridge. And Professor Farquharson's tests were, as far as they went, perfectly valid—a gale could not have blown down Galloping Gertie. The trouble with the experiments was that they were too limited. Professor Farquharson himself felt concern over their incompleteness. The wind is a complex force, and under certain circumstances its action can have very complex results. The wind tunnel, still a novel device in the 1930s, required considerable further sophistication.

At the same time, the dead weight of bridges varied, quite apart from the design. The George Washington, with its eight-lane deck, weighed a solid 56,000 tons. The Tacoma was dramatically lighter, owing to no quirk on the part of the designer, but simply to the fact that the project called for only a two-lane roadway plus sidewalks. Anticipated traffic was not heavy enough to justify a wider, heavier bridge.

Galloping Gertie, in short, was long, narrow, shallow, and light. All the same—as Moisseiff's experience, Melan's theory, and Professor Farquharson's wind-tunnel tests agreed—such a bridge would stand up. What then was the trouble?

The three-man board of engineers appointed by the Federal Works Agency, which had sponsored the project, consisted of Theodore von Kármán of the California Institute of Technology, an expert on wind effects, Glenn B. Woodruff, design engineer of the Golden Gate and Transbay suspension bridges, and Othmar H. Ammann. Their report, a heavy volume dated March 28, 1941, four and a half months after Gertie's fall, attributed the failure to "excessive oscillations caused by wind action." These excessive oscillations, in the opinion of the distinguished engineers, were "made possible by the extraordinary degree of flexibility of the structure and of its relatively small capacity to absorb dynamic forces." They noted significantly: "At the higher wind velocities torsional [twisting] oscillations, when once induced, had the tendency to increase their amplitudes."

Their investigation showed that the initial failure was the slipping of the cable band on the north side of the bridge to which the center ties were connected, a slipping that apparently triggered the torsional oscillations, causing breaking stresses at several points. The remedial installations that the engineers had been considering at the time of the failure were described as "rational" but probably insufficient. More study of aerodynamic forces was called for. Finally, the public was reassured that perfectly safe suspension bridges could be built even in the then current state of knowledge, the "further study" being needed not to make bridges safe, but to determine the economic limits of safety.

While the report was in preparation, two interesting articles appeared in the *Engineering News-Record* of December 5, 1940. One was a description of corrective measures taken to combat oscillations on the Bronx-Whitestone Bridge in New York. The measures consisted of the installation of stays running from the tops of the towers to the roadway. The other article was entitled "Two Recent Bridges Stabilized by Cable Stays," and by it hung an extraordinary experience.

Two years earlier, David Steinman had built the Thousand Island bridge complex, consisting of five separate bridges, including two suspension spans. Like all the bridge projects of the depression-bound 1930s, the job was constricted by a tight budget. One week before the dedication ceremony, at which President Franklin D. Roosevelt and Prime Minister Mackenzie King were to speak, Steinman received a telephone call in New York from his engineer on the spot. It was a third enactment of the drama in which James B. Eads and Theodore Cooper had been earlier protagonists: Steinman's superintendent reported that both the suspension spans at the Thousand Islands were acting oddly—vertical heaving motions with back-and-forth longitudinal motion in a quartering wind.

Steinman took the next train, went straight to the bridge and waited for a quartering wind. It came, and the span Steinman was watching began to waver. Making an on-the-spot analysis, Steinman came up with two physical answers to the problem: first, a pair of inclined stays forming an inverted V at the middle of the span, rigidly connecting each plate girder to the cable above it; second, stays running radially from the ends of the roadway to selected points on the cables. Borrowing some steel hoisting rope, Steinman rushed his stays in time for the dedication, replacing them some months later with specially fabricated steel struts.

As a matter of fact, Steinman himself did not entirely understand what he had done, for the Thousand Islands spans never went into torsional oscillation. Steinman, who had translated Melan's epoch-making exposition of the deflection theory back in 1908 (Moisseiff had applied it to the Manhattan Bridge the following year), took immediate note in 1940 of the motions reported at Tacoma Narrows. Similar though less dramatic disturbances were also occurring on the Bronx-Whitestone, which was long and shallow like the Tacoma, though with a wider (originally four-lane, today a tight six) roadway, and was stiffened with a plate girder. Steinman wrote the engineers at Tacoma offering to help. Tacoma referred him to Moisseiff in

New York. Steinman apparently telephoned Moisseiff, and received a polite no-thank-you to his offer.

According to Steinman's biographer, the engineers of the Tacoma Bridge "took over Steinman's idea of mid-stay spans," but copied it incorrectly. Because his photographic slides showed the stays made of wire rope, they used wire-rope stays for the Tacoma design. Steinman asserted:

> They did not know that the wire-rope mid-span stays on the Thousand Islands Bridge were only an emergency, a temporary installation that we replaced a few months later by the permanent stays made of rigid structural-steel angle members. Even so, the mid-span stays at Tacoma, copied from me, although inadequate, were the only thing that kept the bridge from going into destructive oscillations during the four months of its life. On the fatal morning, one of the rope-stays became slack and snapped, whereupon the span went into its dance of death. . . . If they had let me help them, I could have saved the bridge, as I have saved several other bridges. I could have made the Tacoma span safe for a very small expenditure. But my offer went begging.

Whatever validity there was in Steinman's claim, this style of talk was hardly calculated to endear him to fellow engineers. Steinman already had a reputation as a thorny individualist and a "self-advertiser"—this last as great a sin among engineers as it is among doctors. Without mentioning him by name the three-man board investigating Galloping Gertie dealt rather rudely with Steinman's opinion:

> These bridges [the Thousand Island and Deer Isle] are more nearly comparable in size to some of the early flexible suspension bridges. They give no clue to the possible behavior of a suspension bridge 3½ times longer and 6 times heavier.

However, in the Summary of Conclusions the report stated:

> It was not realized that the aerodynamic forces which have proven disastrous in the past to much lighter and shorter flexible suspension bridges would affect a structure of such magnitude. . . .

The reference to disasters of the past was principally to the suspension bridge Charles Ellet built in 1849 at Wheeling, West Virginia, and which collapsed in 1854 under a moderate wind. Steinman has pointed out in his own books that the eyewitness reports of the fall of Ellet's bridge are strikingly reminiscent of those of the Tacoma Narrows (see page 192). For that matter, Ellet's span was not so short: 1010 feet.

It should be emphasized that until Steinman's experience at the Thousand Islands, his bridge theory differed in no way from that practiced by Ammann, Moisseiff, and the rest. The Thousand Islands bridges, of 800 and 750 feet, had stiffening girders only 6½ and 6 feet deep—a ratio of 1/125. Steinman always had had an exceptional interest in aerodynamic theory. During the First World War, he had taught the first course in aeronautics in an American university at City College of New York. After reading the Tacoma board's report, Steinman wrote a paper entitled, "Rigidity and Aerodynamic Stability of Suspension Bridges" and submitted it to the American Society of Civil Engineers. It was not immediatly accepted, and a fair guess is that it was returned to Steinman for revision because it was thought to reflect unfairly on Moisseiff. If so, Steinman himself changed his views, for in his book, *Bridges and Their Builders,* he defends Moisseiff and places the blame for Galloping Gertie on the whole profession. His paper was accepted in 1943 and published in the Society's *Proceedings* for November. It touched off a tempest. The controversy ran on for several years, marked in 1945 by a revision of Steinman's original article with replies to criticisms.

In his 1945 article, Steinman revised a list of bridges studied in his earlier article, with factors showing their aerodynamic stability. This second list may be compared with that on page 255 showing ratios of truss depths and roadway widths to lengths of span. They are given in descending order of stability:

Williamsburg
Manhattan
Philadelphia-Camden
Transbay (San Francisco)
George Washington
Golden Gate
Bronx-Whitestone
Tacoma Narrows

Galloping Gertie inspired a series of wind-tunnel tests, notably at the California Institute of Technology under Professor von Kármán and at the University of Washington under Professor Farquharson. These singled out the plate girder solid section as the major villain. Cutting holes in the existing eight-foot girder would have had "a marked and favorable effect on the incidence of torsional instability," Professor Farquharson found. Experiments on bridge models with open-grill sidewalks, slotted roadways, etc., gradually developed a new type of bridge cross-section design, one with sufficient openings to break up wind gusts and cut down turbulence.

The air, of course, is a solid mass, with weight and volume. As such, it has the characteristic common to such masses—it can be broken up into pieces. When a large mass of moving air strikes an obstacle, such as a bridge, it both parts to go around and over the obstacle and fragments into small masses acting independently. These smaller masses have momentum and obey the same laws of motion as all masses. Hitting a wall, open above and below, a wind goes into a sort of tumbling act (*Figure 67*).

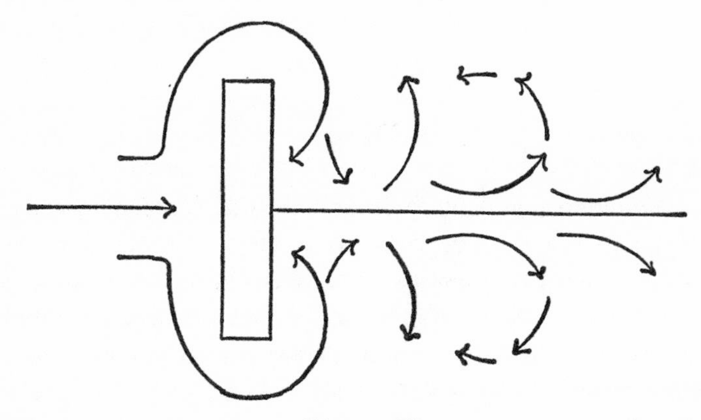

Figure 67

This action can be pictured as a double line of big puffs of wind tumbling over and under the wall. As these puffs roll over and under, they produce the Von Kármán effect (analyzed by one member of the three-man Tacoma investigating board). This is the sort of symmetrical oscillation which one sees in a cattail or other water reed in the current. The plant moves alternately left and right in an ordinary head-on current (*Figure 68*).

When a truss is substituted for the solid plate girder, the puffs are broken up into small eddies, effectively reducing turbulence.

Summing up the whole bizarre accident, Galloping Gertie tore itself to pieces because of two characteristics:

1. It was a long, narrow, shallow, and therefore very flexible structure standing in a wind-ridden valley;

2. Its stiffening support was a solid girder, which, combined with a solid floor, produced a cross section peculiarly vulnerable to aerodynamic effects.

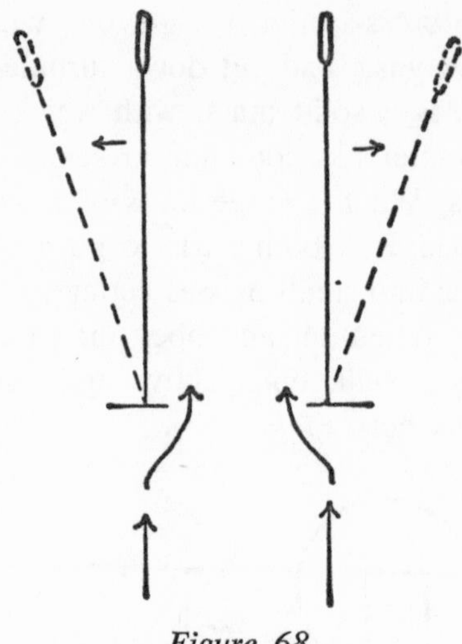

Figure 68

Neither Steinman nor Ammann nor Von Kármán nor anyone else knew the full answer to the profound mystery of Galloping Gertie. In a quite real sense it remains unsolved today, for aerodynamics is a still-growing science. "We haven't any more got the wind all figured out than the space people have the sky all figured out," one engineer remarked to this writer.

Leon Moisseiff, who never attempted to pass the Tacoma failure off on the shoulders of colleagues or subordinates, and did his best to aid in the investigation, is remembered today very differently from Thomas Bouch. His disaster is universally attributed to the state of engineering and aerodynamics in 1940, and so esteemed was he by his colleagues in the American Society of Civil Engineers that a few years after his death a fund was established for the Moisseiff Award, to be given annually for an important paper on structural design.

Nonetheless, in the immediate wake of Galloping Gertie, Moisseiff's services were not exactly in demand for the design of suspension bridges. Some hasty steps were being taken in several places where bridges were under construction, in the design stage, or even fully completed. The Bronx-Whitestone acquired a truss. The Golden Gate underwent alterations running to three and a half million dollars. It is impossible to say how many other bridges, slim and fashionable on drawing boards in engineers' offices, suddenly took on added weight and web trusses in place of plate girders.

In Michigan's state capitol at Lansing, some second thoughts in

1940 were reminiscent of those in London following the Tay Bridge collapse. For in the active planning stage in Michigan was a tremendous suspension bridge across the historic and very windy Straits of Mackinac—designed, complete with plate girder, by Leon Moisseiff.

23.

After Gertie, What?

THE Second World War, interrupting bridge-building in the United States and Europe, provided a breathing space for engineers to stop and think. The need for stopping and thinking was underlined further by the fate of one of the few big bridges built during the period. The mathematical problem of the continuous truss having been mastered by then, a two-span truss was built over the Mississippi at Chester, Illinois, in 1942. In 1944 it blew down in a storm. This was not a case of the arcane "aerodynamic instability" of suspension spans that shook Galloping Gertie, but a much simpler affliction—"insufficient anchorage against wind uplift," the disease of the Tay Bridge.

The Chester Bridge was promptly rebuilt—fastened down tighter on the same piers. Meantime, the State of Michigan recoiled from the Moisseiff design for a Mackinac suspension as if from the presence of a rattlesnake.

But the Mackinac Bridge, a sixty-year-old dream at last on the threshold of realization, could hardly be put aside. An actual construction operation had even been carried out: a mole from the St. Ignace (northern) side of the Straits (*Figure 69*).

The war intervening, the Mackinac project was shelved temporarily while Michigan built tanks and airplanes. After the war a new enabling act was passed by the legislature. The new act contained a helpless layman's solution to the design problem. The Dean of the Engineering School at the University of Michigan was requested to name a three-man board of engineers to report on the project. Dean Ivan Crawford named, in alphabetical order, Othmar H. Ammann, David B. Steinman, and Glenn B. Woodruff. According to reports, this troika resolved itself into two belligerents—Ammann and Stein-

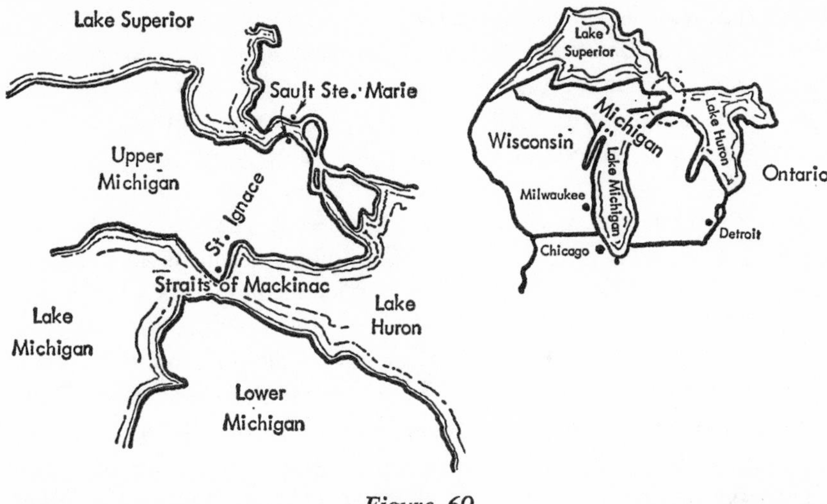

Figure 69

man—and a referee, Woodruff. In the end, Ammann withdrew entirely and Steinman was commissioned to design the bridge.

The Mackinac Bridge, whose robust nickname is Big Mack, presents something of the same contrast with the ribbon-like Tacoma Narrows as the Firth of Forth monster does with the spidery Tay. In each case, a too-weak predecessor that collapsed led to a bridge that almost could be criticized for being too strong. At the Straits of Mackinac, Steinman faced four separate problems:

1. caverns believed to lie under the Straits bed;
2. huge ice masses that piled up every winter and threatened to smash piers and foundations;
3. terrific winds, very reminiscent of those that tunneled down Puget Sound onto Galloping Gertie;
4. high tolls to redeem the $100 million in bonds sold to pay for construction. Mackinac is at the top of Michigan, almost three hundred miles from Detroit, in sparsely settled country.

Geological exploration disposed of Point One. Point Two, the ice masses, was dealt with by brute force—pier foundations weighing an aggregate of nearly one million tons. Point Three was Steinman's particular triumph. His cables and anchorages were extraordinarily strong, and his bridge design was calculated carefully to foil wind forces. The truss (*not* a plate girder) was 38 feet deep, exactly 1/100 of the tower-to-tower distance of 3800 feet. But in addition, Steinman provided wide open spaces between the trusses and the outer edges of the roadway. The trusses are spaced 68 feet apart, and the roadway is only 48 feet wide, leaving a 10-foot space on either side. Finally, Steinman made the two outer traffic lanes solid and the two inner lanes and central mall open-grid. This combination, according to Steinman, raised the critical wind velocity of the bridge to infinity. As a literal claim this may be taken *cum grano salis,* in view of the fact that wind pressure increases as the square of wind velocity, yet there is no question that Steinman's design is an absolute answer to the wind problems—both hurricane and aerodynamic instability.

In November 1955, a 76-mile-per-hour gale hit the unfinished bridge, hurling tremendous piles of ice against the foundations. The 552-foot towers withstood the pressure easily, even though lacking half of their 220,000 rivets.

The Big Mack is undoubtedly there to stay. In fact, only Point Four has given the slightest trouble since construction. And Michigan state government experts are convinced that completion of the new through expressway north from Detroit will assure tolls enough to retire the bonds ahead of time, even apart from the virtual certainty of population growth in northern Michigan. But the ready flow of the bond market in the 1950s, contrasted with the dollar-by-dollar calculations of the 1930s, gives at least one clue to the dramatic structural differences between Gertie and Mack.

The Mackinac Bridge, completed in 1957, is David Steinman's chief monument. Steinman died in 1960, his aerodynamic theories largely vindicated, his reputation the highest in the bridge engineering profession—with the possible exception of that of his rival of nearly fifty years, Othmar H. Ammann, who has just captured the world's span-length record with his Verrazano-Narrows Bridge over New York Harbor—a bridge Steinman had hoped to build.

This tremendous link from Staten Island to Brooklyn, with an ultimate capacity of twelve traffic lanes on two decks, is suspended between two great towers, one standing in shallow water 250 feet off the Staten Island shore, the other off the Brooklyn shore on the site formerly occupied by Fort Lafayette. From tower to tower the span is 4260 feet, exceeding the Golden Gate by sixty feet. The bridge will be open to traffic in 1965.

"Everything about the Narrows Bridge," observed the *Engineering News-Record,* is "big, bigger or biggest." The four steel cables cost more than the whole Golden Gate Bridge, and must support a dead weight of 120,000 tons plus their own weight of 39,000 tons. The maximum anticipated live loading, by contrast, is only 15,600 tons. Picked by the A.S.C.E. as one of "Seven Wonders of the World Under Way in 1963" (the Chesapeake Bay Bridge-Tunnel is another), the Narrows design actually had to take account of the curvature of the earth. The towers, exactly perpendicular to the earth's surface, are one and five-eighths inches farther apart at their summits than at their bases.

Possibly the most interesting feature of the Narrows Bridge is its cost, $325 million. While it was under construction, the Throgs Neck Bridge over Long Island Sound was completed at a cost of $90 million, and the double-decking of the George Washington, involving erection of huge new approach viaducts, was carried out at a cost of $180 million. Thus New York bridge construction costing $595 million will be completed in a space of seven years, 1958–65.

No private company could have done it. The old privately promoted, privately financed bridge is a thing of the past in the United States. (One of the last major bridges built by a private company is the Bear Mountain, a 1632-foot span over the Hudson above New York, finished in 1924.) Modern bridges are built by "authorities," that is, public corporations usually set up by state or municipal governments. The Narrows Bridge, like the Throgs Neck, is a project of the Triborough Bridge and Tunnel Authority, the public corporation that collects tolls on the Triborough Bridge, which connects Manhattan and Long Island with each other and with the New York mainland by means of a three-and-a-quarter-mile complex of suspension, truss, viaduct spans, and a major lift, and which was built in the 1930s at a cost of $60 million. At a quarter a car it turned out to be a brilliant financial success. The Triborough Authority also owns the Bronx-Whitestone, the Henry Hudson, the Marine Parkway, the Cross-Bay Parkway bridges and the Queens-Midtown and Brooklyn-Battery tunnels. Its latest, most towering offspring, the Narrows, not only will eventually pay for itself, but also will have a salubrious effect on tolls collected by three bridges that connect Staten Island and New Jersey by encouraging motorists going from New Jersey to Long Island and Connecticut to bypass New York City. These three bridges, the Bayonne, the Goethals, and the Outerbridge Crossing, which among them anticipate an increase in traffic between 1963 and 1975 of 150 percent—from ten million vehicles to twenty-five million—do not belong to the Triborough Authority but to its older sister, the New York Port Authority. This was set up back in 1921 by New York and New Jersey, and has financed the Holland and Lincoln tunnels, the Lincoln Third Tube, and the George Washington Bridge, including the new double-deck and approach construction.

When one speaks of long-span bridges, distinctions must be made. Suspension bridges are normally compared in terms of the center span, tower to tower (midpoint to midpoint). Thus the Golden Gate, with relatively short side spans, is longer than the Mackinac, tower to tower, but shorter from anchorage to anchorage.

Further, many bridges, suspension and otherwise, are prolonged enormously by approach viaducts. The Mackinac's total length—five miles—is far short of a record. Across Lake Pontchartrain in Louisiana runs a 24-mile trestle. Viaducts and causeways run over the Great Salt Lake in Utah, over the Florida Keys, over the Thousand Islands in the St. Lawrence, across the Danube estuary, across Lake Maracaibo in Venezuela, and in many other places. The longest in the world probably is the ninety-mile pile-and-trestle structure at Tsao-chow, in the Hwang-Ho Valley of China. Viaducts run through shallow water, hop across islands, and here and there vault deeper water with suspension, cantilever, or truss spans, giving the motorist or railroad passenger the odd sensation of riding on wheels across open water. Usually these long trestles have been carried out with little more than ordinary difficulty, though two locomotives plunged into Great Salt Lake during construction of the Salt Lake trestle. Among the bridge complexes of the twentieth century, the most difficult of construction was the eight-mile San Francisco-Oakland Bay Bridge, a more formidable engineering project than even its glamorous sister, the Golden Gate, which was difficult enough. The principal Golden Gate problem was sinking the foundation for the south pier, sited 1125 feet from shore in 85 feet of water. The pier had to hit bedrock to give the bridge an earthquake-proof foundation. The rapidly running tides, frequent storms (one carried away practically the whole access trestle to the pier), and fog (a wandering freighter crashed into the access trestle and destroyed 300 feet of it), plus the problem of blasting rock deep under water, made this pier a fair-sized headache for Chief Engineer Joseph B. Strauss. The rock-blasting was carried out by an ingenious trick: a steel shaft chipped a hole in the bedrock, then a long, slim bomb was carried down and detonated by a time fuse. The towers rise a record 746 feet and the roadway itself carries traffic at the dizzy height of 265 feet above the water. Yet the Golden Gate represented more an exercise in size, like the Firth of Forth, than a pioneering of new ground in design or construction.

The Bay Bridge also involved no new design principles. But the basic problem of bridging the eight-mile Bay, broken by the rocky outcropping of Yerba Buena Island, presented a challenge unmatched by any other contemporary bridge project (*Figure 70*).

Figure 70

Chief Engineer C. H. Purcell had a choice between trying to bridge the San Francisco-to-Yerba Buena gap in a single span of over a mile and trying to sink intermediate foundations in water from 200 to 300 feet deep. He chose the second alternative. The result is the only double suspension bridge in the world—two suspension bridges with main spans of 2310 feet and a common anchorage at the midpoint. To reach bedrock at a distance (265 feet) far below that in which men can work, a revolutionary caisson was needed. It was invented by Daniel Moran, leading expert on deep-water engineering. Moran's invention was a "multiple-dome caisson," a stupendous honeycomb of separate 15-foot-diameter cylinders. Each of these could be sealed and filled with compressed air, but this was rarely done. Usually a single diver descended to handle the rock problem.

The central anchorage, the common anchorage of the two spans, was built inside the world's largest caisson, 92 by 197 feet, sunk in over a hundred feet of water and pushed one hundred feet through the bottom of the Bay. Giant clamshell buckets, dropped down inside the cylinders, hauled out mud and rocks. Sometimes the weird monster tilted capriciously as one side or the other encountered soft ground. Then the men above ran round like Lilliputians around Gulliver, shouting orders, turning valves, bringing pressure on one side and reducing it on the other, until the mammoth was under control again.

Two tower foundations were sunk in deep water, one between the central anchorage and the San Francisco shore, the other between the central anchorage and Yerba Buena. The two other tower foundations were constructed in shallow water, the two end anchorages on either shore. On the Oakland side of Yerba Buena, a cantilever was built to carry the roadway over deep water, to where it could be taken over by viaduct spans. The one problem remaining—Yerba Buena itself—was solved by blasting the world's largest-bore tunnel through the rock.

An even stranger combination crossing is the new Lower Chesapeake Bay Bridge-Tunnel, scheduled to be completed early in 1964. The Upper Bay is already spanned by a seven-and-three-quarter-mile bridge complex, made up of three cantilevers, a suspension, a truss, and a long viaduct. The new crossing of the bay's mouth will eliminate the ferry delays on scenic Ocean Hiway and, more important, will tie the Norfolk-Hampton Roads region to the Eastern Shore of Virginia. Altogether, the project spans seventeen and a half miles of water at a cost of $140 million, virtually all of which has gone for the work itself. The key consideration in the project, of course, was the navigation channels. How high should a bridge over so important a national waterway as Chesapeake Bay be built? The answer was rendered academic by the decision to cross the navigation channels not with bridges but with tunnels. Tunnels are usually almost as cheap to build as high-level bridges, and leave the channel completely clear. On the other hand, trestles are cheaper to build than tunnels, and no one ever suggested taking the whole seventeen-mile crossing under water.

The final design called for twelve miles of prestressed concrete trestles for the approaches, two tunnels of a mile each for the navigation channels, and two high-level bridges near the north end for subsidiary channels (*Figure 71*).

Problem: how do you dig a tunnel a mile long in the middle of an open stretch of water, and how do you connect it to a bridge or viaduct? Solution: you build an island. Since there were to be two

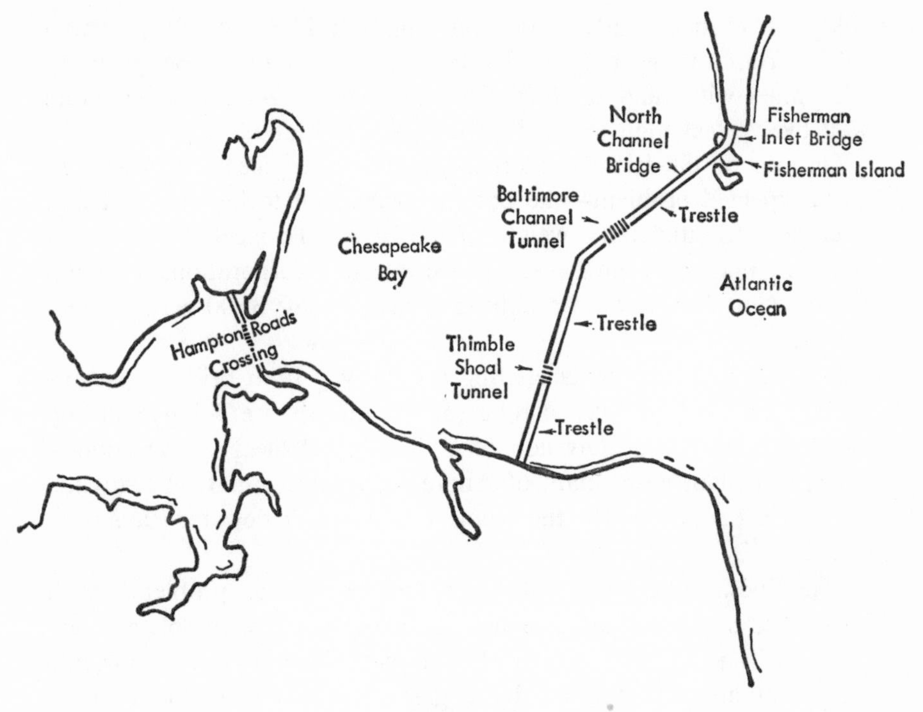

Figure 71

tunnels, it took four islands to provide portals and bridge connections.

Still another "island," a De Long "floating island," is involved in the construction. A sort of super-Texas-Tower, this huge rig floats into position, then puts legs down into the bay to give it a good firm hold. Then it does the pile-driving for the twelve-mile trestle. Another rig, nicknamed the "two-headed monster," follows along, rolling on top of the piles. It levels the piles ahead with one head while with the other it caps those behind and prepares them for the roadway units, which are added by a third traveling monster.

The tunnels themselves are relatively simple, built by the build-and-sink method. Prefabricated sections of steel tube are dropped into position in a dredged trench. The portal islands are something else again. Merritt-Chapman and Scott, the New York firm engaged in this part of the operation, builders of build-and-sink tunnels at Pasadena (Texas), Norfolk, Hampton Roads, and Baltimore Harbor, admitted that they never had come up against anything quite like this job. Each island is a "truncated pyramid," in cross section a trapezoid with rounded ends, 1500 feet long and 230 feet wide, sloping gently from top to bottom. Each is composed of a rocky riprap shell filled with sand dredged from the bay. A reinforced concrete wall twelve feet high extends all around the island.

On one of the islands, Merritt-Chapman's engineers encountered an unexpected problem—the bottom turned out to be very soft and likely to settle under the weight of the island. To meet this threat, a company known as the American Dewatering Corporation, of Hackensack, New Jersey, was brought in to install some 3600 vertical sand drains.

Does all this seem to be getting a long way from bridges? Nevertheless, the steel sections of tube for the tunnels are being made by the American Bridge Division of United States Steel Corporation—a sort of distant descendant of Andrew Carnegie and J. H. Linville. The basic contractor for the whole crossing is Tidewater-Raymond-Kiewit.

The Chesapeake has involved hazards as well as problems, with hurricanes several times threatening havoc to the incomplete structure and its $15 million worth of equipment. The huge De Long pile driver actually was toppled by a gale, and two men aboard only survived thanks to a daring rescue by helicopter. Bridge-building cannot be said to have gone completely tame quite yet.

Air and space travel notwithstanding, bridges continue to make news in the 1960s, especially outside the United States. As late as 1958, the fifteen longest suspension bridges in the world were all in the United States. But in 1959, France completed a 1995-foot span over the lower Seine, and Britain, where once the cantilever reigned, undertook three long suspensions—over the Severn, the Forth, and the Tay (where passengers on the railroad bridge still occasionally toss a penny into the tragedy-haunted Firth). These very long (over 3000 foot) British spans are exceeded by the new suspension bridge over the mouth of the Tagus at Lisbon, which at 3317 feet is the longest outside the United States and the fifth longest in the world.

In India, two suspension spans end-to-end in the style of San Francisco's Bay Bridge will connect the island of Bombay to the mainland.

The suspension is not alone in making news. The cantilever is far from dead. New Orleans completed the world's third longest (longest in the United States) in 1958, with a main span of 1575 feet. In

British Columbia, a cantilever replaced a suspension bridge that had been pushed into the Peace River by a mud slide, and another was completed at Vancouver after a delay. The delay was occasioned by a serious accident—yes, serious accidents still happen—in which eighteen men died, a tragedy commemorated by a rock-and-roll song hit entitled "Steel Men."

Bridge records are made to be broken. In 1961 the longest prestressed concrete bridge in the western hemisphere was opened over Lake Oneida, New York, only to be outspanned in 1962 by the new bridge over Lake Maracaibo, Venezuela, the five-and-a-half-mile length of which includes five 771-foot concrete girders. The longest lift bridge in the world, 558 feet, opened across Arthur Kill, Staten Island-to-New Jersey. The longest concrete arch in the world sprang across Sydney Harbor, Australia—910 feet—while in England a new record for prestressed concrete girder was set with a 500-foot main span over the Medway. All these records are temporary.

A record more likely to stand is that of the covered bridge at Hartland, New Brunswick, Canada, over the St. John River. A sign reads, "You are now entering the longest covered bridge in the world, 1282 feet." Still more likely to keep its title indefinitely is the Syre bridge built at Plauen, Germany, in 1903. What record does this bridge hold? It is the longest stone-arch span ever built—295 feet. The arrival of reinforced concrete put a virtual end to stone.

In 1960 one of David Steinman's most interesting records was broken in Switzerland. This was the world's record for a transporter bridge—the single-cable suspension span by which primitive people rode in baskets over ravines. Steinman built his transporter as a "Sky-ride" for the Chicago World's Fair of 1933—an 1850-foot cable from which were hung ten cars in which 360 Fair visitors at a time were swung far above the Fair grounds. Why wouldn't Steinman's fun ride be practical to solve some of the transportation problems of modern cities? It would be. Rouen built one of 466 feet, followed by Marseille, whose transporter truss over the harbor carries cars 541 feet. England built several, including two 1000-footers, at Liverpool and Manchester. In 1960 a cableway over Lake Zurich finally exceeded Steiman's span. The Swiss transporter cable is 3300 feet long.

An unexpected American record is in pontoon bridges. Across Lake Washington, Seattle has built two tremendous floating bridges—6560 feet of concrete pontoon sections. Seattle's twins dwarf such rivals as Tasmania's 3165-foot floating span, also of concrete pontoons, over the Derwent, and the famous floating bridge across the Golden Horn at Istanbul, Turkey, of 1500 feet. All such long-span floating bridges have movable sections of one kind or another to let shipping pass.

In 1958, a 1271-foot steel arch—second only to the Bayonne in the United States—was built under auspices of the Department of the Interior below the Glen Canyon Dam, Utah. Rising 700 feet above the floor of the canyon below, the bridge is breathtaking for the tourist. Second longest arch, it is also the second highest bridge in the United States, topped only by the Royal Gorge Bridge over the Arkansas in Colorado, 1050 feet above the water.

The most glamorous bridge proposed in recent years is not in the United States. It is the project of a French engineering firm for the English Channel crossing. Because of the superior economy of a railroad tunnel, the Channel Bridge probably will not be built, at least within the foreseeable future. But the idea of bridging thirty-six miles of ocean is one to capture the imagination.

Curiously enough, this extraordinary bridge would not be particularly difficult to build. The Channel floor, only ninety feet down at the deepest point, and in places only about fifteen feet, is mostly solid gray chalk, easy to dig in and impervious to water. Planting bridge foundations would present no serious problems. This fact was known a hundred years ago, and proposals to bridge the Channel go back almost as far as the numerous projects for tunneling under it. Thomé de Gamond first designed a bridge in 1849. In the imperfect state of engineering and metal of that day the scheme was not very sound. But forty years later, in 1889, industrialist-politician Eugène Schneider and engineer H. Hersent, with the agreement of British engineers Sir John Fowler and Benjamin Baker (then completing the Forth Bridge) put forward a *Pont sur la Manche* design of impressive practicality. It called for a cantilever viaduct with fifty-five piers in the sea. Each main truss was to be supported by two piers one hundred meters apart; the cantilever truss would extend another 92.5 meters in either direction and be linked to the next cantilever truss by a suspended span of 65 meters. Thus the maximum span would be 250 meters, or 818 feet, hardly an excessive distance. Schneider and Hersent would have had a better chance if they had made their spans bigger, for the French Ministry of Marine promptly rejected the design as a menace to navigation.

Today, oddly enough, this argument against a bridge in the Channel has lost virtually all its force, and in fact has even been turned around. Piers supporting the four main spans of the middle section of the presently discussed bridge would stand 984 feet apart and serve as part of a radar-operated traffic-control system that some experts believe the Channel needs anyway.

Incidentally, one of the companies involved in the Channel Bridge project is Merritt-Chapman and Scott, the Chesapeake Bay Bridge firm.

Despite its cost—perhaps $700 million—we eventually may see a bridge built over the Channel, not perhaps instead of a tunnel, but in addition to one. A bridge has one unquestioned advantage over a tunnel—pleasure-driving.

We certainly will see the ocean bridged—or, more accurately, bridged again. Aside from bridges over narrow straits and bays, the ocean already has been bridged in a significant way by Denmark, whose crossing over the Little Belt is considered a model for pier-building in the open sea. Japan has recently completed a bridge across Ondo Strait between Kure and Kurahashi Islands. A bigger Japanese project calls for linking Honshu, the largest island of the archipelago, with Shikoku at Akashi Strait. The final decision may be in favor of a combination bridge and tunnel, meeting on Awaji Island.

Steinman, Ammann, and others have discussed the practicability of suspension bridges of two miles or more as a means of bridging deep ocean straits. Steinman designed a suspension bridge with a main span of over a mile for the Straits of Messina between Italy and Sicily.

Such a bridge, like the present Danish and Japanese bridges, would remain within the territorial waters of a single nation. In this respect the Channel Bridge would be a very different project, creating a legal problem that well might require United Nations action. In international waters, a potential navigational hazard can be built only with the consent of every maritime nation of the world. Russia, China, the Malagasy Republic, Argentina, Thailand, Ceylon, any nation with ships on the seas (even Switzerland!), can veto a Channel Bridge. If any nation, however small its shipping interest and however remote geographically, had a diplomatic quarrel with either Britain or France, nothing would be simpler for its government than to pigeonhole the request for permission to build piers in the Channel. Bridge-builders have solved all kinds of problems in the past—geological, metallurgical, medical, economic, and political—perhaps they can solve this one too.

24.

"By the Rude Bridge that Arched the Flood"

If little more is likely to be added to the history of the bridge in the future, there is at least a good sufficiency already in the past. Quite apart from their critical contributions to the peaceful development of civilization, bridges since earliest times have played a decisive role in war. Down to the age of missiles, rivers have formed great defensive barriers, and their crossings have been strategic prizes.

Broadly speaking, bridges have been easier to destroy than to rebuild, easier to defend than to capture. The British-invented Bailey Bridge of the Second World War, a series of truss panels that could be bolted together quickly, for the first time made bridge repair under fire a comparatively simple job, at least where the span was not too long.

Caesar, who had no Bailey bridges, used a stratagem on a famous occasion to construct a bridge in the face of the enemy. During the revolt of the Gauls under Vercingetorix, Caesar sought to cross the Allier River, but found the bridges destroyed and the army of Vercingetorix on the opposite bank. Concealing two legions in the forest, he marched the rest of his army upstream as if searching for a ford. The Gauls followed on their own side; the two hidden legions emerged from the forest, quickly rebuilt one of the bridges, and fortified the bridgehead. About-facing, Caesar countermarched and concentrated his army without the Gauls being able to interfere.

Caesar's Rhine Bridge

If we fully credit Caesar's own account, his legions built a bridge over the Rhine in ten days. The Roman legionary was a ready engineer, accustomed to building his own fortified camp at night wherever he found himself, and the account may be no exaggeration. A mechanical pile-driver, consisting of capstan, cable, and lever, to which rock could be fixed, was part of a legion's equipment. The Rhine bridge was built on piles driven in fours, two on the upstream side, two on the downstream, the pairs forty feet apart and inclined toward each other. Surviving members have been discovered in modern times, though the bridge was destroyed on the legions' return from their raid.

Xerxes at the Hellespont

Perhaps the most famous bridge ever built for a military purpose was the mile-long pontoon thrown across the Hellespont (Dardanelles) by the Persian king Xerxes in his expedition against Greece in 480 B.C. Our main source of information is the Greek Herodotus, writing a generation later, in an era of triumphant Athenian patriotism, and his figures inspire a certain skepticism: 1,700,000 Persians crossing the Hellespont in seven days and nights to attack Greece (whose total population probably did not number 1,700,000). Herodotus describes the bridge as composed of 676 ships in two parallel rows and gives minute details on their types, the means of fastening them together, etc. As he gives equally precise details about many obviously fanciful occurrences and reports numerous speeches exactly as the unrecorded speakers gave them, one may doubt these bridge details too. But that Xerxes led a large army into Greece is beyond dispute, and that the Hellespont was bridged is probable. Other ancient writers also refer to Xerxes' bridge. Plutarch has the Greek captain Aristides prudently argue against destroying it: "Instead of destroying that bridge, we should build another, that he may retire the more quickly from Europe." Perhaps Xerxes did not have the waters whipped and manacles cast into them, as Herodotus records, and possibly he did not even have his first, unsuccessful, engineers put to death. But long pontoon bridges are easily constructed, and often were in ancient times. Xerxes' predecessor, Darius the Great, bridged the Bosporus thirty years earlier in his war with the Scythians. In the fourth century B.C., Xenophon and his Greek mercenaries built a pontoon bridge in Persia which the soldier-historian describes in *The Retreat of the Ten Thousand*. Later in the same century, Alexander the Great had a corps of engineers in his army charged with bridging streams with pontoons. Their most notable span was thrown across the Indus during Alexander's brief invasion of India.

The Roman legions built countless bridges, both timber-pile and pontoon, in all the corners of the far-flung Empire. One of the most famous was that thrown across the Euphrates by Julian the Apostate in his campaign against the Sassanid Persian king, Shapor the Great. Shapor's predecessor had captured a Roman army and employed his prisoners in building Valerian's Bridge. Julian fared little better, being mortally wounded in battle and, according to the pious chroniclers, at least, addressing famous last words to heaven: "Thou hast conquered, O Galilean." But the largest of all Roman pontoons was built not for military but for merely recreational purposes. The Emperor Caligula caused a tremendous floating structure to be assembled in the Bay of Baiae for games and displays in front of the summer palace. Part of his aim, at least if we believe another interested historian (Suetonius), was to outdo Xerxes.

Horatius

If Herodotus' account of events that took place a generation earlier is suspect, it is hard to take seriously Livy's very circumstantial story of Horatius' defense of the Sublician Bridge some seven hundred years before. But Livy's rendering of the original legend, if that is what it is, has a certain economical eloquence that surpasses the sonorous verses of Macaulay:

> On the appearance of the enemy the country people fled into the city as best they could. The weak places in the defences were occupied by military posts; elsewhere the walls and the Tiber were deemed sufficient protection. The enemy would have forced their way over the Sublician Bridge, had it not been for one man, Horatius Cocles. The good fortune of Rome provided him as her bulwark on that memorable day.
>
> He chanced to be on guard at the bridge when he saw the Janiculum Hill taken by a sudden assault, and the enemy rushing down from it to

the river, whilst his own men, a panic-stricken mob, deserted their posts and threw away their arms. Reproaching them one after another for their cowardice, he tried to stop them, appealing to them in heaven's name to stand, and declaring that it was in vain for them to seek safety in flight whilst leaving the bridge open behind them, since there would soon be more of the enemy on the Palatine or the Capitoline than there were on the Janiculum.

Then he shouted to them to break down the bridge by sword or fire, or by whatever means they could; he would meet the enemy's attack so far as one man could keep them at bay.

He advanced to the head of the bridge, a conspicuous figure, standing there alone. The enemy were astounded at his courage. Two men were kept by a sense of honor from deserting him—Lartius and Herminius, both men of high birth and renowned bravery. For a brief interval the three repulsed the wild onset of the enemy. Then, while only a small portion of the bridge remained intact and those who were cutting it down called on them to retire, Horatius insisted that his companions retreat.

Turning eyes dark with menace upon the Etruscan chiefs, he challenged them to single combat. For some time they hesitated, each looking to the others to begin. At length shame roused them to action, and raising a shout they hurled their javelins from all sides on their solitary foe. He caught them on his outthrust shield, and with unshaken resolution kept his place on the bridge. They were just attempting to dislodge him by a charge when the crash of the broken bridge and the shout which the Romans raised at seeing the work completed stayed the attack by filling them with sudden panic.

Then said Horatius: "Tiber, holy Father, I pray thee to receive into thy holy stream these arms and this thy warrior." So saying, fully armed, he leaped into the Tiber, and though many missiles fell over him he swam across in safety to his friends.

The State showed its gratitude for such courage; his statue was set up in the Forum, and as much land given to him as he could drive the plough round in one day. Besides this public honor, the citizens individually showed their feelings; in spite of great scarcity each, in proportion to his means, sacrificed what he could from his own store as a gift to Horatius.

"Scots wha' hae . . ."

Possibly the most successful tactical employment of a bridge in military annals occurred in Scotland in September 1297. The Scottish army under Wallace was posted on the heights above narrow Stirling Bridge. The Earl of Surrey led the English army across to attack: Wallace waited till the English were divided in two, then sounded the charge. The head of the bridge was seized by the Scots and held by a small force while the rest of them fell upon and cut to pieces the part of the English army that had crossed.

Burnside at Antietam

On the other hand, a bridge's importance may be exaggerated. On another September day five and a half centuries later, two American armies faced each other across a little Maryland stream called Antietam Creek. The stronger Union Army won the battle, but the better-led Confederates escaped from the field with less loss than the victors. There were various reasons for this, but a Civil War historian, Colonel Joseph D. Mitchell, ascribes part of the Union failure to Major General Ambrose Burnside's concentration on capturing a stone-arch bridge built as part of the National Pike a generation before and known since as Burnside's Bridge. Burnside's troops could have waded the creek more expeditiously. The delay permitted another Ambrose, red-shirted Confederate General Ambrose Hill, to arrive from Harpers Ferry, seventeen miles away, with the missing fraction of Lee's army. The ultimately indecisive battle led to the prolongation of the war.

John Brown's Bridge

In his famous raid of 1859, John Brown crossed to Harpers Ferry over the Baltimore and Ohio Railroad bridge. When the war broke out, one of the first Confederate cavalry raids partly destroyed this bridge, which the railroad rebuilt, and which served Union troops in the Shenandoah Valley. In 1863, in advance of Lee's invasion of Pennsylvania, Confederate cavalry raiders Jones and Imboden wrecked it more thoroughly, but after Gettysburg it was rebuilt once more.

The Stone Bridge at Bull Run

The first musket shots of the Civil War were fired at the famous Stone Bridge over Bull Run which is still standing. Captured in the beginning of the battle by Sherman's brigade, the bridge was held by the Federals all day and provided the principal route for their retreat at the end of the disastrous battle.

Captain Andrews Steals the General

One of the most incredible adventures of the Civil War, or of any war, is the famous attempt by Captain James Andrews in April 1862 to burn the railroad bridges of Georgia and east Tennessee and thereby facilitate the capture of Chattanooga. The idea was his own. With two dozen volunteers, Ohioans like himself, Andrews made his way south in civilian dress from the Union lines in Tennessee to Marietta, Georgia, close to Atlanta. His plan was to seize a Confederate train near Marietta, run it north, burn several covered bridges—thus cutting off the Confederate army in Chattanooga—and then abandon the train and slip back through the enemy lines on foot.

Some of the men never reached the rendezvous, but twenty met in Andrews' hotel room in Marietta according to plan. Several fresh difficulties appeared to make the attempt hopeless—Big Shanty, where the locomotive was to be seized, had been turned into a Confederate army camp and the trains along the line were filled with soldiers. But Andrews announced his determination to carry out the mission or die in the attempt, and offered the privilege of withdrawing to anyone who wished. Not a man withdrew.

Next morning the twenty Ohioans boarded the train north. At Big Shanty, the train stopped for breakfast. The conductor and engineer, along with most of the passengers, left the train. Andrews' two engineers immediately sprang into the empty cab of the *General,* the locomotive. Andrews and other men uncoupled the first three (baggage) cars and, all having clambered inside, Andrews gave the signal. The throttle was yanked wide open. As the train raced away, the conductor, engineer, and passengers came pouring out of the station.

The conductor, W. A. Fuller, proved as determined and resourceful as Andrews himself. He at once took off after the *General*—on foot. Hopeless though it seemed, his quick action proved decisive in the chase that followed. Anthony Murphy, another railroad man, came pounding after him. Some distance down the track the two came to a siding, and on the siding stood a handcar. Running it onto the line, they pumped for dear life.

37. Drawbridges at Chicago have made history, ever since J. A. L. Waddell's famous South Halsted Street vertical lift. The five visible in the picture above are all double-leaf bascules over the Chicago River. They operate on exactly the same principle as the defensive drawbridges of medieval castles.

TWO MIGHTY SUSPENSION BRIDGES

38, 39. *(Above)* New York's George Washington completed by O. H. Ammann in 1931, 3500 feet from tower to tower, doubled the record span length in one leap. Because of its eight-lane breadth and great weight, it stood securely for thirty-one years without any stiffening truss. In 1962 the lower deck and truss were added. *(Below)* The Mackinac Straits Bridge in Michigan is the masterpiece of D. B. Steinman, completed in 1957 with a center span of 3800 feet, and measuring a record 8614 feet from anchorage to anchorage. Built in the light of aerodynamic research inspired by Galloping Gertie, the Mackinac Bridge is notable for its very high safety factor against wind pressure of all kinds.

CHESAPEAKE BAY: A GREAT MODERN BRIDGE COMPLEX

40, 41. *(Above)* An engineer watches as barges float a truss span into position between prestressed concrete piers. *(Below)* The first trestle section extends three and a third miles from Chesapeake Beach, between Norfolk and Virginia Beach, to the first of four man-made islands. The islands were created to provide portals for the mile-long tunnels that carry the crossing under the main traffic channels of the Bay. The whole crossing is seventeen and a half miles with two high-level bridges.

SAN FRANCISCO'S LONG-SPAN BRIDGES

42, 43. The Golden Gate and Oakland-Bay bridges were begun simultaneously in 1933. Three years and several unprecedented problems later, both were nearing completion *(above).* The twin suspension spans of the Bay Bridge meet in a central anchorage sunk to bedrock at the unheard-of depth of 240 feet. The Golden Gate Bridge *(below, from the ocean side),* at 4200 feet, was the longest bridge of any type ever built till completion of the Verrazano-Narrows Bridge, New York, in 1963.

44. The Oakland-Bay Bridge, San Francisco, seen here from the San Francisco side, is a remarkable eight-mile mixture of engineering feats: two suspension bridges end to end, then the world's largest-bore tunnel through rocky Yerba Buena Island, then the 1400-foot cantilever over the East Bay Channel, then five truss spans and a series of girder spans over the shallow water on the Oakland side.

THE ENGLISH CHANNEL BRIDGE

45. Almost as many Channel bridge as Channel tunnel schemes have been propounded. Above is one put forward by Eugène Schneider, French industrialist and political leader, in 1895: a series of cantilevers of unusual design with short suspended spans between. The hard chalk Channel floor made such a design feasible, but it was vetoed by the French government as a navigation hazard. Radar and sonar have mitigated or even eliminated this problem, and today the only real obstacle to a Channel bridge is cost.

46. The Verrazano-Narrows Bridge over New York Harbor is today the world's record-holder, 4260 feet from center to center of towers. *(Right)* Working platform for north catwalk on west side of tower. Note side span catwalk sections being attached to ropes.

CHINESE BRIDGES
OLD AND NEW

47, 48. The zigzag bridge leading to the Willow Pattern Tea House in Shanghai was designed to baffle evil spirits attempt ing to cross.

Almost as unusual is the design for the modern railroad bridge in the mountains of Yunnan, two mutually supporting trusses braced against the mountainside.

THE SAGA OF
REMAGEN

49, 50. World War II was shortened by the capture of this bridge over the Rhine on March 7, 1945, a feat of arms made possible by a still unsolved mystery, the failure of the German demolition charge to go off. An emergency charge blew the hinge of the upstream arch on the east side of the river *(above)*. GIs of the Ninth Armored Division nevertheless crossed and captured the bridge. A fierce battle raged around the bridgehead for ten days, until the sudden collapse of the span on March 17, as Ninth Armored engineers worked desperately to save it. Bottom picture was taken minutes after the collapse.

The road was single track. Andrews planned to follow the train's regular schedule and pass oncoming trains at the designated sidings. There were only three trains to be passed, after which it would be full speed to the Oostenaula and Chickamauga bridges. With these bridges burned, pursuit would be cut off and Chattanooga isolated. Periodic halts were made to rip down the telegraph wire that ran alongside the right-of-way.

Unluckily for Andrews, it had started to rain early in the morning and kept up all day. Also, the scheduled trains from Chattanooga proved to be off schedule and forced the *General* to wait at sidings. Andrews bluffed his way through several delays with a show of temper and a story that he was carrying ammunition for General Beauregard.

Meantime, the resolute Fuller and Murphy pumped their way to Etowah, surviving a derailment caused by Andrews' men tearing up a section of track. At Etowah an old locomotive, the *Yonah,* stood on a siding. Commandeering a detachment of Confederate troops, Fuller now set off in real pursuit. The *Yonah* pulled into Kingston, Georgia, where Andrews had had to wait for two freight trains to pass, just four minutes after the *General* had left there. Fuller commandeered one of the freight trains and resumed chase with a locomotive and a couple of troop-laden boxcars.

A few miles farther on, Andrews and his men stopped to tear down the telegraph wires again. They had just begun to pry up rails when the whistle of the pursuing train was heard. With a last desperate effort the men broke the rail and leaped back on board. Getting up a speed of sixty miles an hour, Andrews made it to Calhoun just as an express was coming out. He talked the express engineer into backing onto a siding and letting him through.

Meantime Fuller stopped short of the broken rail, jumped off with Murphy and again ran on foot, followed by the detachment of troops. They soon met the express train, which Fuller commandeered and backed into a siding. Uncoupling the engine—the *Texas*—and the tender, and piling his soldiers aboard, he started north again.

A few miles farther, Andrews stopped once more to tear down telegraph wires and pry up a rail. William Pittenger, of the 2nd Ohio Volunteers, recalled later:

> If one rail could now be lifted we would be in a few minutes at Oostenaula bridge, and, that burned, the rest of the task would be little more than simple manual labor, with the enemy powerless. We worked with a will.
>
> But in a moment the tables were turned! Not far behind we heard

the scream of a locomotive bearing down on us with lightning speed! The men on board were in plain sight and well armed. Two minutes, perhaps one, would have removed the rail at which we were toiling; then the game would have been in our hands. . . . But the most desperate efforts were in vain. The rail was simply bent, and we hurried to our engine and darted away, while remorselessly after us thundered the enemy.

The chase was resumed at breakneck speed. Andrews cut loose a boxcar, but the *Texas* simply slowed down, bumped it, and pushed it ahead to a siding. Andrews had the crossties, which he had collected to set fire to the bridges, tossed onto the track. The *Texas* slowed and cleared them off. The *General* plunged into the Oostenaula covered bridge; there was no time to start a fire. Andrews ordered the rear boxcar stripped of wood to feed his engine and the car itself set afire. At the Chickamauga covered bridge, the car was cut loose. Ordinarily the bridge would have caught like tinder, but it was soaked from the day's rain. Before the blaze could be started well, the indomitable Fuller caught up once more, moved the *Texas* out onto the bridge, and shoved the flaming boxcar ahead to the next siding.

Too closely pursued to stop for wood and water, the *General* was nearly out of steam. Andrews halted and undertook a last heroic expedient. To cover the escape of his men, he reversed the *General's* engines and ran her back, meaning to crash into the *Texas*. But the *General* barely crawled under her minimal steam pressure, and the *Texas* got only a bump. Andrews and his men, armed only with pistols, nearly all were captured. Latter-day pageantry to the contrary, the Civil War was serious and spies were hanged. That was the fate of James Andrews and seven others. Trial of the remaining fourteen was postponed because of the rapid advance of Union forces. Taken to Atlanta, the fourteen made a daring break, attacking their guards in broad daylight. Eight reached Union lines. The others were recaptured and remained in Confederate prisons until exchanged in 1863 by a special arrangement.

Andrews and all his Ohioans, living and dead, were awarded a special tribute by act of Congress. It was called the Medal of Honor.

Grant's Pontoons Set a Record

The Union army, especially, made frequent use of pontoon bridges. The efficiency of these American constructions was the envy of

European military engineers. The Army of the Potomac bridged the Potomac at Harpers Ferry in eight hours. French and German engineers in the war of 1870 took from two to three days to bridge comparable rivers. At Fredericksburg, however, the army's pontoons were delayed on the road by bad weather, their failure to arrive on time contributing to the Union defeat. Effective employment of pontoons across the Tennessee River, on the other hand, enabled Grant first to open supply lines and then to attack Missionary Ridge successfully.

A year later, commanding the Army of the Potomac, Grant built the biggest military pontoon bridge since Xerxes. This was a 2100-foot span across the James River opposite Richmond. The bridge, consisting of 101 pontoons, was put together in the remarkable time of eight hours. Had some of Grant's subordinate commanders moved as quickly as his engineers, the bridge would have made possible the capture of Petersburg and a quicker ending of the war.

"Bean Poles and Corn Stacks"

But the most important Civil War bridges were the railroad crossings, crucial to the supply lines of all the Union armies. Few were over very wide rivers; most spanned insignificant creeks. But they were the most vulnerable part of a railway line, and Confederate raiders and partisans constantly destroyed them while the Union Army and the railroad companies doggedly rebuilt. Spindly trestles were nailed together in a few hours to fill in breaks. The result was by no means as strong as a Bailey bridge, but locomotives were still small enough to be carried on such light, temporary scaffoldings. Of course there were plenty of accidents. The most endlessly harassed and most tirelessly repaired of all railroad lines was probably the little Louisville and Nashville. For four years the L & N's bridges, as well as its rolling stock, were targets for Morgan's raiders, the armies of Kirby Smith and Bragg, and, above all, the bands of guerrillas who infested Kentucky and Tennessee. The L & N's chief engineer, Albert Fink, a German immigrant and inventor of a well-known truss, reported in 1862 that several of his bridges had been wrecked twice during the year, a few of them three times. So well did Fink do his repair job that the L & N was the only line in combat areas not seized by the government. All the other railroad repair work fell into the laps of Colonel Herman Haupt, another bridge-builder as well as a tunnel-builder of note, and General Daniel McCallum, inventor of the McCallum Arched Truss. Haupt and McCallum repaired a total of *twenty-six miles* of railroad bridges during the war. One of Haupt's feats of rapid trestle construction brought a Lincolnesque comment from the President, who visited it and told government colleagues on his return: "Gentlemen, I have witnessed the most remarkable structure that human eyes have ever rested upon. That man Haupt has built a bridge across Potomac Creek, about four hundred feet long and eighty feet high, in nine days, with common soldiers, over which loaded trains are running every hour, and upon my word there is nothing in it but bean poles and corn stacks."

Napoleon at the Bridge of Lodi

Napoleon captured, defended, destroyed, and built more bridges than any other general. Bridges played an especially important role in his first campaign in Italy in 1796–97, a campaign that had decisive effect on his own fortunes and on history. Twenty-six-year-old General Bonaparte succeeded in using the narrow, deep, swift rivers of Lombardy to divide the larger Austrian army while keeping his own intact. Several bridges won fame as scenes of bloody fighting. On the one over the Adda at Lodi, Napoleon received the nickname "The Little Corporal" from his admiring grenadiers. The one over the Mincio at Borghetto was captured by the French, recaptured by the Austrians seeking to raise the siege of Mantua, and finally recaptured and held by the French. The bridge over the Alpon at Arcola saw the fiercest struggle of all, which raged not only back and forth on the timber bridge but extended to the causeway over the marsh behind it. After three days of fighting, the Austrians, hard pressed to hold the bridge, heard French trumpets sounding the charge behind them. The bridge defenders hastily pulled out to the north, and the whole army was forced to retreat. The trumpets were not from a cavalry regiment at all, but from a file of trumpeters that Napoleon thoughtfully had sent round to the enemy's rear.

Murat Tricks the Austrians

Another ruse, this one by Napoleon's cavalry commander, Murat, captured another bridge for him in 1805, when he was pursuing the Russian army up the Danube. When Murat arrived at the Floridsdorf Bridge, he found the Austrians at the other end preparing to blow it up. Leaving the troops behind, Murat and Lannes, the commander of the advance guard, rode across the bridge with a few staff officers, as if to parley. The two marshals kept up the pretense at the Austrian end, behaving as if an armistice were about to be made. Meantime a few grenadiers slipped across the bridge, and suddenly the French officers drew their sabers. The scuffle that followed gave the French cavalry time to gallop over and the bridge was captured intact.

Six Bridges in a Night

In 1809 the Austrian army under the able Archduke Karl fought Napoleon to a standstill when he tried to cross the Danube south of Vienna. With great difficulty the French engineers lashed pontoons together in the teeth of the spring flood; the Austrians sent floating rams and fire rafts down the river and wrecked the bridge. At the end of a desperate two days' fight, Napoleon's army, badly battered and barely hanging on, pulled back to the island of Lobau, where it was blockaded.

A month later, in June, Napoleon received a strong reinforcement—the Army of Italy, commanded by his stepson, Eugène de Beauharnais. Picking a hole in the archduke's defenses, Napoleon carried out a night maneuver of formidable intricacy in the middle of a terrific rainstorm. His engineers built no fewer than six pontoons across the various Danube channels, and at daybreak Napoleon confronted the enemy with his entire united army of 150,000 men and 400 guns. This tremendous engineering exertion was rewarded by victory in the bitterly fought two-day battle of Wagram, in which the undaunted archduke strove vainly to turn the French left and destroy the precious pontoons again.

The Beresina

Seven years later the tide of fortune that had carried Napoleon so far began its sudden reversal. The frost-bitten remnants of the Grand Army, retreating across the Russian snows, reached the Beresina, a river whose swift current kept it from freezing. General Eblé's pontooners waded out into the icy water and built a bridge. In Balzac's novel *The Country Doctor,* an old Napoleonic veteran, Goguelat, regales a peasant audience in a barn with the story of the emperor. One of his listeners, Gondrin, also a veteran, is deaf, but follows with his eyes the story, which Goguelat has told a hundred times before. When Goguelat, whose narrative is a marvelous mixture of history, personal experience, superstition, and humor, reaches the retreat from Moscow, he pays a special tribute to his deaf friend:

"Well, the next thing is the Beresina. . . . There it was that the pontooners saved the army, for the pontooners stood firm at their posts; it was there that Gondrin behaved like a hero, and he is the sole survivor of all the men who were dogged enough to stand in the river so as to build a bridge on which the army crossed over, and so escaped the Russians, who still respected the Grand Army on account of its past victories. And Gondrin is an accomplished soldier," he went on, pointing to his friend, who was gazing at him with the rapt attention peculiar to deaf people, "a distinguished soldier who deserves to have your very highest esteem."

Goguelat ends his story with "Long live Napoleon, the father of the soldier, the father of the people!" To which the old pontooner adds, "Long live General Eblé!"

The Pont d'Ièna

When Marshal Blücher entered Paris in 1814 with the Allied Armies of Occupation, the old Prussian hero was incensed by the sight of the Pont d'Ièna, a new bridge named after Napoleon's great victory over the Prussians. He is said to have ordered it blown up. Louis XVIII, just returned to Paris after twenty-two years of exile, wrote to the King of Prussia: "I beg your Majesty to interpose his authority. . . . If you do not care to grant this favor, I urge you to let me know at what hour the bridge will be blown up, so that I may place myself in the center."

Concord Bridge

Two bridges above all others are enshrined in American history. The first is the little timber span in Massachusetts on which the shot heard round the world was fired in 1775; the second is the big humpbacked steel girder over the Rhine that a platoon of GIs incredibly seized one hundred and seventy years later.

Modern historians, stripping away some of the patriotic tinsel with which Concord once was festooned, leave a picture that looks almost more like a lynching than a battle. Yet the historic role of Concord Bridge remains. Had there been no North Bridge at Concord it is very possible there would have been no fighting, that the British retreat to Boston would have been unmolested, and that the Revolution would have been averted by more prudent counsel.

The North Bridge does not, as even some historians think, lie on the road from Concord back toward Boston (*Figure 72*). The Minute Men were not trying to block the British retreat. In fact, just why the fight took place remains obscure to this day.

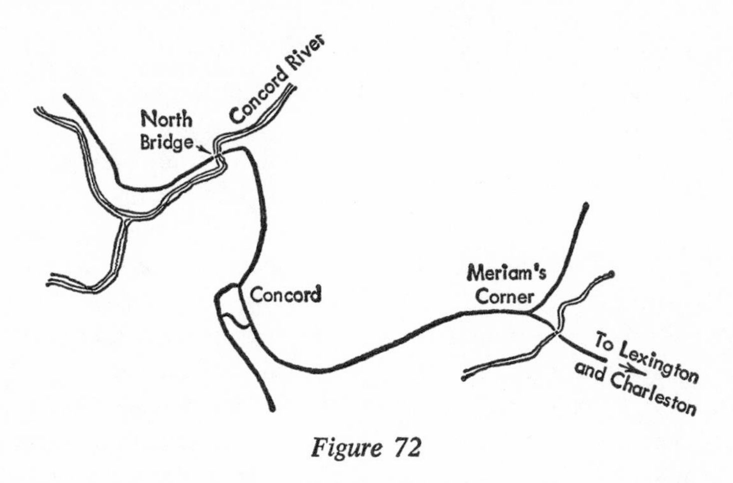

Figure 72

Most of the British were in the town proper; a detachment sent to a nearby farm to search for rebel munitions left a small guard at the North Bridge. The Minute Men, watching from a little hill north of town, apparently grew uneasy at the sight of smoke in Concord—the British were burning a few captured supplies—and some of the hotter heads urged an attack. The British soldiers guarding the bridge began taking up the planking, but on the approach of the Minute Men marching in column, they hastily formed on the eastern (town) side of the bridge and fired a volley, killing two Americans. The Americans, who were in by far the greater number, returned the fire, and several British fell. The rest surprisingly ran off in a panic. They were met by a body of their comrades coming from the town. The Redcoats retreated into Concord, and the Minute Men withdrew in two other directions, some to the hills just north, some back across the bridge. During the shuffle a farm boy committed the first atrocity of the war. For reasons that nobody ever could explain, he finished off one of the wounded British soldiers with a hatchet (an axe—according to Hawthorne, who later lived in the Concord Manse).

The British detachment that had gone out of town to the north now returned, to find the bridge strewn with dead and dying comrades, including the man who had been hatcheted (which, in the British broadside published immediately in Boston, became "tomahawked" and "scalped"). But no Americans remained at the bridge; they all had scattered, and the British detachment was allowed to join the main body without interference.

The Minute Men, of course, were not an army, much less an army at war. They were angry militia. Although they had been organized to resist aggression by British troops, it was hard to say exactly what measure of resistance was appropriate. And waiting outside Concord had a great advantage—more companies kept coming in from the neighboring towns and joining them in the hills.

By the time Colonel Smith, the British commander, tardily had commenced his march back to Boston, more militia were converging on his route from north and south. A mile outside Concord, at Meriam's Corner, another bridge played an important role. The road narrowed for it, and as the grenadiers crowded together to cross, they presented a target that some of the Minute Men on the nearby heights found irresistible. Another story says the British rear guard fired first. The question may seem absurd, but it underlines a point—the war had not yet begun and it would not have been out of the question for the militia to permit the British to return to Boston unmolested.

But once the Americans began firing, they found themselves in the exhilarating situation of being able to shoot at their enemies without receiving effective fire in return. Then began the long and deadly harrying of the retreating column of Redcoats, finally saved from the ignominy of surrender by the arrival of a reinforcing column from Boston. Colonel Smith's men were pretty well worn out, having covered some twenty-five miles since early morning. Lord Percy, commanding the relief outfit, sent out flanking parties that caught a good many militiamen looking the wrong way, and did something to redress the balance of casualties. The Americans lost fewer than a hundred men in the fighting of the whole day, the British nearly three times that number. Percy intelligently avoided a bridge at Cambridge that might have become more famous than Concord's, for the Americans had prepared a barricade and ambush at it.

Fifty years after that famous April day, as a chance result of a visit by Lafayette, an argument almost as violent as the original one between Americans and British broke out between Lexington and Concord. The controversy was over whose was the honor of first resisting. At Lexington, seven Americans were killed, the first blood shed in the war. But the British firing was so nearly accidental (the Lexington militiamen, as Concord triumphantly pointed out, were dispersing in response to British Major Pitcairn's order) that the incident might perhaps not have led to war immediately. The North Bridge on the other hand (especially with its "scalping") made peace much more difficult. Meriam's Corner bridge made it almost impossible.

The Saga of Remagen

At twenty minutes past three on the somber, overcast afternoon of March 7, 1945, a German officer named Captain Friesenhahn, crouching in the entrance to a railroad tunnel just west of the Rhine, wound the key of a firing mechanism. Fully wound, the mechanism should have detonated a set of huge demolition charges encased below the hinges of the massive bridge directly in front of the tunnel. But the charge failed to blow. Frantically, Captain Friesenhahn wound again—still no blast. Thereby hangs a strange story of coincidence, foresight, heroism, and mystery. The only element not present was cowardice—on either side of the battle line—though five German officers later were summarily shot by a Nazi court-martial.

The Ludendorff Bridge at Remagen was born in one world war and died in another. Rushed to completion in 1916–17, it consisted of a single big steel arch of 513 feet flanked by two trusses of 278 feet. On either shore, reminiscent of the ancient castles of the Rhine robber barons, stood a pair of heavy stone towers slotted with narrow windows and topped by observation posts.

A military structure all the way, it contained a feature rare among bridges. Into each of the four stone piers supporting the arch hinges were built two hollow chambers that could be packed with explosive for easy demolition. But the German army of 1918 surrendered before falling back behind the Rhine, and French army engineers, discovering the demolition chambers, efficiently filled them up with cement.

For peaceful purposes, a railroad bridge at this point was so useless that for years after the First World War it served only for pedestrians. But when Hitler came to power, the Ludendorff was reactivated. Immediately a new demolition plan was prepared. Sixty holes were bored at carefully chosen points in the stone and steel around the arch hinges. The charges were stored nearby, and an electric fuse, encased in a heavy steel pipe, was laid under the roadway. A circuit-tester was provided to permit engineers to test the ignition system without setting off the charges.

A few years later, in the fall of 1944, the question of demolition began to be serious. The Americans were threatening. A new feature was added to forestall a *Handstreich* by American armor. If enemy tanks neared the bridge, a ditch thirty feet wide and twelve feet deep would be blown on the Remagen (west) side of the bridge. That would guarantee time to destroy the bridge itself.

In addition to all this, a super-emergency plan existed to blow the bridge with a separate charge, ignited by hand, to be planted at the last moment.

In the early days of March 1945, four things happened to upset these arrangements. First, Adolf Hitler, raging at the retreats on the Western Front, issued a menacing order that bridge demolitions must be carried out only at the last possible minute and on written orders from higher headquarters. Second, the swift American armored thrusts into the Rhineland caused widespread disorganization in the German command structure and at the same time threatened to cut off large numbers of German troops west of the Rhine if any bridges were blown prematurely. Third, within three minutes before Captain Friesenhahn wound up his demolition mechanism, something—to this day no one knows what—happened to the demolition wire.

In desperation, Captain Friesenhahn played his last card. A volunteer, Sergeant Faust, left the shelter of the railroad tunnel, made his way under fire to the point on the bridge roadway at which the emergency fuse terminated, and set off the emergency charge. But because of the first two points mentioned above, this emergency charge had been requisitioned only at the last moment, and less than half the calculated necessary quantity of explosive had been obtained. The charge went off under the roadway at the point where the upstream truss was hinged to the pier. The bridge seemed to rise from the pier, but the next moment settled back again. At the critical point, the vast weight sagged about six inches. But it held.

Now the fourth, and perhaps the most bizarre factor of all, came into play. The Americans firing on the bridge were elements of the Ninth Armored Division. Their mission was not at all to seize the Ludendorff Bridge or to attempt a Rhine crossing. They had come from the north with the object of sweeping south to link up with other American armor and cut off German troops west of the Rhine.

Nor did the Americans, even when they had fought their way into Remagen, the town on the west bank, and stood on the very threshold of the bridge, think of capturing it. Lieutenant Karl Timmermann, brand-new C.O. of Able Company, 27th Armored Infantry Battalion, a First World War baby born a hundred miles from that very spot, looked through his field glasses at three o'clock and remarked to Sergeant DeLisio, one of his platoon leaders, "Looks like they want to get us out on the bridge before they blow it." Sergeant DeLisio's laconic GI comment was "Screw that noise," which may be translated as "Let's not fall into that trap."

Shortly before, on the heights above Remagen, Brigadier General Hoge, commanding general of Combat Command B, Ninth Armored Division, had given his subordinates a chewing-out for not getting into the town of Remagen fast enough. As for the bridge, over which German troops, vehicles and animals still were piling helter-skelter, he vainly sought to get Division artillery to zero in on it.

Remagen did not even represent the main effort of the Ninth Armored, which was directed toward a much smaller bridge over the Ahr, a tributary of the Rhine. That bridge was captured intact by plan and intent, a bold and skillful feat very soon completely forgotten. In the advance, however, a couple of German civilians were encountered who insisted they had important information—that the great Ludendorff Bridge at Remagen was to be blown at precisely four o'clock.

This information was entirely false—no time had been set for demolition of the Ludendorff. Yet, by pure coincidence, it was close to the truth, and supplied the stimulus for the capture of the bridge. The rumor, quickly relayed to General Hoge, who received it at three-fifteen, provoked an immediate order to seize the bridge. This shortly resulted in the following colloquy below at the bridge head:

Major Deevers (battalion commander): "Do you think you can get your company across that bridge?"

Lieutenant Timmermann: "Well, we can try it, sir."

Deevers: "Go ahead!"

Timmermann (after a moment's look at the bridge): "What if it blows up in my face?"

Deevers: (No answer).

Karl Timmermann, German-born, Nebraska-bred, moved toward the bridge, flipped a piece of liberated rock candy to a soldier, and began a sentence: "We're going to cross this bridge before—"

Just then the blast set off by Sergeant Faust roared across the Rhine.

Among the GIs there was first the welcome thought that the Germans had blown up the bridge. Then came the unhappy discovery that they had not.

Lieutenant Timmermann strode forward. The bridge was still there. When would the enemy fire another charge?

"Okay, Jim, Mike, and Joe," he called, addressing his platoon leaders, "we'll cross the bridge. Order of march, first platoon, third platoon, and then second platoon."

The first platoon moved out on the bridge roadway with a reluctance no soldier would misunderstand. The open roadway was covered by machine guns in the pair of grim stone towers on the east bank. And the bridge itself surely would blow up any moment.

The first platoon started down the left catwalk in single file. As they reached the main span, they were pinned down, partly by a cross-fire coming from snipers on a barge anchored two hundred yards upstream. Lieutenant Timmermann ran back and yelled to a Sherman tank near the bridge; in a few minutes the barge, plastered with .75-mm shells, surrendered. But the tank fire was ineffective against the heavy towers across the bridge, and the first platoon still was pinned on the catwalk. Timmermann waved to Sergeant DeLisio, ordering the third platoon forward. Joe DeLisio, a scrappy little New York Italian who had taken over the platoon less than a week before, when its lieutenant had been wounded, ducked low and headed out onto the bridge. As he passed the men on the first platoon prone on the catwalk, one of them muttered one of the famous, oft-repeated lines of the war: "There goes a guy with more guts than sense."

DeLisio worked his way forward to the lead man on the bridge, called to others to follow, and darted on over the main span. To the machine-gun and sniper fire was added a new sound—that of .20 mm antiaircraft shells. One swooshed just over his head. DeLisio ran and ducked onward. Nearing the end of the main span, miraculously untouched, he made a final dash. He reached shelter—directly under one of the stone towers, whose fire still was pinning the men behind him out on the bridge. Not all of them; a half dozen from his own and the first platoon had followed him across. It was a little before four o'clock, the moment rumor had set for the demolition. Actually, the moment had come for the decisive action to capture the bridge.

Somebody yelled, "Who's gonna clean out that tower?"

DeLisio, already beyond the tower, turned back, and began shoving aside the bales of hay with which the tower door was barricaded. A bullet hit the stone wall next to him, and another GI, coming up behind him, shouted, "You're hit, Joe!" DeLisio ran his hands quickly over his field jacket, and finding no blood pushed his way into the tower. Moments later Sergeant Mike Chinchar, leader of the first platoon, and two others broke into the opposite tower.

DeLisio raced up the circular stairway. As he climbed, he heard the machine gun stop firing. Were they waiting for him? He banged open a steel door with one hand and fired his carbine with the other. Three German soldiers, bent over their machine gun, jerked their heads around.

"Hände hoch!" DeLisio yelled. Their hands went up. DeLisio grabbed the machine gun and hurled it out the window. GIs starting across the bridge saw the welcome sight, and came on.

DeLisio shoved his three prisoners ahead of him up to the top floor. There were two men there. A lieutenant dived for a corner, but DeLisio stopped him with a shot. Disarming the officer and a private, he marched all five prisoners back down and told them simply to walk back across the bridge to Remagen. They went.

In the other tower Chinchar found only one German, took him prisoner, and threw his machine gun out the window.

Meantime one of DeLisio's squad leaders, Sergeant Alex Drabik of Toledo, a notably quiet fellow, arrived at the towers. Not seeing

DeLisio, Drabik decided that his platoon leader must be on the east bank.

Drabik took off. As he ran, his steel helmet bounced off. He did not stop to pick it up. Behind him streamed other men of Able Company, including Joe DeLisio, though Drabik did not know that. He became the first Allied soldier to set foot across the Rhine. Turning left, he ran two hundred yards up the river road before finally stopping. There he formed his squad in a skirmish line, taking cover in a series of craters made in a recent air attack.

Meantime, Timmermann gave DeLisio another mission—to check the railroad tunnel directly in front of the bridge. DeLisio and four men crept forward in the gathering darkness toward the black tunnel mouth as shots rang out around them. DeLisio fired two rounds into the tunnel and flushed a half dozen German engineers.

Unknown to DeLisio or Timmermann, many more Germans were in the tunnel. They did not, however, constitute a danger. A demoralized mixture of Volksturm militia, civilians, foreign laborers, service personnel, and convalescent wounded, they were eager to surrender. They did so a little after five o'clock, when more GIs entered the tunnel. Captain Friesenhahn had the good luck to be among the number. His immediate superior, Major Scheller, was less fortunate, and got away a little earlier. Four days later, along with four equally innocent officers, he was court-martialed and shot in a grotesque Nazi travesty carried out to appease Hitler's fury over loss of the bridge.

As early as quarter to five Colonel Engeman, battalion commander, had radioed General Hoge that the bridge was taken—what now? It could be held only if reinforcements were pushed across at once. General Hoge put it up to General Leonard, the division commander. Leonard sent an aide to Corps Headquarters. If all this sounds to civilian ears like hesitation and buck-passing, it should be recalled that the Ninth Armored Division had been given an important mission—to race south along the Rhine's left bank and link up with General Patton's armor, to trap the German elements in the Rhineland. If men and tanks were pushed across the bridge, not enough would be left for the thrust south.

Nor was the decision to expand the bridgehead quite so obvious militarily as it seems. Remagen was not a good place to concentrate strong forces because the east-and-west roads were few and poor. Even if an intensive effort was made, it was entirely possible that the Germans across the Rhine could mount a big counterattack soon enough to wipe out the bridgehead.

So a call went in to III Corps Headquarters, where Colonel James H. Phillips, the Corps chief of staff, made the decision, and made it instantly. The Ninth Armored was ordered to hold up on its mission to the south and push hard across the Rhine. First Army Headquarters was notified immediately, and soon after that, General Courtney H. Hodges phoned the news to General Omar Bradley, commanding general of the Twelfth Army Group.

Up to this point the Remagen bridge operation was a strictly local affair, an opportunity seized by officers on the regimental and battalion level. Now, suddenly, leaping over intermediate division, corps and even army levels, it became a part of the great inter-Allied strategy debate.

The agreed-on plan for the Allied offensive across the Rhine called for the main crossing to be made in the far north, over the Rhine's broad mouth, by the 21st Army Group, commanded by British Field Marshal Bernard L. Montgomery. American generals Patton and Bradley always had objected to the plan, which placed large numbers of American troops directly under British command and gave the rest a subordinate role. Now Bradley and Patton, who met Hodges to discuss the situation on March 9, saw an opportunity. "We all felt," Patton wrote later, "it was essential that the First and Third [American] Armies should get themselves so involved that Montgomery's plan to use most of the divisions on the Western Front, British and American, under his command . . . could not come off. . . ."

Meantime, at Remagen, nine Sherman tanks rumbled across the bridge on a plank flooring thrown down by the engineers, moving to support the thin line of Able Company, now spread out in a 3500-yard arc. A platoon of tank-destroyers started over the bridge, but the lead vehicle, three quarters of the way across, hit the hole in the roadway torn by Captain Friesenhahn's emergency demolition, and crashed sideways, hanging precariously over the river and blocking the roadway. It was five-thirty in the morning before the desperate engineers got the clumsy monster out of the way.

From then on, troops poured over the bridge. Within twenty-four hours the equivalent of four infantry regiments, a tank battalion, a battery and a half of antiaircraft guns, and several special units—a total of some eight thousand men—was east of the Rhine. Within a few days four divisions were across.

The Germans, despite an advantage in road network, could not match the rapid American concentration. Operating in a chaotic state of broken communications, and desperately pressed for reserves, the German command had the utmost difficulty assembling troops for counterattacking. Nevertheless, a continuous series of small and medium assaults was launched day after day, night after night. A huge 17-centimeter gun was employed in an effort to score a direct hit on a vulnerable point. Dive bombers attacked repeatedly. The first jet planes ever used in war joined them. Frogmen attempted to swim explosives to the bridge. At Hitler's personal order, V-2s were fired —the first tactical use of long-range missiles. All these efforts were vain. But on March 17, a little after three o'clock, almost precisely ten days to the minute after Captain Friesenhahn had wound up the firing mechanism in the tunnel, the bridge suddenly collapsed.

The collapse was not caused by the bombs and shells rained by the Luftwaffe and the Wehrmacht. They alone would have accomplished no more than the furious hail of explosive by the United States Air Force a few weeks earlier, which tore up the roadway, but had no more effect on the arch itself than a hailstorm. The bridge fell because of the weakening caused by Sergeant Faust's demolition charge—a shrewd knife stab at the bridge's vitals that left the big humpback standing badly wounded, sustained by one (the downstream) arch alone. In the week following the capture, under air and artillery fire, the GI engineers succeeded in constructing two treadway (pontoon) bridges, one on either side of the Ludendorff, and repaired the wounded giant's flooring enough to keep the flow of men and vehicles piling over. They patched some of the broken stringers supporting the roadway. What they could not improvise, in so short a space of time, was a replacement for the damaged arch hinge. They tried. A heavy crane strove all day on March 16 to rig a cable connection to hold the broken chord together. But the pounding vibrations of trucks and tanks and tank-destroyers on the roadway and of V-2s and bombs and 17-cm. shells close by, toppled the weakened structure before it could be rescued. By this time the bridge had been closed to traffic, but two battalions of engineers were on it when it went down. Twenty-eight died.

Why did the original German demolition charge fail to go off? Ken Hechler, from whose authoritative book, *The Bridge at Remagen,* most of the facts given here are drawn, made a careful investigation, including interrogation of surviving German personnel. He effectively disposed of several reports that circulated later, and made it quite clear that, despite all the chaos and confusion of the last weeks of the war, no negligence or accident on the German side was responsible.

In the weeks after the capture, a Polish forced laborer named Sevinski, liberated by the Americans, told a story about the bridge demolition. Sevinski asserted that a group of foreign laborers, collected in the railroad tunnel on March 7, held a secret meeting and resolved to sabotage the demolition wire. A Pole whose name Sevinski did not know cut the wire, tied the ends together so that the circuit-tester would work, and then, just before Captain Friesenhahn wound up the mechanism, pulled the wires apart. Captain Friesenhahn himself strenuously denied to Hechler that this could have taken place, and indeed it seems difficult to believe.

Yet the alternative is at least equally incredible. It is that during the same three-minute interval a shell from one of the Sherman tanks firing across the bridge at the German positions on the right bank scored a direct hit on the steel tube encasing the demolition wire. This would have been easy to ascertain in the days following if no battle had been going on, but in the midst of combat nobody could take the time to figure out—or stop to wonder—what had gone wrong with the German charge. It remains that ancient cliché—one of the unsolved mysteries of the war. Interestingly enough, Dwight D. Eisenhower, writing in 1948, was entirely unaware of the mystery involved in the Remagen demolition. He attributed the failure to destroy the bridge to "indecision and doubt" on the part of the German defenders.

The bridge's final agony did not invalidate its importance. This importance derived only in part from the actual strategic value of a Rhine crossing. It was greatly enhanced by the German reaction to the capture, particularly Hitler's personal reaction, which caused reserves to be scraped from the length and breadth of the hard-pressed Rhine front to counterattack at Remagen. On the night of March 22, Patton was able to cross the Rhine south of Mainz with almost no casualties, actually two days before Montgomery's "main crossing" of the Rhine mouth. Montgomery himself ran into only very weak opposition. And Hodges' First Army had by then made several more crossings. By the end of March, the German Western Front was shattered beyond recovery, with the American First and Ninth armies moving to encircle the entire Ruhr area and trap the whole main German force, Army Group B. This in turn had far-reaching ramifications, which some historians believe extend even to the Cold War tension over Berlin. Had the Ludendorff Bridge been blown according to plan, Montgomery's thrust across the lower Rhine probably would have remained the principal Allied offensive; into it, instead of the drives of Bradley, Patton, and Hodges, would have been funneled the reserves, the gasoline, the supplies. And Montgomery, backed by Churchill, probably would have attempted to capture Berlin ahead of the Russians—an effort the American commanders refrained from making.

25.

Bridge Firsts, Bridge Cities, Bridge Sports

WHAT was America's first bridge? There are three possible answers, depending on just what is meant by "bridge." The forces of nature created bridges on this continent long before the first Stone Age men crossed from Siberia to North America on the bridge of the Aleutians twenty thousand years ago. No region in the world is so rich in natural bridges as Utah's San Juan County, with Rainbow Bridge, Kachina Bridge, Sipapa Bridge, and Owachomo Bridge. Among other American natural bridges are Virginia's famous arch over Cedar Creek, near Rockville City, and Arizona's Petrified Log Bridge at Apache City.

Our first man-made bridges were logs felled across streams by the Indians, who, in North America, never achieved the bridge-building skill of the Incas and other peoples of South and Central America. The first "real" bridge on the soil of the future United States—built, rather than merely felled or carried into place—often has been credited to the Massachusetts Bay Colony: Israel Stoughton spanned the Neponsett River at Dorsetshire in 1634. But Stoughton's bridge was preceded by almost a hundred years by several bridges built by Hernando de Soto's Genoese engineer, Maese Francisco, during the Spanish exploring expedition of the 1530s and 1540s. One of those built by Francisco was destroyed by the current, recording the first bridge failure in American history.

Massachusetts can claim several firsts in bridge lengths, beginning with the "Great Bridge" of 1662, 270 feet long, mounted on 13 piers. Twenty-five years later, another trestle of 1500 feet was carried by

75 piers. Finally, in 1790 a bridge across the broad and shallow Charles at West Boston was carried a distance of 3580 feet—longer than the George Washington—on 180 "pile bents"—heavy timber pilings. An even longer trestle—running over a mile—was constructed over Cayuga Lake in New York in the same decade.

The first United States suspension bridge, the pioneer forefather of America's great modern bridge form, was that built by James Finley over the Schuylkill at Philadelphia in 1801. The collapse of Finley's bridge inconvenienced a number of employees in a factory across the river. The factory owner, Captain Josiah White, decided to replace it with one specially designed for his workers. The result was the world's first suspension bridge to use wire cables, a generation ahead of Chaley's "Grand Pont" at Fribourg. How does it happen that this notable first is so little known? Possibly because Captain White's bridge, though long, was only eighteen inches wide. It cost the captain $125, and as he collected one penny toll from passengers (only eight of whom were allowed on the footway at one time), he made a tidy profit by the time his creation fell into the Schuylkill under a winter snow. One end of Captain White's bridge was anchored to a tree. The other terminated in the second floor of the factory, through a window of which the bridge users, employees or others, entered.

The antithesis of Captain White's straitened roadway stands today in Providence, R. I.—the widest bridge in the world. The "Crawford Street Bridge" is more than eleven hundred feet wide, but only a hundred and fifty feet long. Most people driving over it never realize that they are on a bridge.

How many covered bridges still remain in the United States? The American Society for the Preservation of Covered Bridges reports the surprising total of 1344, in twenty-nine different states. Pennsylvania has the most, 347, followed by Ohio, Indiana, Vermont, and, unexpectedly, Oregon. (For a complete list by states, see Appendix.)

No country in the world has so many covered bridges as the United States, though Canada, Switzerland, Austria, and Germany have large numbers still in service. Italy has only a few, but certainly the three most famous of all—Florence's Ponte Vecchio and Bridge of Sighs, and Venice's Rialto.

The oldest covered bridge in the United States cannot be identified with certainty. Two known to date to 1810 are the Dellville Bridge, a Burr arch-truss over Sherman's Creek at Wheatfield, Pennsylvania,

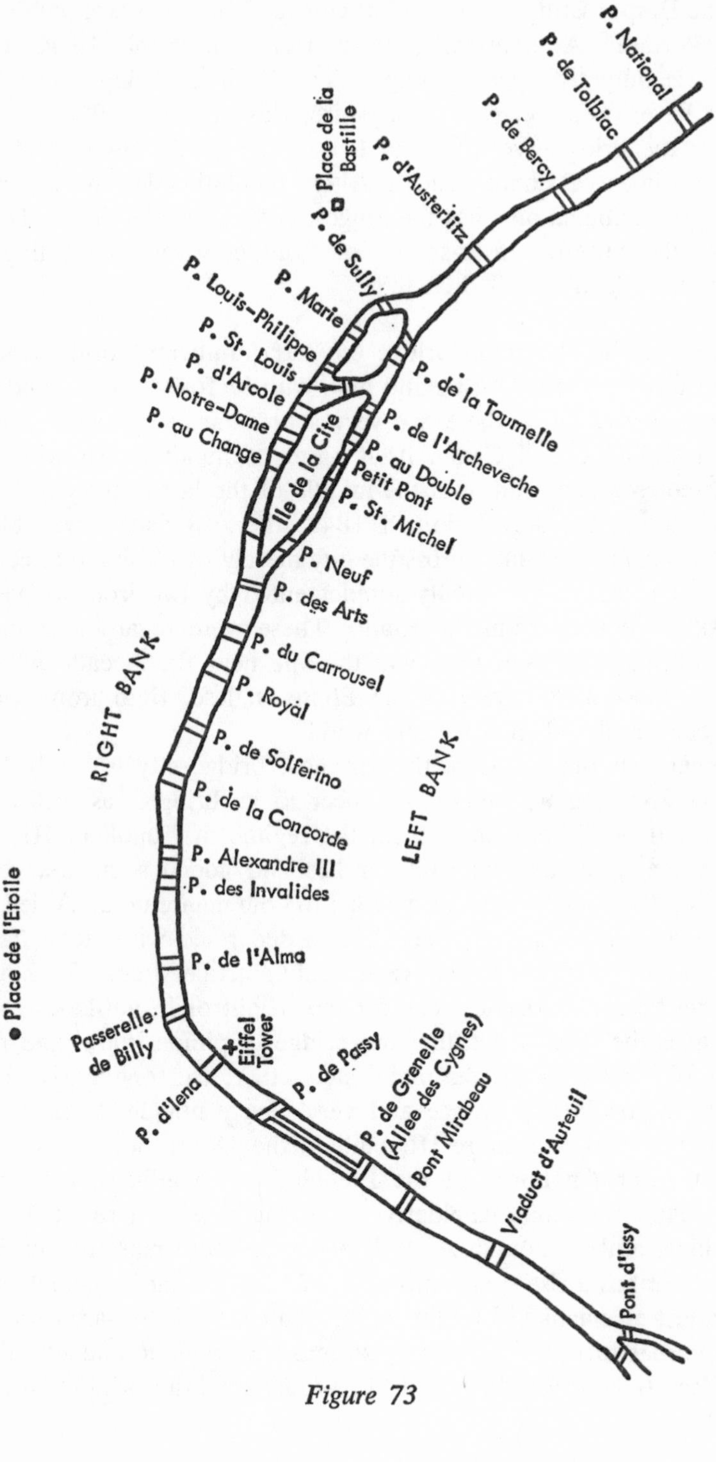

P. National
P. de Tolbiac
P. de Bercy
P. d'Austerlitz
Place de la Bastille
P. de Sully
P. Marie
P. Louis-Philippe
P. St. Louis
P. d'Arcole
P. Notre-Dame
P. au Change
Ile de la Cite
P. de la Tournelle
P. de l'Archeveche
P. au Double
Petit Pont
P. St. Michel
P. Neuf
P. des Arts
P. du Carrousel
P. Royal
P. de Solferino
P. de la Concorde
P. Alexandre III
P. des Invalides
P. de l'Alma
RIGHT BANK
LEFT BANK
Place de l'Etoile
Passerelle de Billy
Eiffel Tower
P. d'Iena
P. de Passy
P. de Grenelle (Allee des Cygnes)
Pont Mirabeau
Viaduct d'Auteuil
Pont d'Issy

Figure 73

and the Halpin Bridge, a Town lattice over Muddy Brook at Middlebury, Vermont. Another Middlebury bridge, the Pulpmill, over Otter Creek, is only five years younger. The Whittier Bridge over Bear Camp River, Ossipee, New Hampshire, was built in 1820, the same year as the bridge over Buzzard Roost Creek at Chisca, Alabama.

According to Richard Sanders Allen, indefatigable covered-bridge historian, Alabama also has the longest covered bridge in the United States: the 600-foot four-span Town lattice over the Tallapoosa River at Dadeville, built in 1887.

Which is the champion bridge city? If number of bridges is the only criterion, Venice must stand first, with its four hundred and fifty bridges. Nearly all of these are very short, hardly more than street crossings. The Grand Canal, itself barely a hundred feet wide, has just three crossings, and until the middle of the last century had only the Rialto. In the Revolution of 1848, the Austrians were able to prevent rebel movements across the city merely by closing that central bridge. The Rialto was finally supplemented by two iron bridges, in opposite directions from the Rialto. These were regarded as excessively ugly by the Venetians, and the one near the Accademia Gallery was known derisively as the Ponte Inglese. Both iron bridges have been replaced in stone and wood.

If beauty is the criterion, the foremost bridge city is surely Paris (*Figure 73*). Paris profited in respect to its bridges, as well as its streets and public buildings, from the regime of Napoleon III, who rebuilt nearly all the old stone arches and added some new ones, including the Pont de l'Alma. Named to commemorate an Allied victory in the Crimean War, the Alma is decorated with stone figures of a grenadier, a Zouave, a chasseur, and an artilleryman. The Zouave has long been a Parisian gauge for the height of Seine floods.

What is the most beautiful Paris bridge? Opinions vary, and most of the old stone arches resemble each other. But one Paris bridge is outstanding in appearance and very nearly unique in the world. This is the Pont Alexandre III, built in the 1890s and named for a Russian Czar (in honor of the French-Russian alliance of 1892). The Alexandre, unlike its elderly stone sisters, leaps across the Seine in a single athletic bound. A steel arch faced with masonry, its 350-foot ellipse has a rise-span ratio of 1/17, duplicating in a single span the flattest arcs achieved by the eighteenth century's five-arch bridges. The familiar form and startling size make a dramatic and ultramodern effect. In contrast, the broad (150-foot) roadway, with pillars surmounted by allegorical figures at either end, creates an unexpectedly baroque impression.

Rome and London also can advance claims. No city, naturally, is so rich in Roman bridges as Rome; and London, for centuries possesor of a single Thames crossing, now has dozens of bridges, many of them of remarkable beauty (*Figure 74*). Several Chinese and Japanese cities are outstanding for both number and beauty of their crossings—Tokyo, from whose Bridge of Japan distances traditionally are measured; Shanghai, on whose Marco Polo Bridge the first clash of the Chinese-Japanese war took place in 1937; Osaka, "the Venice of the East," and many others. To attempt to catalogue Europe's most bridge-beautiful cities would be dangerous—Budapest and Vienna with their interesting variety of long spans over the Danube; Leningrad, Russia's premier bridge city, with its eighteenth- and nineteenth-century arches over the Neva; Amsterdam, rival of Venice for number of bridges; Lyon, with medieval and modern spans crossing the ancient Rhône; Stockholm, an island city of the north; many others.

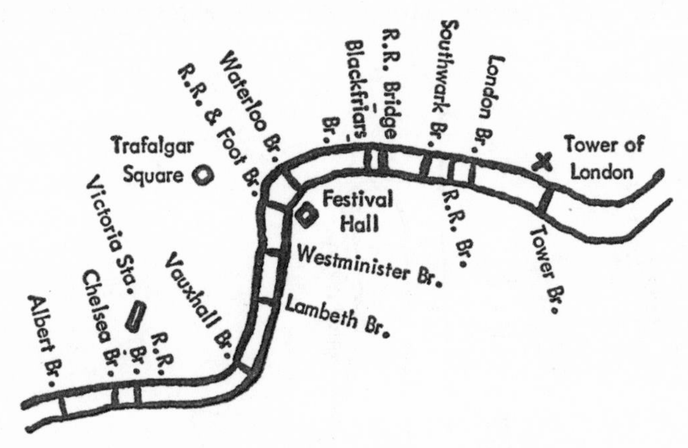

Figure 74

The United States too is rich in bridge cities. No other city in the world has two such bridges as San Francisco's Golden Gate and Bay crossings, not to mention the twin cantilevers over the Carquinez Straits and the new Benicia-Martinez crossing. No other city has such a galaxy of drawbridges as line the Chicago River. Niagara Falls has an abundance and variety of crossings in a stunning setting. Philadelphia, with memories of Timothy Palmer, Lewis Wernwag, and James Finley, has many noteworthy bridges of more recent vintage, such as Ralph Modjeski's "Sesquicentennial" over the Delaware, one of whose foundations goes down 105 feet. New Orleans, almost surrounded by water, is the center of a bridge complex of which the long Lake Pontchartrain causeway is outstanding. Boston, Minneapolis-St. Paul, Pittsburgh, St. Louis, many other United States cities have bridges of historic, structural, and artistic note. Montreal and Quebec have magnificent settings for long spans over the St. Lawrence.

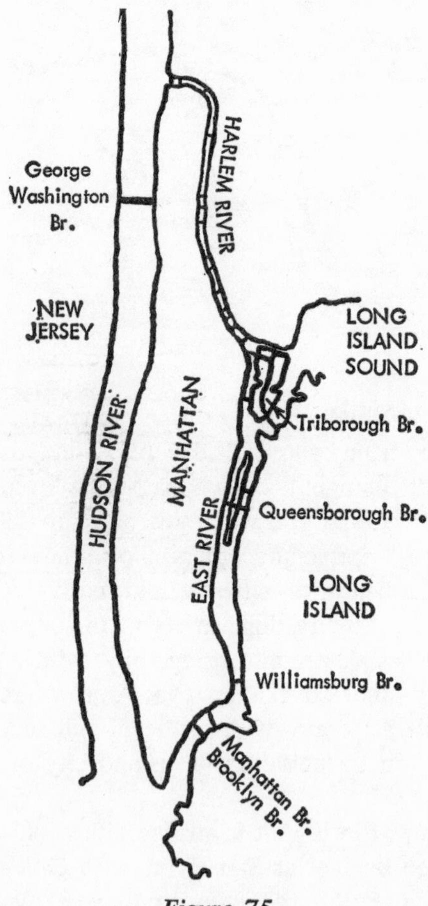

Figure 75

But America's premier bridge city, if not the world's, is New York (*Figure 75*), where the mighty George Washington in solitary splendor over the Hudson now is surpassed by the Verrazano-Narrows, under whose lofty deck the harbor's shipping henceforward will pass.

The East River is filled with bridge fascination—the Brooklyn, Williamsburg, and Manhattan giving three chapters in the history of the suspension bridge; the Queensborough, that badly disguised cantilever, recalling the great bridge-form controversy; the Triborough, whose rich intricacy no single view—from the water, from any of the shorelines, or from the air—can capture entirely. Besides these famous and familiar giants, dozens of others are worth noticing. The Hell Gate and the Bayonne, two mighty bent bows at opposite corners of the metropolis, still rank among the biggest arches in the world. The beautiful Bronx-Whitestone is perhaps outshone by its new sister in the Sound, the Throgs Neck. Over the Harlem River a thick array of lift, truss, and cantilever forms jump, amid them the wonderful old High Bridge aqueduct that ended the great New York water shortage of the 1830s. The High Bridge cost $737,800, a tremendous outlay for 1837. Within a few years enough was known about iron bridges to have done the same job for far less, but in 1837 the only alternative to a wooden bridge seemed to be a stone arch, and so New York's only stone bridge was built—the biggest stone bridge ever erected in the United States, 1460 feet long, composed of fifteen arches, eight of which span the river.

We have already referred to the knightly combat between Sir David Lindsay and Lord Wells on Old London Bridge. A Spanish bridge was the scene of an even more memorable passage of arms. In 1434 a certain Don Suero de Quinones got permission from the king, Juan II, to defend a bridge near Beguellina for thirty days, against all comers, at the time of the jubilee feast at Santiago. Don Suero imposed this combat on himself as a condition for his removing an iron ring that he wore around his neck every Thursday in token of his captivity to his mistress. Any lady who came by the bridge without a cavalier to do battle had to forfeit her right-hand glove, and any knight who declined combat had to forfeit his sword and right spur. Seventy-eight combatants appeared; 727 courses were run; 177 lances were broken; one knight was killed, eleven were wounded seriously. Suero having fulfilled his vow, the iron link was removed with great solemnity. This egregious chapter in chivalry was well known to Cervantes, writing a century and a half later.

Two Italian bridges were for many generations scenes of regular combats. The Ponte di Mezzo, in the center of Pisa, was the arena for the "Giuoco del Ponte," or Bridge Game. Factions drawn from the city and the suburbs faced each other on opposite sides of the river, rushed onto the bridge armed with helmets and shields and fought to hold the span. No hitting was allowed below the belt. The fight was followed by numerous banquets. A similar mass combat took place on the Ponte dei Pugni (Bridge of Fisticuffs) in Venice.

The more peaceful bridge game, the one with cards, probably derives its name from some now lost connection with a bridge. In his newspaper feature, "Believe It or Not," Robert Ripley once offered an explanation. Two English couples played whist at each other's houses on alternate weeks. To go between, either couple had to cross a bridge of doubtful condition, and they came to remark to each other in parting, "Well, it's your bridge next week."

Still another form of bridge amusement: at Isfahan, Iran, a famous seventeenth-century bridge, the Pul-i-Khuju, produces a wild sport, half-spectatorial, half-participant. The bridge is a pointed-arch structure, typical of the time and region, brick arches mounted on stone piers, with a covered gallery on either side of the roadway. The huge piers leave only constricted room for the waters, and in floodtime the citizens throng the stairs that lead from the piers to the water, the lower deck of the bridge and the upper parapet, singing, shouting and having the time of their lives while the roaring waters creep upward. They abandon their perilous grandstand only at the last moment.

An even madder bridge sport long was practiced in the American West, and still is in some places in Western Canada: flume-riding.

A flume is a miles-long timber trestle that wanders down a mountainside, jumping over an occasional gorge. Its deck is a trough about three feet wide with a few inches of water from a stream at the top sluicing through it. Its invention was an ingenious answer to the problem of taking lumber down from the green mountain tops to the sawmills without the expensive trouble of building roads and the laborious process of using horse- or ox-drawn wagons or sledges. Hewn timbers were thrown into the flume at the top and taken out, sometimes fifteen miles later, at the bottom. Along the way there were some difficulties, and the flume line had to be manned by operators armed with hookaroons, long-handled pick hammers used to break jams.

But once a week the flume acquired a different function and significance. On Saturday night, after their 72-hour week of backbreaking labor, the lumberjacks headed for town—down below. Writer Bert Goldrath of *Argosy Magazine* talked to some of the old-timers, who recalled the flume-riding days of fifty years ago. "We'd save out some good timbers to ride on," one veteran said, "and balance ourselves with a piece of edging, like a tightrope walker. An eight-by-sixteen timber, eighteen or twenty feet long, worked fine." Down the flume the loggers slid, at an average speed of ten miles an hour, but sometimes whirling around mountain bends or shooting over gorges three or four times that fast, singing, yelling, careening, sometimes falling off. Unfortunately, they had to get back to work Monday morning by walking uphill. Flumes were a great, but strictly one-way, form of rapid transportation.

The bridges of the Orient are as famous for the beauty of their names as their designs. Western bridges, usually named for towns, quays, streets, etc., rarely compete with such Chinese names as "Bridge of Ten Thousand Ages," "Fruit Basket Bridge," "Flowing Flowers Bridge," "Bridge of the Gods," or with the Japanese "Bridge of Heaven" and "Bridge of the Damask Girdle." An exception must be made of some of the bridges over Venice's canals: "Bridge of Paradise," "Bridge of Courtesy," "Bridge of Humility," "Bridge of the Honest Woman." Igor Stravinsky records in *Expositions and Developments*—the "Bridge of Kisses" over a canal in Leningrad, so-called because departing sailors and marines said good-by to wives and sweethearts there.

Kings aside, surprisingly few bridges are named after men. The George Washington got its name from the fact that the New Jersey approach is at Fort Washington. The Verrazano Bridge, named for the Italian explorer who first sighted New York Harbor (in 1525) seems destined to be known more familiarly and generally as the Narrows Bridge.

Of all New York's great girdle of bridges, the one farthest out from the heart of the city is the Outerbridge Crossing, between Staten Island and New Jersey. Why is it so named? For Eugenius H. Outerbridge, a former Port of New York Authority chief.

The old confidence trick allegedly played on newly arrived immigrants in New York—"selling the Brooklyn Bridge"—sounds meaningless to modern ears, accustomed to the idea of publicly owned bridges. But in the days when many bridges were built by private companies for the toll profits, the sale of a bridge was not itself an absurdity.

The bridge, like most of man's institutions, has a shady side to its past. Many bridges have become notorious to police for suicide attempts. The high pedestrian deck of London's Tower Bridge has been closed for this reason. Pedestrian bridges also have been favorite haunts for pickpockets. A famous covered bridge at Kwanhsein, China, remembered for its green porcelain-tiled roof, once had a sign: "No opium-smoking on the bridge."

Some bridges have provided strategic points for assassins. European history's most famous instance came in 1419, when John the Fearless, Duke of Burgundy, was slain on the bridge of Montereau by the partisans of the Dauphin, an assassination that backfired in the alliance the Duke's successor made with Henry V of England, leading to the renewal of the Hundred Years' War. Gavril Princip and the Serb youths who shot the Archduke Franz Ferdinand and his wife in Sarajevo in June 1914, waylaid their victims at the entrance to a bridge. James V of Scotland, father of James I of England, once was attacked on Cramond Old Bridge, near Edinburgh, by the suitor and relatives of a peasant girl to whom the king had been addressing his attentions. On the point of being overpowered, he was rescued by one Jock Howieson, who did not recognize the king, but simply pitched in because he saw six attacking one. Jock's valiant and timely aid won him the land of Barehead, according to the British historian F. W. Robins, and to this day the owners of the fief present a ewer, a basin, and a towel for the sovereign to wash the royal hands whenever he passes Cramond Old Bridge.

In more recent times bridges have been associated, at least by frequently recurring rumor, with the end rather than the beginning of murder. Many a bridge foundation in America is reputed to provide a final resting place for the victims of gang feuds.

And apropos of the bridge and crime, a bridge recently was stolen in Illinois—from a state-owned scrap pile.

A bridge's endurance depends on three things: the original strength of its design and materials; the amount of strain from traffic and weather, and maintenance. Every bridge must be repaired now and then, and often the repair job is as big a project as the original construction. Rome's ancient Tiber bridges were allowed to fall to pieces in the Dark Age, and were reconstructed in Renaissance and modern times. One, the Ponte Rotto, was briefly given a unique repair fillip—a suspension span to fill in for a lost arch.

Roadways are the most often worn-out and most often repaired parts of bridges. On suspension bridges the suspenders may need replacing. When the second deck was given to the George Washington Bridge, 22 of the 584 suspenders were found to have deteriorated. Cables may need strengthening or replacing; older suspension bridges using iron-wire cables have been given new leases by replacement in steel wire.

Brooklyn Bridge needed a general overhauling in the 1940s, after over half a century of heavy duty. The job of repairing John and Washington Roebling's masterpiece went to their greatest admirer and chief biographer—David Steinman.

Often bridges are built with future expansion in mind. The Narrows Bridge will have an initial capacity of six lanes on a single deck, the second deck to come in 1980 as traffic increases. San Francisco's Oakland-Bay Bridge ran into a curious problem when it was double-decked. Where the roadway runs through Yerba Buena Island, it was found that the outside lanes of the upper deck would not accommodate trucks that required a clearance of fourteen feet. This was because of the arched cross section of the big tunnel. Because part of the advantage of the double-decking would be lost if trucks had to be restricted to the interior lanes, a method was sought for economically improving the clearance of the two troublesome lanes. One method would have been to narrow each lane slightly, so that the outer lanes would run a little nearer the middle of the tunnel and avoid the low-roofed extreme edges. But this would have meant slowing down traffic slightly. Widening the tunnel bore itself would have been prohibitively expensive for such a small gain. Finally an ingenious solution was applied: the upper roadway simply was lowered a few inches.

Unfortunately the process of lowering the roadway while keeping the bridge open to traffic involved a rather dramatic inconvenience to motorists—a six-foot "hump" in the roadway under which the construction crew worked and which moved forward with them.

New bridges are always insured for a period after construction. Galloping Gertie's coverage was due to be radically reduced within a few days after the fatal morning. This resulted in an unhappy experience for an insurance agent. He had sold a large policy and pocketed the premium, trusting the bridge to stand up long enough to bring the cancellation clause into effect. Gertie did not quite make it, and the insurance man went to jail.

Nothing so inevitably calls for ceremony as a bridge inauguration. The pattern is universal and timeless: band music, a parade, speeches, and refreshments. In modern times, publicity releases have been added. New York indisputably holds the world's championship for these ceremonies. One of the biggest was to celebrate the opening of the biggest bridge, the George Washington, in 1931. The Hon. Alfred E. Smith, former governor of New York, was among those on the speakers' stand. At that time the tradition persisted that marching troops could make a bridge fall down—partly perhaps deriving from the famous Angers, France, disaster of eighty years earlier and partly from the precaution always taken by troops crossing a pontoon bridge. Governor Smith expressed apprehension to Othmar H. Ammann over the arrival of a detachment of troops, marching in step, on the roadway. The engineer dryly assured the governor that the detachment could be composed of elephants marching in step without endangering the bridge.

Several airplanes flew under the new bridge and one—according to reliable eyewitnesses—incredibly flew through both towers, tilting over to squeeze between the steel-web pillars that make up each great arch.

Lafcadio Hearn tells two stories about inaugural ceremonies in Japan. A certain bridge, rebuilt in the nineteenth century, had a dark chapter in its remote past. Having encountered foundation troubles the engineers had appeased the river-god by burying a man alive under the troublesome pier. The story still was told in the region, and when the rebuilding was carried out, the country folk were afraid to come into town for fear of being chosen as the new victim. A rumor that the choice would be made among the men who wore their hair in the old style caused old men for miles around to cut off their queues. Another rumor, that the thousandth person to cross the bridge would be seized by the police as the victim, completely spoiled the inauguration ceremony—nobody came.

A more cheerful tradition was embodied in another bridge-opening that Hearn observed. It was the custom in a certain region to have the happiest person in the community be the first to cross a new bridge. Hearn especially paid a visit to a bridge opening to see who would be chosen for the honor. It was divided between two aged men married more than half a century, each with twelve children, not one of whom had died. The two old men solemnly walked across the bridge first, followed by their wives, their children, their grandchildren and their great-grandchildren, as fireworks were shot off.

26.

The Endless Bridge

A BRIDGE is to a road what a diamond is to a ring. To labor its beauty is as supererogatory as to labor its usefulness. Long before Robert Maillart, Eugène Freyssinet, and others gave civil engineering its sometimes uncomfortable place in the gallery of modern art, the complex appeal of bridges was evident. Bridge beauty is not always conventional. The two arches that curve upward at opposite ends of New York's skyline, at Hell Gate and Bayonne, or the triple-backed Victorian monster that guards the Firth of Forth, give less a sense of grace than of power. The old covered bridge upon which one suddenly comes is also not likely to be beautiful in the usual sense; rather, it conveys the special mystery of the recent past, the outdoor civilization of the horse-and-buggy days. When we go back to the intimate stepped arcades over the Grand Canal or the Arno, the flattened arches of seventeenth- and eighteenth-century France, or the ancient semicircular arches of the Romans, we recover a sense of the deep past, authentic, meaningful, almost disturbing. Whose hands cut those stones, whose shoulders moved them into place? Why did intelligence and brawn labor for years, perhaps for decades, to provide an indestructible river crossing to serve mankind for centuries? (It requires no great cynicism to doubt that serving mankind for centuries was the primary consideration.)

Yet all these aspects of the bridge—its enduring Roman stone, its geometric modern steel, its evocative weathered timber—all signify beauty to the artists. For them the bridge in all its forms remains the most beautiful of man-made structures. Over the centuries, as painting evolved, the bridge, which was evolving too, became a more and more favored subject. At first a bit of decoration in the background, it presently took over the center of the canvas. Still later, changing, fragmenting, exploding in abstractions, it became a leading symbol of modern art as of modern literature.

In the Annunciations, Madonnas, portraits, and mythological paintings of the Renaissance, a glimpse of a bridge is often visible through a window, or as part of a dreamily remote vista. Raphael's *Madonna of the Goldfinch,* Botticelli's *Annunciation,* Giovanni Bellini's *St. Jerome among the Rocks,* Veronese's *Finding of Moses,* Jan Van Eyck's *Madonna Enthroned, with the Chancellor Nicholas Rolin*—in these and many more, bridges edge unobtrusively into corners of the composition. Leonardo da Vinci, always preoccupied with mathematics and geometric forms, painted the perfect semicircle of a Roman arch into the dark landscape against which Mona Lisa smiles.

Most of the bridges in Renaissance paintings are Roman. In the centuries that followed, when painters moved outdoors, not only did bridges move to the front of the canvas, but they were a new species of bridge; the noonday of bridge landscapes was also that of bridge esthetics, when the appearance of the structure assumed importance to its builders. And the most painted bridges were those built with beauty most in mind, like the Rialto in Venice. (In the eighteenth century, Francesco Guardi painted the Rialto that everyone knows.) Second place perhaps belongs to the Ponte Vecchio.

The nineteenth century made the bridge one of art's favorite subjects. Pre-Impressionist Corot depicted Hadrian's famous Roman span in *Bridge and Castel Sant'Angelo,* and in his *Bridge at Mantes* showed the masonry arch whose construction led Perronet to the discovery that perfected the arch form. John Rennie's Waterloo Bridge was painted by Constable (*Waterloo Bridge from Whitehall Stairs*) and later by Monet, who with Pissarro and Sisley painted numerous London bridge pictures. Seurat, Cézanne, Gaugin, Derain, Marquet, Van Gogh, and all the other Impressionists painted bridges, from the stone arches of Paris to the little timber beam at Arles.

The most painted bridge of Paris (if not of the world) is the three-hundred-and-fifty-year-old Pont-Neuf. Best known in Renoir's representation, it has been sketched, drawn, painted over and over, scores and hundreds of times, the long arm to the Right Bank, the short arm to the Left, from the upstream side and the down, looking into the roadway from the Quai des Augustins or from the side of the Louvre, or from the Square du Vert-Galant on the tip of the Ile de la Cité, where bronze Henry IV still surveys with satisfaction the bridge he completed.

Some artists have found bridges irresistible and taken up residence next to them. Monet lived over the Thames embankment for three years, painting Waterloo and Charing Cross bridges at various times of day and night. Matisse, a studio painter, nevertheless lived on the Quai St.-Michel on the Left Bank and came outdoors to paint the Pont St.-Michel. A corner of the same bridge is visible through the window of several Matisse interiors.

James McNeill Whistler was an admirer of London's docks and bridges. He painted the dismantling of Charles Labelye's historic Westminster Bridge with a fairly conventional realism. But a Whistler exhibition in 1877 contained four *Nocturnes* done in a distinctly Impressionist style. John Ruskin, a critic of strong and out-of-date opinions, delivered a diatribe, climaxed by a famous phrase—"a pot of paint flung in the public's face." This characterization was restricted to one of the Nocturnes, that in *Black and Gold: the Falling Rocket*. But it sounded the keynote of conservative taste's reaction to the new painting style. Whistler sued for libel on the grounds that Ruskin had asserted that he was incapable of painting recognizable pictures, and in support of his suit submitted to the court another of the Nocturnes, *Blue and Gold: Old Battersea Bridge*. In this misty blue picture, with distant lights and stars dropping from the sky like sparks, the familiar bridge was a bit murky but quite discernible, and Whistler won his case. The victory was on a Pyrrhic scale, for the damages granted were only one farthing, and the painter was assessed half the court costs for stirring up all the trouble. Whistler was forced into bankruptcy, had to sell his house, china, prints, and some of his pictures. Quitting London, he retreated to Venice, where there were even more bridges than in London, and produced a series of etchings that soon retrieved his fortune. In this realm of art, money, and bridges, the recent sale of Monet's *Bridge at Argenteuil* for 1,470,000 francs ($264,000) makes one wonder how many bridge pictures cost more than the bridges they portray.

In Japan, bridges of a special character were discovered by a painting school of equally original flavor. Japanese bridges were depicted as part of the landscape they so enchantingly fitted, and for themselves. Two artists emerged: Hokusai, who designed a famous series of woodcuts of bridges, and Hiroshige, in whose prints bridges figured prominently. Both had a marked influence on the Impressionists of the West, already bridge enthusiasts.

Primitive painters, too, were attracted by bridges. Henri Rousseau forsook his tropical dreams to paint the footbridge at Passy and a geometric, precise Pont de Grenelle. American primitives turned out such works as John H. Smith's *Burning of Richmond,* with its flaming bridges, and Joseph Pickett's *Manchester Valley,* with railroad bridge. Grandma Moses painted covered bridges. And John Kane, miner, railroad worker, and Sunday painter of Pittsburgh, represented the longest reinforced-concrete arch in the United States, the George Westinghouse Bridge, in his *Turtle Creek Valley.*

In the early years of this century, there was even a group of young artists in Germany who called themselves *Die Brücke* (The Bridge) and regarded their work as a bridge from old to new.

The bridge that contemporary artists paint is a far different one from the gracefully simple masonry arch of the Renaissance. It has not lost its beauty, but the beauty has become complex. The big steel bridge is built to serve an industrial society, and in the artist's eyes is a symbol of that society. The Brooklyn Bridge has exerted a fascination on many American painters, notably John Marin and Lyonel Feininger.

Modern artists ceased to paint the bridge representationally, painting instead the force it concealed or expressed. In Paul Klee's *Revolution of the Viaduct,* the elements of a bridge seem to have come unstuck, and are converging menacingly on the viewer. Other painters were occupied with geometrical shapes, as in Niles Spencer's *Two Bridges,* which contrasts a masonry arch and a metal truss, or in Feininger's bridge series. Joseph Stella, who painted Brooklyn Bridge over and over, declared it to be "the shrine containing all the efforts of the new civilization in America," moving him "as if in the presence of a new divinity."

Marcel Duchamp, the cubist-futurist (*Nude Descending a Staircase*), put somewhat the same thought in more trenchant words: "The only works of art America has given are her plumbing and her bridges."

A bridge is a place of life. The conditions that caused it to be built may change, but the fact that it is there forces life to come to it. In the Middle Ages a bridge built to supplant a ferry on a well-traveled road very often led to construction of two, three, or four more roads converging at the spot. London Bridge had much to do with the development of London, as the Karlsbrücke did with that of Prague. In more than one place in Europe the bridge has been the real reason for a town's survival.

No wonder bridges have recurred endlessly in literature, both the formal sort and the popular.

Everyone knows the metaphorical bridge of popular speech, that you cross before you come to, or burn behind you. (A Chinese emperor invading Korea in the seventh century literally burned the bridges as his army crossed them.) The folklore of bridges is less familiar. In Poland, evil spirits are believed to haunt bridges; when a child is being taken to a christening, it is awakened if a bridge is passed. In Portugal, if an expectant mother fears a difficult delivery, or if a previous child was stillborn, the woman goes to the middle of a bridge in the dead of night, accompanied by a male relative other than her husband. There she draws a bucket of water from the river and awaits the first man to cross after midnight. When he appears, she asks him to baptize the unborn child, lowering her garments and having him make the sign of the cross with water on her bared body.

Bridges appear frequently in Oriental legend. Lafcadio Hearn tells a gruesome tale of the Bridge of the Washing of the Peas, at Matsue, Japan, on which a phantom woman sat nightly washing peas. A certain flower song was tabu on this bridge; one night a samurai braved the tabu and loudly sang the forbidden song: as no ghost appeared, he went home merrily. On his way he was met by a beautiful woman who presented him with a lacquered box. Inside it lay the head of his child.

Hearn retells an ancient Chinese legend, in its Japanese popular version:

The great god of the firmament had a lovely daughter, Tanabata-tsume, who passed her days in weaving garments for her august parent. She rejoiced in her work, and thought that there was no greater pleasure than the pleasure of weaving. But one day, as she sat before her loom at the door of her heavenly dwelling, she saw a handsome peasant lad pass by, leading an ox, and she fell in love with him. Her august father, divining her secret wish, gave her the youth for a husband. But the wedded lovers became too fond of each other, and neglected their duty to the god of the firmament; the sound of the shuttle was no longer heard, and the ox wandered, unheeded, over the plains of heaven. Therefore the great god was displeased, and he separated the pair. They were sentenced to live thereafter apart, with the Celestial River between them; but it was permitted them to see each other once a year, on the seventh night of the seventh moon. On that night—providing the skies be clear—the birds of heaven make, with their bodies and wings, a bridge over the stream; and by means of that bridge the lovers can meet. But if there be rain, the River of Heaven rises, and becomes so wide that the bridge cannot be formed. So the husband and wife cannot always meet, even on the seventh night of the seventh month; it may happen, by reason of bad weather, that they cannot meet for three or four years at a time. But their love remains immortally young and eternally patient; and they continue to fulfill their respective duties each day without fault—happy in their hope of being able to meet on the seventh night of the next seventh month.

A Japanese bridge, the Long Bridge of Seta, which crosses the waters of the Setagawa, near the picturesque Buddhist temple of Ishiyamadera, appears in another Lafcadio Hearn story, in which a poor young man passing over the Long Bridge rescues a Samebito—a Shark Man—who has been banished from the Dragon Palace because of a small fault he has committed. The young man takes the Samebito home to dwell in the pond in his garden. Half a year later, the young man falls in love with a girl of extraordinary beauty whose family demands a betrothal gift of ten thousand jewels. Haunted by her memory, he becomes ill. The Samebito nurses him, and when the young man announces himself about to die, the Shark Man begins to weep bitterly—tears of blood, which turn into rubies. The young man springs from his bed, overjoyed, whereupon the Shark Man stops weeping, unfortunately, somewhat short of the ten thousand jewels demanded by the girl's parents. The Samebito cannot produce tears at will—"Do you think that I am like a harlot, able to weep whenever I wish?" But he suggests that the young man take him to the Long Bridge of Seta. There, gazing in the direction of the Dragon Palace and thinking of the happy days he spent there, he manages to produce the requisite number of ruby-tears. And then an amnesty is declared for him in the Dragon Realm, and he leaps from the bridge, never to be seen again; and the young man obtains the beautiful girl.

In a Burmese legend, the Shan king of Yunna promised the hand of his beautiful daughter to whoever, dryshod and without boat or bridge, could reach her on the island where he had placed her and strike the palace gong there. The son of a dragon princess takes the magic wand left him by his mother and strikes the ground three times. His dragon-mother appears, stretches herself bridgelike from shore to island, and enables him to cross and win his bride.

Nigerian folklore provides a story about the people of a town who crossed a narrow creek to attack their enemies on the other side; defeated, they were cut off by the rising water. Their protector, a great python, stretched himself across the creek, enabling them to cross; then as the victors tried to follow, he sank and drowned them. Moses did not think of building a miraculous bridge over the Red Sea to serve the same purpose as the Nigerian python. The Egyptians of the Middle Kingdom were not bridge-builders. There was not even a word for "bridge" in ancient Coptic.

An American Indian funeral oration addresses the soul of a dead warrior: "As you journey on, you will come to a fire running across the earth from one end of it to the other. There will be a bridge across this fire, but it will be difficult to cross because it is continually swaying. You, however, will cross it safely, for you have as guides the souls of those enemies whom the warriors at your funeral wake placed at your disposal. . . . If at the funeral wake any of the warriors, in recounting his exploits, tells any falsehoods, you will fall off this bridge and be burned. Do not, however, worry, for you surely will pass it safely." The perilous bridge to heaven occurs in other religions, notably Islam. The "Bridge of Mahomet" opens under the feet of the wicked and precipitates them into the abyss. The Rainbow Bridge over which the warriors of the Teutonic sagas passed to Valhalla had no such treacherous feature. Still another unearthly bridge was that by which Charlemagne crossed the Rhine in a later poetic legend:

> When the bright moon shines by Rudesheim
> Its beams made a bridge to carry the king
> Who passed o'er the Rhine like a bird on the wing.

Faust-like legends of Devil's bridges are part of the great folklore of the Middle Ages, when bridge-building perhaps seemed too difficult to be accomplished without supernatural help. Typical is the Ratisbon story of the Devil's Bridge. An architect was building Ratisbon Cathedral. His apprentice wagered that he could build the bridge before the copestone of the church was laid. After several failures, he made a compact with the Devil, who undertook to build fifteen arches of the bridge in return for the first three living creatures who crossed. But the apprentice sent across the bridge a dog, a cock, and a hen. The enraged devil tore the animals to pieces and disappeared; a carved representation of the three animals adorns the bridge. In a story about the Pont de Valentré, the handsome medieval war bridge at Cahors, France, the architect also sold his soul to the Devil and also tricked him, but the Devil had the last word. If the Devil refused his help in any phase of the work, the architect could recover his soul; the Devil performed prodigies in bringing stone and mortar from distant places; finally the architect gave him a sieve and demanded that he fill it in the river and supply the workmen with water. When he was unable to comply, the bet was lost, but the Devil in revenge removed a stone from the northwest corner of the central tower, and though it was replaced, took it again, so that it still is missing.

England has its version—about Dibble's Bridge (a corruption of Devil's Bridge) in Yorkshire, over the River Dibb. A shoemaker was crossing one night with a sackful of shoes to be repaired and he fell asleep at the ford. As he awoke, a stranger asked his way. After being directed, the stranger asked what the shoemaker would like in return. "A bridge over this river so I could cross it dryshod in flood times," the shoemaker replied. "Come here next Sabbath morning, and it will be there," the stranger promised. The shoemaker's friends were skeptical, but when they all came the next Sabbath, the bridge was there.

Longfellow tells a Devil's bridge story in "Christus: A Mystery." No bridge could be built across an abyss, the Devil's hand overthrowing by night what was built in the day. At last the Abbot Giraldus of Einsiedel built a single-arched bridge for pilgrims on their way to Rome, and the Devil promised to let it stand:

> Under compact and condition
> That the first living thing which crossed
> Should be surrendered into his hand,
> And be beyond redemption lost . . .
> At length, the bridge being all completed,
> The Abbot, standing at its head,
> Threw across it a loaf of bread,
> Which a hungry dog sprang after,
> And the rocks re-echoed with the peals of laughter
> To see the Devil thus defeated!

Another bridge legend, repeated in various versions, comes from Valladolid. A gallows stood on a bridge, and whoever passed over had to answer truthfully the question, "Where are you going?" If he lied, he was hanged. One man answered, "I am going to be hanged." No solution has been given to this riddle.

The Three Billy-Goats-Gruff have trip-trapped, in crescendo, through many a bedtime story, over the bridge under which the troll, a sort of devil, hides. That tale too probably goes back to the Middle Ages. And to pass from the comic to the sublime, we have an inscription on Akbar's Gate of Victory, from the Jamma Masjid, Fatehur Shah: "Said Jesus, on whom be peace: 'The world is a bridge, pass over it, but build no house there!'"

Poets and novelists have found the bridge as rich a source of inspiration and imagery as did the singers and sages of long ago. More than twenty books—novels, plays, autobiographies, poetry—have been titled simply "The Bridge." For Wordsworth and Byron, two famous bridges made excellent observation posts. Westminster Bridge, whence Wordsworth scanned sleeping London and reflected, "Earth has not anything to show more fair . . ." was the second stone arch ever to span the Thames. Now, like so many other historic bridges, it is gone. Byron, in *Childe Harold's Pilgrimage,* pauses in Venice, city of four hundred and fifty bridges, to memorialize a bygone grandeur:

> I stood in Venice on the Bridge of Sighs,
> A palace and a prison on each hand;
> I saw from out the wave her structures rise
> As from the stroke of the enchanter's wand:
> A thousand years their cloudy wings expand
> Around me, and a dying glory smiles
> O'er the far times, when many a subject land
> Looked to the winged Lion's marble piles,
> Where Venice sat in state, throned on her hundred isles.

And everyone knows Longfellow's much quoted (and parodied) "Bridge over the Charles":

> I stood on the bridge at midnight,
> As the clocks were striking the hour . . .

Bridges have provided dramatic stages for playwrights and novelists: Robert Sherwood's *Waterloo Bridge;* Maxwell Anderson's *Winterset,* which opens with the stage direction, "Scene is on the bank of a river under a bridgehead," a somewhat cryptic direction which turns out to mean not a defensive fortification, but merely the end of a bridge (apparently the Brooklyn).

"On the Nikolaevsky Bridge he was roused to full consciousness again by an unpleasant incident. A coachman, after shouting at him two or three times, gave him a violent lash on the back with his whip, for having almost fallen under his horses' hoofs. The lash so infuriated him that he dashed away to the railing (for some unknown reason he had been walking in the very middle of the bridge in the traffic). He angrily clenched and ground his teeth."

The passage is from *Crime and Punishment,* the setting of which is St. Petersburg, whose Neva River and canals are rich in bridges. Dostoievsky's hero, Raskolnikov, who receives the whiplash on the Nikolaevsky Bridge, later sees a woman fling herself into the canal from a bridge and has various other adventures of mind and spirit on bridges, ending with the sober reflection, as he prepares to confess murdering the old woman pawnbroker:

"In another week, another month, I shall be driven in a prison van over this bridge, how shall I look at the canal then? I should like to remember this! . . . Look at this sign. How shall I read those letters then? . . . What shall I be feeling and thinking then? How trivial it all must be, what I am fretting about now!"

The Hunchback of Notre Dame carries a reminder that medieval European bridges had houses on them, in defiance of the inscription on Akbar's Gate. Victor Hugo uses a house on the Pont Saint-Michel as setting for the scene in which Captain Phoebus is stabbed by Claude Frollo, who then escapes through a window overlooking the river, leaving Esmeralda to be arrested for the crime. In *Treasure Island,* Jim Hawkins and his mother hide from Old Pew and his cutthroats under a bridge. In Dumas's *The Three Musketeers,* a bridge assists d'Artagnan in acquiring his memorable valet, Planchet:

The meal had been ordered by Athos, and the lackey furnished by Porthos. He was a Picard, whom the glorious Musketeer had picked up on the Pont de la Tournelle, where he was amusing himself by spitting in the water and watching the circles spread.

Porthos claimed that this occupation was a proof of a reflective and contemplative temperament, and he had brought him away without any other recommendation. . . .

Dorchester Bridge appears as a trysting place in Thomas Hardy's *Far From the Madding Crowd,* and in *The Mayor of Casterbridge* one of Hardy's passages of thoughtful, painstaking realism is concerned with bridges:

Two bridges stood near the lower part of Casterbridge town, the first of weatherstained brick . . . the second bridge of stone. . . . These bridges had speaking countenances. Every projection in each was worn down to obtuseness, partly by weather, more by friction from generations of loungers. . . . To this pair of bridges gravitated all the failures of the town. There was a marked difference of quality between the personages who haunted the near bridge of brick, and the personages who haunted the far one of stone. Those of lowest character preferred the former, adjoining the town; they did not mind the glare of the public eye. They had been of comparatively no account during their successes; and, though they might feel dispirited, they had no particular sense of shame in their ruin. Their hands were mostly kept in their pockets; they wore a leather strap round their waists, and boots that required a great deal of lacing, but seemed never to get any. Instead of sighing at their adversities they spat, and instead of saying the iron had entered into their souls, they said they were down on their luck. . . .

The *misérables* who would pause on the remoter bridge were of a politer stamp. They included bankrupts, hypochondriacs, persons who were what is called "out of a situation" from fault or lucklessness, the inefficient of the professional class—shabby-genteel men, who did not know how to get rid of the weary time between breakfast and dinner, and the yet more weary time between dinner and dark. The eyes of this species were mostly directed over the parapet upon the running water below. A man seen there looking thus fixedly into the river was pretty sure to be one whom the world did not treat kindly for some reason or other. While one in straits on the townward bridge did not mind who saw him so, and kept his back to the parapet to survey the passers-by, one in straits on this never faced the road, never turned his head at coming footsteps, but, sensitive to his own condition, watched the current whenever a stranger approached, as if some strange fish interested him, though every finned thing had been poached out of the river years before. . . .

Some had been known to stand and think so long with this fixed gaze downward, that eventually they had allowed their poor carcasses to follow that gaze; and they were discovered the next morning in the pool beneath out of reach of their troubles. . . .

H. L. Davis' Pulitzer Prize but inadequately appreciated story of homesteading Oregon, *Honey in the Horn,* begins picturesquely:

There was a run-down old tollbridge station in the Shoestring Valley of Southern Oregon where Uncle Preston Shively had lived for fifty years, outlasting a wife, two sons, several plagues of grasshoppers, wheat-rust and caterpillars, a couple or three invasions of land-hunting settlers and real-estate speculators, and everybody else except the scattering of old pioneers who had cockleburred themselves onto the country at about the same time he did. The station, having been built in the stampeding days when people believed they were due for great swarms of settlement and travel around them, had a great many more rooms and a whole lot more space than there was any use for; and so had the country behind it. . . .

In a few cases, bridges step out of the background and become the chief actors in poems or stories, as in Robert Burns's "The Brigs of Ayr," in which the "Auld Brig," built in the thirteenth century, argues with the "New Brig," of 1788. The newer structure opens the colloquy with:

> Auld Vandal, ye but show your little mense,
> Just much about it wi' your scanty sense;
> Will your poor, narrow foot-path of a street,
> Where twa wheelbarrows tremble when they meet,
> Your ruined, formless bulk of stone and lime,
> Compare wi' bonny Brigs o' modern time? . . .

The "Auld Brig" sputters back:

> Conceited gowk! puffed up wi' windy pride!
> This mony a year I've stood the floor an' tide . . .
> And tho' wi' crazy eild I'm sair forfairn,
> I'll be a brig when ye're a shapeless cairn!

Burns writes about Brig o' Doon in "Tam o' Shanter"; the hero is being pursued by a pack of witches, but his mare, Meg, gets him to the bridge in time:

> Now do thy speedy utmost, Meg,
> An' win the keystone of the brig;
> There, at them, thou thy tail may toss,
> A running stream they darena' cross;
> But ere the keystone she could make,
> The fient a tail she had to shake!
> For Nannie, far before the rest,
> Hard upon noble Maggie prest,
> An' flew at Tam with furious ettle;
> But little wist she Maggie's mettle—
> Ae spring brought off her master hale
> But left behind her ain grey tail:
> The carlin claught her by the rump
> An' left poor Maggie scarce a stump.

A bridge is the chief character, too, in a contemporary novel by Una Troy called *The Other End of the Bridge,* in which two feuding Irish villages joined by a narrow, decrepit, outmoded bridge, quarrel over the cost of replacing it with a modern structure, ignoring the peace-making efforts of the Apostle Blaney, a religious fanatic who preaches that pacifism alone will solve the world's problems. When he blows up the bridge, and himself with it, the two towns meet in reconciliation at a dedication ceremony on the bridge. But suddenly the Apostle's familiar umbrella is seen floating on the water.

> Murmurs of grief and horror echoed along the bridge . . . "He'd be alive today only for being driven out of his mind with the antics of the other end of the bridge!"—"You worried him to his death there at the other end of the bridge!" . . . The first missiles came simultaneously from both ends of the bridge.

The most memorable bridge in modern fiction is the stone arch in Nobel Prize-winner Ivo Andrić's novel, *The Bridge on the Drina.* Built by the Ottoman Turks in Bosnia in the sixteenth century, the construction profited from the expert knowledge of an Italian, Mastro Antonio, brought in to direct the stone dressing. Like London Bridge, the bridge over the Drina was used to expose heads of rebels, and a Serbian curse ran, "May your mother recognize your head on the *kapia!*" The *kapia* was the broad central promenade deck. The bridge witnesses the passage of the centuries, the transfer of Bosnia from Turkish to Austrian rule, the First World War and the mining of the bridge, and finally its demolition by the retreating Austrians in 1918 as the Serb troops enter the town. This demolition consists of a tremendous explosion that knocks out one heavily mined pier. A stone-arch bridge is not so easily destroyed, and today the bridge over the Drina at Visegrad stands for the visitor to Yugoslavia to see, just as it is described in Andrić's novel.

Bridges in war play a dramatic part in literature. The Sublician Bridge that Macaulay's "Horatius" defended used to be known to every schoolchild:

> Hew down the bridge, Sir Consul,
> With all the speed ye may;
> I, with two more to help me,
> Will hold the foe in play.
> In yon strait path a thousand
> May well be stopped by three.
> Now who will stand on either hand,
> And keep the bridge with me?

As often recited was Ralph Waldo Emerson's shorter, better "Concord Hymn":

> By the rude bridge that arched the flood,
> Their flag to April's breeze unfurled,
> Here once the embattled farmers stood,
> And fired the shot heard round the world.
>
> The foe long since in silence slept;
> Alike the conqueror silent sleeps;
> And Time the ruined bridge has swept
> Down the dark stream which seaward creeps. . . .

Arthur Hugh Clough, that Victorian romantic and skeptic, stood on a battlefield where the Austrian Whitecoats had crushed an Italian independence uprising in 1849:

> What voice did on my spirit fall,
> Peschiera, when thy bridge I crost?
> 'Tis better to have fought and lost,
> Than never to have fought at all.

Ambrose Bierce begins his haunting story of the Civil War, "An Occurrence at Owl Creek Bridge," with the words:

> A man stood upon a railroad bridge in northern Alabama, looking down into the swift water twenty feet below. The man's hands were behind his back, the wrists bound with a cord. A rope closely encircled his neck. It was attached to a stout cross-timber above his head and the slack fell to the level of his knees. Some loose boards laid upon the sleepers supporting the metals of the railway supplied a footing for him and his executioners—two private soldiers of the Federal Army, directed by a sergeant who in civil life may have been a deputy sheriff. . . ."

From this opening paragraph, the reader's interest is held unflaggingly to the final sentence, a dash of icy water in the face.

Contemporary writers have dealt with the military aspect of bridges with varying success. There is Russian M. A. Aldanov's *The Devil's Bridge,* an undistinguished story of a young lieutenant with Suvarov pursuing the French across an Alpine bridge over an abyss. There is James Michener's *The Bridges at Toko-Ri,* a novel about the Korean War. Michener's Air Force hero notes that of the four bridges he is to attack two are permanent, mounted on stone piers, while the other two are "emergency" and lie close to the water. He considers the first two "decidedly vulnerable," apparently because they stick out of the water so far. Actually it is the two "emergency" spans, presumably wooden trestles, that would be vulnerable to bombs. The two stone-pier bridges, which presumably would have steel trusses and roadways, would be virtually bombproof. In the novel all four bridges are "destroyed" with comic-strip facility.

In two other popular novels, bridge demolition by fixed charges plays a central narrative role. In Ernest Hemingway's *For Whom the Bell Tolls,* the hero, a somewhat incredible soldier of fortune named Robert Jordan, goes about his mission of destroying a bridge in the Spanish Civil War of 1936–39 with a great show of expertness. First he carries out a reconnaissance, in which he makes a sketch of the bridge from a safe distance. The bridge is described as a "single-span steel bridge," which seems to imply an arch, or perhaps a truss or girder. Surprisingly it is not a railroad bridge, but a steel highway bridge, something of a luxury for a remote region of a backward country. Jordan figures out from his observations and sketches how he will blow up the bridge—apparently how much explosive he will use, and where he will plant the charges—the novelist is unclear on these points. An army engineer (Jordan is pictured as a bridge-demolition expert) would hardly require an advance study of a bridge before blowing it up, and looking at it from a distance could not possibly help him ascertain such details as whether the chords were seven-eighths of an inch thick or an inch and an eighth. For an expert, Jordan chooses an unusual place to plant his charges—under the middle of the bridge. Here he climbs around in the "trestle work" —a very unexpected feature of a "single-span bridge"—and ties his charges in place with hand grenades as detonators. Hemingway is adroit at lending verisimilitude to the scene, but Robert Jordan's feat nevertheless remains a little reminiscent of those of James Thurber's immortal Walter Mitty.

The Bridge on the River Kwai is the most interesting case of all. In this novel, Pierre Boulle depicts the ironic adventure of a rigidly old-school British Army colonel who, as a prisoner of the Japanese, undertakes to build a bridge for his captors in order to demonstrate the superiority of Western civilization. The author contrasts the primitive and badly put together structures of the Japanese military, which would last "a few days, a few weeks, sometimes even a few months," with the "Western" creation that rose under the appreciative eye of Colonel Nicholson. Even the Japanese colonel is impressed: "Since he had not fully understood . . . the subtler aspects of Western civilization . . . he could not realize to what extent method, organization, calculation, theoretical planning and expert co-ordination of human activities facilitate and eventually accelerate any practical undertaking." In the end, Colonel Nicholson, after thoughtlessly assisting the Japanese invasion of Burma by building the bridge over the Kwai, dies trying unsuccessfully to save it from destruction by British Commandos.

Unluckily for M. Boulle, his novel has deeper ironies than he intended. The bridge that Colonel Nicholson's engineering officer constructs is quite simple and would require no such recondite technical knowledge as the author imagines. The river is shallow and no attention needs to be paid to navigation, so an ordinary trestle, of which any nineteenth-century (or earlier) carpenter would be capable, is all that is necessary.

Captain Reeves, the British engineering officer whose theoretical training reflects, in M. Boulle's mind, "the fierce struggles and countless experiments by which a nation gradually raises itself in the course of centuries to a state of civilization," has some remarkable gaps in his education. When the Japanese propose building the bridge in a certain place, Captain Reeves drives a pile into the water near the bank with a sledgehammer. Failing to find "solid bottom," he pronounces the site unfit. A Roman engineer, who might spend a lifetime building bridges without ever finding "solid bottom," would be incredulous. A nineteenth-century engineer would laugh out loud.

M. Boulle's picture of the Japanese as technically backward is peculiarly inappropriate. Japan is full of bridges of all types, excellently constructed, not to mention even more formidable engineering feats. The Kanmon Tunnel, for example, the world's first under-ocean tunnel, a truly historic achievement, was under construction at the very time in which M. Boulle's novel takes place. And as for military bridges, the United States Army's *Engineer Field Manual* (Fourth Edition) is illustrated on page 246 with three drawings of Japanese bridges—this in 1912!

But the bridge over the River Kwai was no mere fiction. It actually was built by British prisoners of war under the whip of Japanese soldiers and officers whose brutality in the Second World War won their country a reputation it cannot shake off even today. Ernest Gordon, one of the men who helped build the real Kwai bridge, has told the story in a recent book. It is not ironic—merely horrifying. The bridge was a minor link in what the thousands of prisoners called "The Railroad of Death." The piles were heavy square beams of teak, floated into the river, tilted upright, and driven into the riverbed by hand-operated pile drivers. A trestle was built and the track laid. The whole operation took less than two months. "We worked at bayonet point and under the bamboo lash," Gordon says, "taking any risk to sabotage the operation whenever the opportunity arose."

In literature as in history there is the bridge of disaster. No one who has read *Around the World in Eighty Days* can forget the bridge at Medicine Bow, "a suspension bridge thrown over some rapids." The train, bearing Phileas Fogg and Passepartout, is halted by a signal man who insists that the bridge is in a ruined condition—several of the iron wires being broken—and that it is impossible to risk the passage. "It may be taken for granted," Jules Verne comments, "that, rash as the Americans usually are, when they are prudent there is good reason for it." The conductor explains that he has telegraphed to Omaha for a train, but it will not reach Medicine Bow for six hours, and that period of time will be necessary, at any rate, for them to reach Medicine Bow on foot. Passepartout is in despair, but the engineer, "a true Yankee, named Forster," calls out, "Gentlemen, perhaps there is a way after all, to get over. I think that by putting on the very highest speed we might have a chance of getting over." Passepartout counsels prudence, but is shamed into agreeing. "But," he reflects, "they can't prevent me from thinking that it would be more natural for us to cross the bridge on foot, and let the train come after!"

Then, with another whistle, [they] began to move forward; the train increased its speed, and soon its rapidity became frightful; a prolonged screech issued from the locomotive; the piston worked up and down twenty strokes to the second. They perceived that the whole train, rushing on at the rate of a hundred miles an hour, hardly bore upon the rails at all.

And they passed over! It was like a flash. No one saw the bridge. The train leaped, so to speak, from one bank to the other, and the engineer could not stop it until it had gone five miles beyond the station. But scarcely had the train passed the river, when the bridge, completely ruined, fell with a crash into the rapids of Medicine Bow.

Phileas Fogg and Passepartout traversed the United States in 1872, three years after the opening of the first transcontinental railway. At that time there was only one major railroad suspension bridge in America, built by John Roebling in 1855, at Niagara Falls, and suspension spans were in very doubtful repute. Railroad bridges of the conventional truss type, however, were failing at an appalling rate in 1872, and for one to fall down at Medicine Bow that year would have been perfectly believable. What is less believable is that a locomotive engineer (even a rash American) would not realize that the speed of the locomotive proportionally increased the strain on a bridge. Across a suspect bridge a train crawled rather than raced. But Passepartout's own idea, of letting the passengers cross on foot first, is one that could have saved a lot of lives in real-life railroading of that era.

The most famous novel about a bridge disaster is Thornton Wilder's *The Bridge of San Luis Rey,* which begins, "On Friday noon, July the twentieth, 1714, the finest bridge in all Peru broke and precipitated five travellers into the gulf below." In a single sententious Latin phrase, *"Misericordia Domine inter pontem et fontem"* (The mercy of God [may be found] between the bridge and the stream), St. Augustine dealt with the case of a man who fell off a bridge and was drowned. Thornton Wilder is less concise.

The Bridge of San Luis Rey, like the Bridge over the River Kwai, is a fictional version of a real bridge. About a hundred years old in 1714, it was made up of parallel cables woven of osier, with slats laid across as a walkway, and with handrails of vine. According to the novelist, it could be used by foot traffic only, baggage having to descend to the gorge. In the novel, Brother Juniper, who happens to witness the disaster, makes up his mind to investigate the lives of the five victims, to find God's purpose. "If there were any plan in the universe at all, if there were any pattern in human life, surely it could be discovered mysteriously latent in those lives so suddenly cut off. Either we live by accident and die by accident, or we live by plan and die by plan." The book goes on to examine the lives of the five, one by one. Brother Juniper's researches are not very fruitful, in spite of a system of tabulation that would stagger a modern social scientist—and which seems to prove neither that evil is punished nor that God takes those who are valuable to him. Brother Juniper bravely dies a martyr's death, his problem unsolved. But Thornton Wilder interprets the disaster in his own way:

> There is a land of the living and a land of the dead, and the bridge is love, the only survival, the only meaning.

Which brings us to a final use of the bridge in literature: as a symbol. Mathematicians will recall the name given to one of Euclid's propositions, *"Pons asinorum"* (Bridge of Asses)—in other words, a proposition too difficult for asses to get over. And, on a different level, Sir Richard Francis Burton's translation of the Kasidah of Haji Abdu

El-Yazdi: "Why meet we on the bridge of Time to 'change one greeting and to part?" Cervantes recommends furnishing "a flying enemy a bridge of silver," a counsel echoed by Rabelais, as well as by Byron who, however, transmutes the silver to gold. Shakespeare turns an unexpected metaphor: when Claudio, in *Much Ado About Nothing,* begins a long speech about his love for Hero, Don Pedro cuts him short with, "What need the bridge much broader than the flood?" Longfellow, that bridge-lover, used the covered bridge in an often-quoted passage, referring not to the bridge of his native New England, but to the Kapellbrücke at Lucerne:

> The Grave itself is but a covered bridge,
> Leading from light to light through a brief darkness.

Longfellow's New England contemporary, Thoreau, drew a metaphor at once more homely and more sophisticated: "The youth gets together his materials to build a bridge to the moon, or, perchance, a palace or temple on the earth and, at length, the middle-aged man concludes to build a woodshed with them."

Symbol, actor, stage, and theme—Brooklyn Bridge is all these things in Hart Crane's masterpiece, *The Bridge,* still far too little known and appreciated.

Crane begins with an invocation to the bridge itself:

> And Thee, across the harbor, silver-paced
> As though the sun took step of thee, yet left
> Some motion ever unspent in thy stride,—
> Implicitly thy freedom staying thee!

In the main body of the poem, Crane crosses from Brooklyn into Manhattan in the morning and returns at night, in the course of his journey exploring America's past—Columbus, Pocahontas, Pizarro and Cortez, Rip Van Winkle, the pioneers, the Mississippi, the railroads roaring West, and the industrial civilization—

> New verities, new inklings in the velvet hummed
> Of dynamos, where hearing's leash is strummed . . .
> Power's script—wound, bobbin-bound, refined—
> Is stropped to the slap of belts on booming spools, spurred
> Into the bulging bouillon, harnessed jelly of the stars . . .

In the tunnel of the subway, going back to Brooklyn, he takes us into the inferno of the new age:

Whose head is swinging from the swollen strap?
Whose body smokes along the bitten rails,
Bursts from a smoldering bundle far behind
In the back forks of the chasms of the brain,—
Puffs from a riven stump far out behind
In interborough fissures of the mind . . . ?

Then he lifts us once more to the bridge:

Through the bound cable strands, the arching path
Upward, veering with light, the flight of strings,—
Taut miles of shuttling moonlight syncopate
The whispered rush, telepathy of wires.
Up the index of night, granite and steel—
Transparent meshes—fleckless the gleaming staves—
Sibylline voices flicker, waveringly stream
As though a god were issue of the strings . . .

Finally he apostrophizes the bridge again, insigne of the industrial age, man-made machine, instrument of man's future. Addressing it as "Tall Vision-of-the-Voyage, tensely spare," as "Thou steeled Cognizance," "Swift peal of secular light, intrinsic Myth, Whose fell unshadow is death's utter wound,—O River-throated," "Deity's glittering Pledge," he concludes:

So to thine Everpresence, beyond time,
Like spears ensanguined of one tolling star
That bleeds infinity—the orphic strings,
Sidereal phalanxes, leap and converge:
—One Song, one Bridge of Fire! Is it Cathay,
Now pity steeps the grass and rainbows ring
The serpent with the eagle in the leaves . . . ?
Whispers antiphonal in azure swing.

Appendix

LONG SUSPENSION SPANS (still standing)

Bridge	*Site*	*Length in feet*	*Date*
Verrazano-Narrows	New York	4260	1965
Golden Gate	San Francisco	4200	1937
Mackinac Straits	Michigan	3800	1957
George Washington	New York	3500	1931
Lisbon over Tagus	Portugal	3317	196–
Forth Suspension	Scotland	3300	196–
Severn	England	3240	196–
Bosporus	Turkey	3100	1961
Tacoma Narrows	Puget Sound	2800	1950
Transbay (Oakland-Bay)	San Francisco	2310 (2 spans)	1936
Bronx-Whitestone	Long Island Sound	2300	1939
Delaware Memorial	Wilmington, Delaware	2150	1951
Walt Whitman	Delaware River	2000	1957
Tancarville	Seine River, France	1995	1959
Ambassador	Detroit	1850	1929
Delaware River	Philadelphia	1750	1926
Bear Mountain	Hudson Valley	1632	1924
Williamsburg	New York	1600	1903
Chesapeake Bay	Chesapeake Bay	1600	1952
Brooklyn	New York	1595	1883

LONG STEEL ARCHES

Bridge	*Site*	*Length in feet*	*Date*
Bayonne	New Jersey	1652	1931
Sydney Harbour	Australia	1650	1932
Mersey River	Liverpool	1082	1961
Birchenough	S. Rhodesia	1080	1935
Saikai	Nagasaki	1042	1955
Hell Gate	New York	977	1917
Rainbow	Niagara Falls	950	1941
Clifton	Niagara Falls	840	1898
Duisburg-Rheinhausen	Germany	838	1951
Sukkur	Indus River, Pakistan	806	1963
Volta River	Ghana	805	1956
Henry Hudson	New York	800	1936
Louisville (2 decks, 2 tied arches)	Louisville, Ky.	800	1961

CONTINUOUS TRUSSES AND GIRDERS

Bridge	*Site*	*Length in feet*	*Date*
Belgrade	Save River, Yugoslavia	856	1956
Dubuque	Iowa (Mississippi River)	845	1943
Duisburg	Germany	839	1935
Earle C. Clements	Shawneetown, Illinois	825	1956
St. Louis County, Mo.	Mississippi River	804	1944
Kingston-Rhinecliff	Hudson River	800	1956
Sciotoville	Ohio	775	1917
Chain of Rocks	Mississippi River	699	1929
Neuwied	Germany	698	1935
New Jersey Turnpike	Delaware River	682	1956
Düsseldorf-Neuss	Germany	676	1951
Cincinnati	Ohio	675	1929
Cape Girardeau	Missouri	672	1928
Cologne	Germany	605	1948

LONG-SPAN CANTILEVERS

Bridge	*Site*	*Length in feet*	*Date*
Quebec	Canada	1800	1917
Firth of Forth	Scotland	1700 (2 spans)	1889
New Orleans-Algiers	Louisiana	1595	1958
Howrah	India	1500	1943
Transbay (Oakland-Bay)	San Francisco	1400	1936
Tappan Zee	Hudson River	1212	1955
Longview	Columbia River	1200	1930
Queensborough	New York	1182 (longest span)	1909
Balboa	Panama Canal Zone	1120	1962
Carquinez Strait	San Francisco	1100 (two parallel spans)	1927
Vancouver	British Columbia	1100	1961
Montreal Harbour	Quebec	1097	1930
Cooper River	Charleston, S.C.	1050	1929

CONCRETE ARCHES

Bridge	*Site*	*Length in feet*	*Date*
Sydney Harbour	Australia	910	1963
Sandoe	Sweden	866	1943
Esla	Spain	645	1940
Plougastel	France	612	1929
Antas River	Brazil	612	1953
Traneberg	Sweden	594	1934
La Roche-Guyon	France	528	1937
Svinesund	Sweden	509	1946
Medway River	England	500	196–

SIMPLE TRUSS SPANS

Bridge	*Site*	*Length in feet*	*Date*
Metropolis	Ohio River	720	1917
Paducah	Ohio River	716	1929
Tanana	Tanana River, Alaska	700	1922

Bridge	Site	Length in feet	Date
Douglas MacArthur	St. Louis	668	1911
Henderson	Ohio River	665	1933
Louisville	Ohio River	644	1919

SUCCESSIVE HOLDERS OF WORLD'S RECORD SPAN LENGTH, ALL TYPES

Bridge	Site	Type	Length in feet	Date
Trajan's Bridge	Danube River	timber arch on stone piers	170	104
Trezzo	Italy	stone arch	236	1371
Wettingen	Germany	timber arch	390	1758
Menai Strait	Wales	chain suspension	580	1826
Fribourg Grand Pont	Switzerland	wire cable suspension	870	1834
Wheeling	W. Va.	suspension	1010	1849
Lewiston	Niagara Falls	suspension	1043	1851
Cincinnati	Ohio River	suspension	1057	1867
Clifton	Niagara Falls	suspension	1268	1869
Brooklyn	New York	suspension	1595	1883
Firth of Forth	Scotland	cantilever	1700	1889
Quebec	Canada	cantilever	1800	1917
Ambassador	Detroit	suspension	1850	1929
George Washington	New York	suspension	3500	1931
Golden Gate	San Francisco	suspension	4200	1937
Verrazano-Narrows	New York	suspension	4260	1965

LONG-SPAN MOVABLES (Drawbridges)

Vertical Lift

Bridge	Site	Length in feet	Date
Arthur Kill	New York	558	1959
Cape Cod	Massachusetts	544	1935
Philadelphia-Camden (longest double-track)	Pennsylvania-New Jersey	542	1960
Marine Parkway	Jamaica Bay, New York	540	1937
Burlington, N.J.	Delaware River	534	1934
Sault Ste. Marie	Michigan	369	1959

Swing Bridges

Bridge	Site	Length in Feet	Date
Fort Madison, Iowa	(over Mississippi)	525	1927
Portland, Oregon	(over Willamette River)	521	1908
East Omaha	(over Missouri River)	519	1903

Single-leaf Bascules

Bridge	Site	Length in Feet	Date
Sixteenth Street	Chicago	260	1919

Double-leaf Bascules

Bridge	Site	Length in Feet	Date
Sault Ste. Marie	Michigan	336	1914

AMERICAN COVERED BRIDGES

(Compiled by Philip and Betsy Clough for "World Guide to Covered Bridges," published by The National Society for the Preservation of Covered Bridges, Reading, Mass.)

State	Number	State	Number
Alabama	45	Michigan	6
Alaska	2	Missouri	7
California	17	New Hampshire	57
Connecticut	5	New York	31
Delaware	4	North Carolina	3
Georgia	44	Ohio	234
Illinois	11	Oregon	106
Indiana	152	Pennsylvania	347
Iowa	12	South Carolina	3
Kentucky	31	Tennessee	9
Louisiana	1	Vermont	121
Maine	11	Virginia	8
Maryland	8	Washington	11
Massachusetts	15	West Virginia	40
		Wisconsin	1
		U. S. Grand Total:	1,342

CANADIAN COVERED BRIDGES

Province	Number	Province	Number
New Brunswick	214	Ontario	1
Nova Scotia	1	Quebec	240

Bibliography

I. GENERAL: *Books on bridges and bridge engineering*

Billings, Henry. *Bridges*. Illustrated by author. The Viking Press, New York, 1956.

Black, Archibald. *The Story of Bridges*. McGraw-Hill Book Co., New York, 1936.

Burr, William H. *Ancient and Modern Engineering and the Isthmian Canal.* John Wiley & Sons, New York, 1902.

Comolli, L. A. *Les Ponts de L'Amerique du Nord*. Librairie scientifique, Ambroise Lefevre, Paris, 1879.

Finch, James Kip. *A Century of American Civil Engineering*. Transactions of the A.S.C.E., Vol. ct, 1953.

———. *The Story of Engineering*. Doubleday & Co., Garden City, N.Y., 1960.

Jenkin, Fleeming. *Bridges, an Elementary Treatise on Their Construction and History*. Adman and Charles Black, Edinburgh, 1878.

Merdinger, Charles J. *Civil Engineering Through the Ages*. Transactions of the A.S.C.E., Vol. ct, 1953.

Mock, Elizabeth B. *The Architecture of Bridges*. Museum of Modern Art, New York, 1949.

Smith, H. Shirley. *The World's Great Bridges*. Harper & Brothers, New York, 1953.

Steinman, David B., and Sara Ruth Watson. *Bridges and Their Builders*. G. P. Putnam's Sons, New York, 1941; Dover Publications, New York, 1957.

Straub, Hans. *A History of Civil Engineering,* an outline from ancient to modern times. Translated by E. Rockwell. Leonard Hill, Ltd., London, 1953.

Tyrrell, Henry Grattan. *History of Bridge Engineering*. Published by the author, Chicago, 1911.

Watson, Wilbur J. *Bridge Architecture,* containing two hundred illustrations of the notable bridges of the world, ancient and modern, with descriptive, historical, and legendary text. William Helburn, Inc., New York, 1927.

Whitney, Charles S. *Bridges, a Study in Their Art, Science, and Evolution,* with photographs and drawings of old and new bridges of many lands. William Edwin Rudge, New York, 1929.

II. SPECIAL: *Books and articles on aspects of bridge engineering and bridge history*

Abel, Derek. *Channel Underground,* a new survey of the Channel tunnel question, with a foreword by Sir Ivone Kirkpatrick. The Pall Mall Press, London, 1961.

Allen, Richard Sanders. *Covered Bridges of the Northeast.* Stephen Green Press, Brattleboro, Vt., 1957.

Ammann, O. H., and others. *George Washington Bridge across the Hudson River at New York.* Published by the American Society of Civil Engineers in collaboration with the Port of New York Authority. Reprinted from A.S.C.E. Transactions, Vol. 97, 1933.

Ammann, Othmar H. "The Narrows Bridge at New York." Presented at the 76th annual meeting of the Connecticut Society of Civil Engineers, Inc., at Cheshire, Conn., April 7, 1960.

Besant, G. B. *London Bridge.* Selwyn and Blount, Ltd., London, 1927.

Bill, Max. *Robert Maillart—Bridges and Constructions.* Erlenbach, Zurich, 1948.

Boucher, François. *Le Pont-Neuf.* 2 vols. Chez le Goupy, editeur, Paris, 1926.

Carnegie, Andrew. *Autobiography.* Edited by John C. Van Dyke. Houghton Mifflin Co., Boston, 1920.

Daley Robert. *The World beneath the City.* J. B. Lippincott Co., Philadelphia, 1959.

Dempsey, G. Drysdale. *Tubular and Other Iron Girder Bridges,* particularly describing the Britannia and Conway Tubular Bridges. John Weale, London, 1850.

Dorsey, Florence L. *Road to the Sea,* the story of James B. Eads and the Mississippi River. Rinehart & Co., New York, 1947.

Dredge, James. *Thames Bridges from the Tower to the Source,* "Engineering," London; John Wiley & Sons, New York.

Dubly, Henry-Louis. *Les Ponts de Paris.* Éditions des Deux Mondes, Paris, 1957.

Edwards, Llewellyn Nathaniel. *A Record of History and Evolution of Early American Bridges.* University of Maine Press, Orono, 1959.

Finch, James Kip. *Perronet, Master of the Stone Arch,* Consulting Engineer, 1961.

Fletcher, Robert, and J. P. Snow. *History of the Development of Wooden Bridges.* (Papers relating to early American Bridges with pictures, clippings, letters, etc., in Engineering Center Library, New York.)

Fowler, John W. "Chesapeake Bay Bridge-Tunnel Construction," *Civil Engineering,* January 1962.

Fugl-Meyer, H., (member Inst. Danish Civil Engineers). *Chinese Bridges.*

Kelly and Walsh, Ltd., Shanghai and Singapore; Kegan Paul, Trench, Trubner & Co., Ltd., London, 1937.

Gautier, Hubert, (inspecteur des grands chemins, ponts et chaussees du Royaume). *Traité des Ponts.* A. Cailleau, Paris, 1728.

Gibb, Sir Alexander. *The Story of Telford, the Rise of Civil Engineering.* A. & C. Black, Ltd., London, 1935.

Goldrath, Bert. "River in a Box," *Argosy Magazine,* March 1961.

Grant, Michael. *The World of Rome.* The New American Library, New York, 1961.

Greene, Stephen, ed., and Arthur W. Peach, Ralph N. Hill, Walter Hard, Jr. *A Treasury of Vermont Life.* The Countryman Press, Woodstock, Vt., 1956.

Harrod, Kathryn E. *Master Bridge Builders,* the Story of the Roeblings. Julian Messner, Inc., New York, 1958.

Home, Gordon C. *Old London Bridge.* Dodd, Mead & Co., New York, 1931.

Jakeman, Adelbert M. *Old Covered Bridges,* the story of covered bridges in general, with a description of the remaining bridges in Massachusetts and Connecticut. Stephen Daye Press, Brattleboro, Vt., 1935.

Kingman, Edward Dyer. *Frères du Pont,* a Religious Brotherhood of the Middle Ages. Boston, 1938. (Bound MS in library of A.S.C.E., New York)

Mehrtens, Georg C. *A Hundred Years of German Bridge-Building.* Translated by Ludwig Mertens. Published for the Paris Universal Exposition, Berlin, 1900.

Mensch, E. Cromwell. *The Golden Gate Bridge,* a technical description in ordinary language, illustrated by Chesley Bonestell. The author, San Francisco, 1935.

Morris, James. *The World of Venice.* Pantheon Books, New York, 1960.

Noble, Celia Brunel. *The Brunels, Father and Son.* R. Cobden-Sanderson, Ltd., London, 1938.

Polo, Marco. *The Travels of Marco Polo.* Orion Press, New York, 1958.

Prescott, William H. *History of the Conquest of Peru.* David McKay, Philadelphia.

Ratigan, William. *Highways over Broad Waters,* the Life and Times of David B. Steinman, Bridgebuilder. William B. Eerdmans Publishing Co., Grand Rapids, Mich., 1959.

Rondelet, Antoine. *Essai Historique sur le Pont de Rialto.* Paris, 1837.

Rostem, Osman R. "Bridges in Ancient Egypt," *Annales du Service des Antiquités de l'Egypte,* tome xlvii (premier fascicule), Le Caire, Imprimerie de l'Institut Français d'Archéologie Orientale, 1948.

Sandburg, Carl. *Abraham Lincoln, the Prairie Years.* 2 vols. Harcourt, Brace & Co., New York, 1926.

Schuyler, Hamilton. *The Roeblings,* a Century of Engineers, Bridge-Builders and Industrialists, 1831–1931. Princeton University Press, Princeton, N.J., 1931.

Sloane, Eric. *American Barns and Covered Bridges.* Wilfred Funk, Inc., New York, 1954.

Smiles, Samuel. *The Life of George Stephenson and of His Son Robert Stephenson,* comprising also a history of the invention and introduction of the railway locomotive. Harper & Brothers, New York, 1868.

———. *The Lives of the Engineers,* with an account of their principal works, comprising also a history of inland communication in Britain. 2 vols. John Murray, London, 1861.

Steinman, David B. *The Builders of the Bridge,* the story of John Roebling and his son. Harcourt, Brace & Co., New York, 1945.

———. *Rigidity and Aerodynamic Stability of Suspension Bridges.* A.S.C.E. Proceedings, November 1943 and April 1945.

Telford, Thomas. *The Life of Thomas Telford,* Civil Engineer, written by himself; containing a descriptive narrative of his professional labours; with a folio atlas of copper plates. Edited by John Rickman, one of his executors; with a preface, supplement, annotations and index. James and Luke G. Hansard & Sons, London, 1838.

Thomson, R. *Chronicles of Old London Bridge,* by an Antiquary. Smith, Elder & Co., London, 1827.

Vose, George L. *Bridge Disasters in America.* Lee & Shepard, Boston, 1887. (Originally published in *The Railroad Gazette.*)

Watson, Wilbur J. *A Decade of Bridges, 1926–1936.* J. H. Jansen, Cleveland, 1937.

Woodward, C. M. *A History of the St. Louis Bridge.* G. I. Jones & Co., St. Louis, 1881.

Yonge, Samuel, ed. *Testimony at Coroner's Inquest of the St. Charles Bridge Disaster, November 8, 1879.* St. Charles, 1880.

"Bridge-Tunnel's $3.5 Million Offspring," *Construction,* 1961.

Examples of Structures Built by the Keystone Bridge Co. Keystone Bridge Co., Pittsburgh.

The Failure of the Tacoma Narrows Bridge, a report to the Hon. John C. Carmody, Administrator, Federal Works Agency, Washington, D.C. Board of Engineers: Othmar H. Ammann, Theodore von Karman, Glenn B. Woodruff. March 28, 1941.

The Forth Bridge in Its Various Stages of Construction. R. Grant and Son, Edinburgh, 1899.

Japan, vol. xv, No. 3, March 1926, San Francisco.

"London Bridge before the Great Fire," *The Guildhall Miscellany,* London, January 1952.

Il Messagero, Florence, Italy, November 7, 1961.

Notes and Comments on the Failure of the Bridge on the Lake Shore and Michigan Southern Railway over Ashtabula Creek, December 30, 1878. Bound volume of clippings, Engineering Societies Library, New York.

"One of the Great Crossings—the Chesapeake Bay Bridge-Tunnel," *Engineering News-Record,* November 23, 1961.

Le Pont sur la Manche, avant-projets de M. Schneider et Cie., et H. Hersent. Imprimerie et librairie centrales des chemins de fer. Imprimerie Chaix, Paris, 1889.

Tay Bridge Disaster: Report on the Court of Inquiry and Report of Mr. Rothery upon the Circumstances Attending the Fall of a Portion of the

Tay Bridge on the 28th of December, 1879. Eyre & Spottiswoode, London, 1880.

Technical Record and Design and Construction of Glen Canyon Bridge. U. S. Dept. of Interior, Bureau of Reclamation. Denver, 1959.

III. *The Bridge in War*

Burton, Lieutenant Colonel R. G. *Napoleon's Campaigns in Italy.* George Allen & Co., Ltd., London; The Macmillan Company, New York, 1912.

Caesar, C. Julius. *The Gallic War.* Translated by H. Y. Edwards. Harvard University Press, Cambridge, Mass., 1958.

Eisenhower, Dwight D. *Crusade in Europe.* Doubleday & Co., Garden City, N.Y., 1948.

French, Allen. *The Day of Concord and Lexington, the nineteenth of April, 1775.* Little, Brown & Co., Boston, 1925.

Herodotus. *History,* a new English version, translated and edited by George Rawlinson, M.A., in four volumes. D. Appleton and Co., New York, 1880.

Johnson, Robert Underwood, and Clarence Clough Buel. *Battles and Leaders of the Civil War.* 4 vols. Century Co., New York and London, 1884.

Livy, Titus. *History of Rome.* Translated by D. Spillan and Cyrus Edmunds. 2 vols. George Bell & Sons, Ltd., London, 1892 and 1896.

Mèneval, Baron C. F. de. *Memoirs of Napoleon Bonaparte.* P. F. Collier & Son, New York, 1910.

Mills, Dorothy. *Book of the Ancient Romans,* an introduction to the history and civilization of Rome from the traditional date of the founding of the city to its fall in 476 A.D. G. P. Putnam's Sons, New York, 1927.

Mitchell, Lieutenant Colonel Joseph B. *Decisive Battles of the Civil War.* G. P. Putnam's Sons, New York, 1955.

Murdock, Harold. *The Nineteenth of April, 1775.* Houghton Mifflin Co., Boston, 1925.

Preston, John Hyde. *Revolution, 1776.* Harcourt, Brace & Co., New York, 1933.

Suetonius. *The Lives of the Twelve Caesars.* Edited by Joseph Gavorse. Modern Library, Inc., New York, 1931.

Tacitus. *The Annals.* Translated by Arthur Murphy. J. M. Dent & Sons, Ltd., London and Toronto, 1908.

Tarbell, Ida M. *A Short Life of Napoleon Bonaparte.* S. S. McClure, Ltd., New York, 1895.

Thompson, R. W. *Battle for the Rhineland.* Hutchinson & Co., London, 1958.

Wilmot, Chester. *The Struggle for Europe.* Harper & Brothers, New York, 1952.

The Bridge. Official publication of the Ninth Armored Division. Printed in Bayreuth, Germany, by Carl Giessel, 1945.

A Circumstantial Account of an Attack that happened on the 19th of April 1775 on his Majesty's troops by a number of the people of the Province of Massachusetts Bay. Printed at Boston, 21 April 1775. (John Howe)

Engineer Field Manual. Professional Papers No. 29, Corps of Engineers, U. S. Army, Washington, Government Printing Office, 1912.

IV. *The Bridge in Art and Literature*

Aldanov, M. A. *The Devil's Bridge.* Translated by A. E. Chamot. Alfred A. Knopf, New York and London, 1928.

Andrić, Ivo. *The Bridge on the Drina.* Translated by Lovett F. Edwards. The Macmillan Co., New York, 1959.

Barr, Alfred H. *Matisse, His Art and His Public.* Museum of Modern Art, New York, 1951.

Baur, John I. H., ed. *New Art in America,* fifty painters of the twentieth century. New York Graphic Society, Greenwich, Conn., 1957.

Bierce, Ambrose. *In the Midst of Life,* tales of soldiers and civilians. Albert & Charles Boni, New York; Modern Library, New York, 1927.

Boswell, Peyton. *Modern American Painting.* Dodd, Mead & Co., New York, 1939.

Botkin, Benjamin A., and Alvin F. Harlow, eds. *A Treasury of Railroad Folklore,* the stories, tall tales, traditions, ballads and songs of the American railroad man. Crown Publishers, New York, 1953.

Boulle, Pierre. *The Bridge over the River Kwai.* Translated by Xan Fielding. Vanguard Press, New York, 1954.

Byron, G. G. N. *Poetical Works.* Oxford University Press, London, 1926.

Cather, Willa. *Alexander's Bridge.* Houghton Mifflin Co., New York and Boston, 1912.

Cheney, Sheldon. *Story of Modern Art.* The Viking Press, New York, 1941.

Crane, Hart. *Collected Poems.* Waldo Frank, ed. Liveright Publishing Corp., New York, 1933.

Davis, Harold L. *Honey in the Horn.* Harper & Brothers, New York, 1935.

Dickens, Charles. *American Notes and Pictures from Italy.* Vol. 11 of the Complete Works of Charles Dickens, edited by Richard Garnett. Chapman & Hall, Ltd., London, 1900.

Dostoievsky, Feodor. *Crime and Punishment.* Translated by Constance Garnett. The Macmillan Co., New York, 1927.

Dumas, Alexandre. *The Three Musketeers.* Translated by William Robson. D. Appleton & Co., New York and London, 1911.

Hardy, Thomas. *The Mayor of Casterbridge.* Boni & Liveright, New York.

Hearn, Lafcadio. *The Romance of the Milky Way, and Other Studies and Stories.* Houghton Mifflin Co., Boston and New York, 1905.

————. *Shadowings.* Little, Brown & Co., Boston, 1900.

Hemingway, Ernest. *For Whom the Bell Tolls.* Charles Scribner's Sons, New York, 1940.

Hugo, Victor. *Notre-Dame de Paris.* Translated by Jessie Haynes. Heritage Press, New York, 1955.

Jean, Marcel, and Arpad Mezei. *The History of Surrealist Painting*. Translated by Simon Watson Taylor. Grove Press, New York, 1960.

Longfellow, Henry Wadsworth. *Complete Poetical Works*. Houghton Mifflin Co., Boston and New York, 1863.

McGonagall, William. *Poetic Gems*. David Winter & Son, Ltd., Dundee, Scotland, 1951.

Michener, James. *The Bridges at Toko-ri*. Random House, New York, 1953.

Rewald, John. *The History of Impressionism*. Museum of Modern Art, New York, 1946.

Ritchie, Andrew Carnduff. *Abstract Painting and Sculpture in America*. Museum of Modern Art, New York, 1951.

———, ed. *German Art of the Twentieth Century*. Museum of Modern Art, New York, 1957.

Robins, Frederick W. *The Story of the Bridge*. Cornish Bros., Ltd., Birmingham, England, 1948.

Stravinsky, Igor, and Robert Craft. *Expositions and Developments*. Doubleday & Co., Garden City, N.Y. 1962.

Troy, Una. *The Other End of the Bridge*. E. P. Dutton & Co., New York, 1960.

Verne, Jules. *Around the World in Eighty Days*. Translated by George M. Towle. Dodd, Mead & Co., New York, 1956.

Watson, Wilbur J., and Sara Ruth Watson. *Bridges in History and Legend*. J. H. Jansen, Cleveland, 1937.

Wilder, Thornton. *The Bridge of San Luis Rey*. Albert & Charles Boni, New York, 1928.

Woods, George Benjamin, ed. *Poetry of the Victorian Period*. Scott, Foresman & Co., Chicago, 1930.

Zigrosser, Carl, ed. *A Book of Fine Prints*, an anthology of printed pictures and introduction to the study of graphic art in the West and the East. Rev. ed. Crown Publishers, New York, 1948.

Also: Standard guidebooks, encyclopedias, atlases, historical atlases, standard histories, newspapers, magazines, special publications, etc.

Index